Dynamic Psychopathology in Childhood

DYNAMIC PSYCHOPATHOLOGY IN CHILDHOOD

Edited by

LUCIE JESSNER, M.D.

and

ELEANOR PAVENSTEDT, M.D.

with Fifteen Contributors

GRUNE & STRATTON New York and London 1959

Library of Congress Catalog Card No. 59–7826

Grune & Stratton, Inc.

381 Fourth Avenue

New York City 16

Printed and bound in U. S. A. (B)

Editors

LUCIE JESSNER, M.D., Professor of Psychiatry and Director of Child Psychiatry, University of North Carolina, School of Medicine, Chapel Hill, North Carolina; Faculty and Training Analyst, Washington Psychoanalytic Institute, Washington, D.C.; Formerly, Director, Child Psychiatry Unit, Massachusetts General Hospital, Boston, Massachusetts.

ELEANOR PAVENSTEDT, M.D., Associate Professor and Director of Child Psychiatry, Department of Psychiatry, Boston University School of Medicine, Boston, Massachusetts; Faculty and Training Analyst, Boston Psychoanalytic Institute, Boston, Massachusetts.

Contributors

JOHN BENJAMIN, M.D., Professor of Psychiatry, Department of Psychiatry, and Psychiatrist, Child Research Council, University of Colorado School of Medicine, Denver, Colorado.

GASTON E. BLOM, M.D., Associate Professor of Psychiatry, Director of Children's Division, Department of Psychiatry, University of Colorado School of Medicine, Denver, Colorado; Formerly, Director, Child Psychiatry Unit, Massachusetts General Hospital, Boston, Massachusetts.

HELENE DEUTSCH, M.D., Lecturer and Training Analyst, Boston Psychoanalytic Institute, Boston, Massachusetts; Formerly (1923–35), Director, Vienna Psychoanalytic Institute, Vienna, Austria.

RUDOLF EKSTEIN, PH.D., Coordinator, Training and Research, Reiss-Davis Clinic for Child Guidance, Los Angeles, California; Formerly, Consultant in Training and Research Division, Child Psychiatry, Menninger Foundation, Topeka, Kansas; Formerly, Training Analyst, Topeka Institute for Psychoanalysis, Topeka, Kansas.

SEYMOUR W. FRIEDMAN, M.D., Staff, Reiss-Davis Clinic for Child Guidance, Los Angeles, California; Formerly, Department of Child Psychiatry, Menninger Foundation, Topeka, Kansas.

EUGENIO GADDINI, M.D., Former Director and Chief of the Department of Medicine, Red Cross Hospital, "F. Aurelia," Rome, Italy; Member, Italian Psychoanalytic Society.

RENATA DE BENEDETTI GADDINI, M.D., Assistant in Pediatrics and Head of the Center for Mental Hygiene, Pediatric Clinic, University of Rome, Rome, Italy.

PHYLLIS GREENACRE, M.D., Professor of Clinical Psychiatry, Cornell University Medical College, New York; President, New York Psychoanalytic Institute, 1948–50; President, New York Psychoanalytic Society, 1956–57.

EARLE L. LIPTON, M.D., Commonwealth Fund Fellow, Department of Pediatrics, College of Medicine, State University of New York, Syracuse, New York.

RICHARD MEILI, PH.D., Professor of Psychology, University of Bern; Director, Psychological Institute, Bern, Switzerland; Formerly, Professor, Institut des Sciences de l'Education, Geneva, Switzerland.

JAMES T. PROCTOR, M.D., Assistant Professor of Psychiatry, Department of Psychiatry, University of North Carolina School of Medicine, Chapel Hill, North Carolina.

EVEOLEEN N. REXFORD, M.D., Director, Douglas A. Thom Clinic for Children; Faculty, Boston Psychoanalytic Institute, Boston, Massachusetts.

JULIUS B. RICHMOND, M.D., Professor and Chairman, Department of Pediatrics, College of Medicine, State University of New York, Syracuse, New York.

MELITTA SPERLING, M.D., F.A.P.A., F.A.A.C.P., Associate Clinical Professor of Psychiatry, State University of New York, Downstate Medical Center; Training Analyst, Psychoanalytic Institute of the State University of New York, Medical Center at New York.

BABETTE WHIPPLE, PH.D., Research Psychologist, Child Psychiatry Unit, Department of Psychiatry, Massachusetts General Hospital, Boston, Massachusetts; Formerly, Analyst, Russian Research Center, Harvard University, Boston, Massachusetts.

Contents

Introduction

After a half century of significant progress in our knowledge concerning the human being, both by discovery and rediscovery, we have come to a point where we experience the urge and feel the obligation to validate our findings and concepts.

The clinician confronted with the task of validation must thread his way between the devil of the rigid and constraining models from other disciplines and the deep blue sea of the absence of controls. With the former he may impoverish and sterilize his living material and with the latter leave our subject matter open to belief without sufficient warrant.

This volume is an attempt to bring examples from the entire range of individual clinical observations, which have led their authors to meaningful connections or to more controlled systematic research. The reader may prefer one or the other approach; the editors are convinced that both are means of enriching our knowledge. The studies include observations on both pathologic and normal development because the former illuminates the latter. We are all familiar with the insights which studies of pathologic emotional and mental states have given us in adults. It is, however, particularly important in the evaluation of childhood disorders to develop a more precise knowledge of the wide range of normative phenomena, which, without reference to their developmental stage, may readily be misinterpreted.

All the contributions are new with one exception which was published forty years ago, although never in English. Helene Deutsch's paper is such an outstanding example of clinical material accurately observed, material which gives substance from a child's life to theories originally derived from reconstruction, that we were delighted to have it as a contribution. Like all good research, it shows further problems to be studied: for example, why did the child use a particular mode of regression, a question that still occupies our minds today.

But how is one to approach this wealth of clinical observations and theoretical formulations in order to validate them? Basic research on the order of carefully, but not rigidly, controlled scrutiny of the developing personality, whether it be of cross-sections or of the entire longitudinal process, is one such avenue.

John Benjamin describes and exemplifies the predictive method of orienting data and testing our theories. It has always been the task of science to remove the supernatural from a foretelling of the future. A thoughtful and painstaking analysis is given by Benjamin of types of predictions and of carefully defined criteria which have to be met in order to state that a prediction was correct and to guard against self-deception. This investigation of the incorrect prediction bears fruit.

Richard Meili, one of our contributors from Europe, has undertaken to study the development of character in much the same way as Piaget has systematically investigated the stage-by-stage evolution of thought processes. He presents the child with the same, gradually modified experimental tasks at various age levels and relies heavily on moving pictures, complemented by on-the-spot recording of observations, in the home. His data thus are available for repeated review for analysis and refinement of observations. The editors take this opportunity to thank Sibylle Escalona for calling this work to their attention. It seemed important to include this research for our English-speaking readers; we bring here the first translation of a summary prepared by the author.

Julius Richmond and Earle Lipton present the significant data available concerning the central and autonomic nervous systems of the newborn infant. This follows from their succinct formulation that "studies of newborn infants can only be *oriented* psychologically, since data collection must necessarily be physiological or biochemical."

The next three papers by Blom and Whipple,* Gaddini, and Rexford * represent the conscientious efforts (with the inherent growing pains) of clinicians desirous of submitting their findings to critical and systematic conditions which approach experimental research at least to the extent that they can be repeated and/or examined by others.

Melitta Sperling discusses her contribution to the investigation of child psychopathology: the simultaneous analysis of mother and child. Simultaneous analysis constitutes a kind of control and, furthermore, opens up a deeper understanding of the transactions between mother and child.

It is followed by four essentially clinical papers.

Phyllis Greenacre advances our understanding through the concept of focal symbiosis. She perceives an interdependence of a child with one other person, which is intensely strong in one circumscribed area. Symptom formation in the older child and in the adult can be recognized as sequelae of such unresolved partial union.

Lucie Jessner gathers together, from her long experience, descriptions of children during and after illness and discusses the relevance of illness to the child's regressive or constructive further development. The paper

* The description of the gradual evolution of the research methods in these contributions was done at the editor's request.

contains many suggestions which might be fruitful springboards for research.

The last two papers, by Ekstein and Friedman and by Proctor, scrutinize the therapeutic process. Ekstein and Friedman give a thoroughgoing analysis of play in the treatment situation, and Proctor of the countertransference. Each is a crucial point in the therapy of the particular kind of pathology the author deals with.

A book of this kind is homage to Sigmund Freud. The impact of his patient seeking for the origins and evolution of the human being through reconstruction made it possible to investigate these data progressively through analysis of children and through unembarrassed observation of their behavior.

We think these chapters, as a whole, give a picture of where we stand now in child psychopathology, and what the avenues are to the future. If this volume serves to stimulate more clinical observations and more attempts at validation, its purpose will have been fulfilled.

LUCIE JESSNER
ELEANOR PAVENSTEDT

1

A Two Year Old Boy's First Love Comes to Grief

By HELENE DEUTSCH

RUDI WAS just two when his nurse left him. Because of his mother's heavy professional schedule and because of the pressure of external events, this nurse had been a mother surrogate to little Rudi for two years. It was she who from the beginning served all his autoerotic needs; it was she who fed him, assisted him with his excretory functions, and fulfilled his wishes. Consequently, in his first object choice Rudi disregarded his mother. Indeed, the nurse well knew how to make little Rudi's object choice even more exclusive, for she did not allow anyone else to perform the tasks of love.

On the surface, the relationship between Rudi and his nurse did not appear to be too tender. His mother's wish not to spoil the child was quite in keeping with the views and temperament of his nurse. She cared for Rudi with great devotion and yet with a certain detachment. He responded with a similar attitude: there were no demonstrations of tenderness, no kisses, no embraces. Any show of tenderness by his mother was received by Rudi with an air of stolid endurance.

The nurse left the home without saying good-bye to the little boy who had been in her care. A young and lively nursemaid took her place, assuming the role of playmate and friend. The child was delighted with her. He brought out all his toys to show his "new friend." He let her sing to him, show him pictures, and did not want to let her out of his sight. The whole transition appeared to be much easier than one would have thought. True, the child was so caught up in his play that he did "forget" several times to mention his toilet needs, and when he did ask to go, he refused help from anyone but his mother.

At mealtime his manner was somewhat distant but he did accept food from the new nurse. At bedtime he asked for his mother, and let her

Published in 1919 in the *Int. Ztschr. f. Aerztl. Psa.* This is the first English translation, by Marianne Sommerfeld, Boston, Mass.

undress him and put him to bed without protest. After an hour or two he awoke, which was unusual, and wept aloud. His despair grew when the nurse attempted to calm him. Crying, Rudi asked for his mother and would not let her go during that whole sleepless night. This behavior was strange indeed, for ordinarily Rudi had quite decidedly warded off his mother and asked only for his "La" (Paula, the name of the first nurse). During the night Rudi put his arms around his mother, asked her to lie down beside him, kissed her, and called her many tender names. Every few minutes he reassured himself by asking, "Mummy, are you there?" Toward morning he fell asleep for a short time. When he awoke he remained quietly in bed without a sound. His little misdeed made itself known only by the odor: Rudi had soiled his bed, although this had not happened for a year. This ambitious little boy, who normally showed signs of the greatest repugnance and remorse when he occasionally wet his pants, now remained quite indifferent when his misdemeanor was discovered. There was no sign of affect, neither triumph nor remorse; it was as if this were an everyday event.

Rudi then let himself be dressed without resistance and played happily and cheerfully with the new nurse, but he absolutely refused any offer of food. With every attempt to offer him something to eat, his face took on an expression of extreme despair such as had never been seen in him before. He was neither angry nor obstinate; on the contrary, to the nurse he made tender gestures with his hands as if to console her for his behavior. His mother finally succeeded in getting him to eat a little, although Rudi, who had called for her in despair when the nurse attempted to feed him, let his mother feed him only with the greatest resistance.

Rudi, who had been fully toilet trained, now wet and soiled his pants. If attempts were made to "catch" him and put him on the potty, he would let go of a few drops of urine, only to wet his pants a few minutes later. Sometimes he would announce his need to go, but when the nursemaid hastened to help him he would say, "Oh no, Rudi goes wee wee only for Mummy."

Until now, Rudi had shown great obstinacy in withholding his excretory products. He had clearly enjoyed retaining his always constipated stool and waiting until the last moment to urinate. Now he relinquished this source of pleasure. His feces, which were found in his bed or in his pants, were now ideally soft, a state of affairs no medical or dietary measures had been able to produce. It was as if he were protesting, "I have something. I have something precious, but it is a gift. It is only for my loved one." Now that his love object was gone, he would not yield his most highly prized and love-laden possession. Occasionally, he offered it to the substitute closest at hand: "Only for Mummy."

Rudi's need for demonstrations of tenderness increased during the following days. He embraced and kissed everyone around him. He talked to his dolls with expressions of tenderness he had learned from his mother: "My sweet, lovely bunny," etc. He even lavished expressions of tenderness upon all inanimate objects, as if he were seeking an outlet for his newly freed love.

The name of the lost one was never mentioned in all this time. Rudi often made a slip in addressing the new nurse, but always corrected himself ("La . . . Rosa, please . . .," etc.). When the nurse, now somewhat more certain of her success, asked him, "Are you going to cry when Rosa goes away?" Rudi answered, "No, but Rudi would like to cry when Paula goes away."

During the nights that followed, his behavior remained the same. His mother had to stay with him, to assure him of her love, to cuddle him. At times Rudi would look with a horrified expression at the nurse's bed. When the latter was requested to put out the light beside her bed and did so, Rudi said, "The light went out by itself." When told that Rosa put it out, he insisted, "Oh, no, it went out by itself."

On the third day, the mother gathered her courage and asked him, "Where is Paula?" Rudi answered with an air of the greatest indifference, "She went to the tailor" (where Paula had been in the habit of going on her brief outings).

On the fifth day, Rudi no longer wet and soiled but still would allow no one but his mother to help him with toilet functions. Only when his mother was away did he permit the nurse to help him. At this time he also began to sleep normally again.

His refusal of food, however, persisted. When attempts were made to feed him, he would turn his head away, press his lips together, and begin to cry bitterly. In a pitiful voice, as if pleading for help, he would cry "Mama, Lina, Mama, Lina" (Lina was the cook and was greatly liked by Rudi). When one of them hastened to his side, Rudi calmed down, ate a few spoonfuls, only to return to his former despair. He still did not mention the name of his beloved.

Attempts to withhold food until Rudi got hungry did not succeed. On the days when he refused food, Rudi had been in the habit of stilling his hunger with snacks which had been cut up for him and which he ate without help. Forcing fluids upon him turned into a long drawn-out ritual. On the sixth day of his mourning, Rudi was given nothing to eat in the morning. He was taken for a walk and returned with a good appetite. At lunch he wolfed down his soup quite greedily. But for the rest of the meal, which consisted (as did all meals during this period) of his favorite foods, he returned to his former behavior. His hitherto good mood once more turned into despair, and he pushed his food away.

On the ninth day of separation Rudi returned to reality. He seemed to be his old self once more, but there was a change in his personality. In a sense, he had become socialized; he was more tender and more in need of tenderness. His erotic needs appeared to be greater and he showed a greater interest in people around him, treating them with a certain respect and considerateness. He was tender toward his dolls, animals, and other toys, and at every opportunity would ask: "What is that?" "What is it called?" The poems which were recited to him he learned by heart avidly. He loved his new nurse tenderly, but not with the same intensity and single-mindedness as his former nurse. His sleeping, eating, and toilet habits had returned to normal, except that his constipation had given place to regular bowel movements.

For the psychoanalyst, Rudi's little misdemeanors during the nine days described above serve to confirm facts with which we have long been familiar. It is the particularly clear-cut and unequivocal nature of his behavior which made this episode from his life seem worth reporting.

We know that infantile autoerotic sexuality obtains its satisfaction through the organic needs of the child's own body, that is, in eating and excretory activities. For the infant, the satisfaction of hunger becomes at the same time the first means of deriving pleasure from his own body. Strong feelings of pleasure are also obtained from the elimination of urine and feces. Children learn to give up the pleasure derived from excretory functions in order to gain the sympathy and praise which those in charge of their training offer them as a reward. From the moment that this exchange has taken place, a great value is placed upon the child's libidinized excretory activities, and his excremental products become a cherished gift to the chosen love object. Little Rudi appears to have valued his excretory products very highly. He was as grudging in his gifts to his beloved as he was sparing of his tenderness: this is evidenced by his constipation as well as by his urinary habits.

Upon the loss of his love object, Rudi no longer denied himself the pleasure derived from excretory functions which educative measures had previously compelled him to give up. When he lost the object for whose sake he had relinquished these pleasures, he indulged in them without restraint. And, further, he would not yield this precious gift unless a substitute object was present. At times his mother seemed to him worthy of this gift, apparently because she reminded him of his former libidinal tie: "I will do it only for Mummy." It was only when his libido was freed for new object cathexes that Rudi was able to give up a form of libidinal gratification which he had already abandoned once before. Together with the change in the nature of his object relationships, there was a change in his excretory functions: when Rudi became an affectionate child, lavish with his tenderness, his constipation ceased and his urinary needs were announced on time.

In his eating habits, Rudi expressed the cannibalistic phase of his pregenital sexual development. In him, eating remained closely connected with sexuality, but his sexual drive from here on, like his excretory functions, was object-directed. This was evidenced by the fact that he would eat only to please his love object. Upon the loss of his object, his sexual drives won out over his hunger, and it was only when new object relations were formed that both functions were served harmoniously.

It is not quite clear why the decathexis of that portion of the libido connected with the oral stage took place at a slower rate. We do not know whether this was due to Rudi's individual predisposition or whether it is the norm. It is possible that there is some connection between this behavior and the fact that Rudi was not given to expressing his affection by kisses.

Little Rudi overcame his first bitter disappointment in a period of nine days. The completion of this task represented a major step in his adjustment to his external environment. We do not know how this first great accomplishment will influence the future of his psychic functions, the vicissitudes of his life, and his further strivings. As analysts, however, we cannot help but engage in some conjectures.

2

Prediction and Psychopathological Theory*

By JOHN D. BENJAMIN

Introduction

It is one of the apparent paradoxes of psychoanalysis as a theoretical system that it is so rich in explanatory propositions and so poor in attempts to demonstrate hypothesized relationships between variables through prediction and control. One of several factors responsible for this state of affairs is, I believe, the unusual nature of the relationship between psychoanalytic data and psychoanalytic theory. The wealth of clinical and even semi-experimental data from which theory was and is built is in no way matched by the availability of such data in systematic form for the purposes of testing, correcting, and expanding theoretical formulations. What is published is, almost of necessity, and with some important exceptions, seldom primary data themselves (the homologues of protocols of experiments in the experimental sciences), but anecdotally selected summaries of them, impressions about them, or secondary and tertiary inferences from them. Beyond these, then, the theoretically minded clinician has at his disposal his own clinical experiences, and those of a few colleagues and students, in addition to more systematically treated data from allied fields; and he is dependent upon these for whatever additional observational and experimental facts he needs for further theory building, in the ordinary scientific sense of the term. Thus, we find in fact that original theorizing in psychoanalysis, where it exists, is in general concerned with problems of clarification, of redefinition of accepted concepts and intervening variables in terms of logic and plausibility, in correcting one-sided points of view, or in introducing new explanatory concepts †; much less often do we find the introduction of newly observed and

* From the Child Research Council, University of Colorado School of Medicine. This work was supported in part by grants from the Field Foundation.

† Cf., e.g., the theoretical contributions of Hartmann,[45, 48] Hartmann et al.,[49, 52] Kris,[59, 61] and Rapaport.[82, 83, 86]

described phenomena or relationships between phenomena, within the context of theoretical amplification or revision; * and even more rarely the use of theory as a guide to observations and experiments aimed at testing its validity, generality, and predictive value. The sort of clarificatory contemplative theorizing exemplified by the best in Hartmann's work is, in my opinion, a valuable and even indispensable contribution to progress in the development of psychoanalytic psychology, for the reason that semantic and systematic clarification and amplication [5, 47, 49] of many parts of existing theory are needed before meaningful testing of validity and predictive potential can be fully exploited. For the same reason, I would attribute great value to efforts, such as Rapaport's,[81, 84, 87] to clarify and organize systematically Freud's own profound and still not fully appreciated theoretical writings. For it remains true that it is "frankly nonsensical to test a theory while ignoring its most essential parts." [5] To which I would add that ignorance of Freud's metapsychological theorizing is by no means confined to those without psychoanalytic training! Even if one believes, as I do, that some parts of Freud's theories will eventually prove to need basic revision rather than just clarification and amplification, psychoanalysis as he created it has proved so productive of facts, ideas, hypotheses, and explanations, in terms both of psychopathology and general psychology, that one has good reason, historically reinforced, to mistrust the rejection of any of it without the certainty that it has been, first, thoroughly understood and then that it has been thoroughly tested

* One among several notable exceptions to this statement is to be found in the work of Erik Erikson,[22, 26] whose conceptualizations, although not yet systematically formulated nor integrated into the body of psychoanalysis (but cf. Rapaport [85, 87]), may be said to derive directly from an expansion of the field of facts to be accounted for.

At the other end of the chronologic scale of childhood, the work of Spitz,[90, 91] Spitz and Wolf,[96, 97] Escalona et al.,[29, 30] Wolf,[102] this author and others [72, 103] in the study of infants also offers exciting challenges to the psychoanalytic theoretician for both confirmation and revision of previous extrapolative theory, as well as for new theory building. The recent contributions of Spitz [93, 94, 95] in particular are examples of important and creative attempts to integrate more data within the conceptual framework of psychoanalytic theory; and this holds true even though the data themselves may not always have as much generality as is ascribed to them. The theoretician in this area, as in all others, must also, if his theories are to be "good" ones, take into account the facts derived from the many important experiments and observations of other than psychoanalytic investigators. The failure of Piaget,[76a, 76b] for example, to consider motivation as a variable in his experiments, restricts the scope of their applicability but in no way invalidates them nor deprives them of first-rate importance for developmental theory. It suggests the systematic repetition of his experiments with varyingly cathected objects rather than the rejection of his findings as "inconsistent with" psychoanalytic theory.

wherever meaningful testing is possible. Where it is *not* possible, either directly or indirectly (as in the case of intervening variables between two or more observables), either now or in the foreseeable future through new psychological and biological method development, it is rather meaningless to speak of acceptance or rejection of a theoretical proposition except in a philosophic or esthetic sense. In any case, it seems necessary to distinguish this sort of theorizing, at a great distance from clinical or experimental data although originally arising from it, from theory as we know it in science in general, with the constant two-way flow from observation and experiment to theory, and back again.*

Psychopathological Theory

It is useful, following Hartmann and Rapaport,[87] to distinguish between psychoanalysis as a theory of psychopathology and as a general psychological theory. Clearly, this is not a dichotomous distinction; and it is perhaps as useful to distinguish between general and special psychopathology as between these and general psychology. Although I would agree with Rapaport's implication that the clinical theories of psychoanalysis stand in less need of further investigation, development, and testing than do some aspects of general theory, I would emphasize that this is a purely relative statement, both as a generalization and in terms of the differential status of various parts and levels of psychopathological theory. To be more concrete: patients, and psychoanalytic students, are people; and in studying them it was possible for Freud and others, using the methods of psychoanalysis, to make many major discoveries about personality development and functioning in general, as well as about psychopathology in general and about specific forms of pathology in particular. The major factual discoveries, explanatory concepts, and first-order constructs of psychoanalysis (the dynamic unconscious, transference, dream theory, libidinal stages, the defensive and adaptive mechanisms, fear of object loss, fear of loss of love, fear of castration, conflict and conflict derivatives, secondary narcissism, the functional concepts of structures, etc., etc.) have just as close a relationship to general and developmental psychology as they do to psychopathology, even though their discovery in most instances took place in, and was facilitated by, therapeutic need and a therapeutic setting. Conversely, second- and third-order constructs, hypotheses, and assumptions (much of metapsychology, parts of instinct theory, etc.) are just as important for and pertinent to psychopathological

* For a somewhat fuller, though still only partial, handling of these and other considerations, see a forthcoming publication (ref. 11).

theory as to general and developmental psychology. And the whole of modern ego psychology (which involves constructs of all orders) is surely of equal pertinence to both fields, giving us, as it does, our best hope for meaningful distinctions between the normal and pathologic.[48]

What is really meant, then, by the relatively more "validated" state of psychopathological theory can be reduced to a series of statements about the association of specific behaviors with specific dynamic and structural constellations, of varying degrees of explanatory value and of largely unknown, because untested, predictive value. I have discussed elsewhere[5, 6] the impressive magnitude of this achievement of psychoanalysis, as well as its limitations, and shall not repeat myself here. For our present purposes it is sufficient to say that since psychoanalysis arose from the study of patients, and since, in addition, psychopathology lends itself somewhat more easily to behavioral categorization[6] than do the varieties of "normal" behavior, we are more firmly grounded in certain aspects of psychoanalytic psychopathology than in certain aspects of normal psychology. But in both fields there are many analogous, homologous, and even identical empirical and theoretical problems awaiting solution.

A more essential distinction than the above as regards the relative need for validation and new discovery, however, can be based on that originally made by Hartmann and Kris[49] between the *dynamic* and the *genetic* propositions of psychoanalysis. Much necessary work remains to be done in giving greater precision, differentiation, flexibility, and, when possible, operational definition to some dynamic, topographic and structural constructs. I think it a fair statement, though, that the existential probability[5] of many of them is so high that their validation as constructs has little interest, although some propositions involving them as variables are certainly not beyond the need for further investigation and revision. But it is the genetic propositions which constitute a major segment of both psychopathological and general personality theory, at least insofar as we subsume developmental theory under the latter. And it is these, along with some *economic* concepts almost always invoked in genetic considerations, which are particularly in need of the sort of systematic, controlled investigation without which, in my opinion, it is not possible to speak meaningfully of validation, invalidation, elaboration, and necessary revision. Some of these questions may, as I have suggested elsewhere[5] and as Rapaport strongly emphasizes, best be approached through other methods than those of analysis proper or of the clinic in general, that is, through experimentation or experimentally controlled observation. But others demand primarily the use of clinical methods of the same nature as those by which the findings were originally made, but with greater scrutiny of the methods themselves, with greater attention to the question of interpretation as a scientific tool, and with greater consideration of the nature of the relationships between the data and the theories based on them. In both instances, new method development under the guidance of theory, leading to new or newly organized data, leading in turn to new theory development, is what is most needed.[5, 6, 81]

Prediction as a Method

In two previous communications,[5, 7] I discussed briefly some of the potentials, limitations, and technical problems, as I then saw them, in the use of prediction as a major tool in personality-theoretical research. I should now like to continue and amplify this discussion. I am at present engaged in the systematic analysis of a large population of predictions, of different sorts and on different levels, made over the past ten years as one of many interlocking methods in a long-term longitudinal study of personality development. The results of this analysis will be presented elsewhere when it is completed. In this chapter, I shall use only a few of the data to illustrate some of the points previously made, as well as to raise some new ones.

Predictability is a goal of science; prediction a method to test, among other things, how far along toward that goal a science is. There are theoretical as well as technical limits to predictability in all sciences; and both of these increase with the complexity of the level or levels of organization with which the science deals.[6] Any implication that psychoanalytic knowledge and theory are at a stage of development permitting total predictions of behavior and development comparable to those possible in the physical, and to a lesser but increasingly significant extent, in the biological sciences would, therefore, be completely absurd. Our interest in and advocacy of prediction as a *method* stems from quite different sources than a desire to demonstrate that psychoanalysis is a mature science today. Quite obviously it is not, although on the level of conviction [8, 9] I feel, and on the level of science I think I shall be able to demonstrate, that its facts, assumptions, and theories, once understood, are at present by far the most promising base for further advances and closer to the realities of human functioning than many of its opponents, lukewarm adherents, and even some of its practitioners are inclined to find plausible.

Our aims in using prediction as a method are by no means confined to questions of validation and invalidation of specific propositions, as I have already emphasized strongly in the two earlier publications referred to.*

* It is therefore surprising to find the contrary stated in a recent paper of M. Kris,[62] particularly in view of earlier references to this aspect of our work.[19, 58]

Rather, they seek suggestive, approximate, or, if possible, definite answers to a wide range of questions, stressing particularly the heuristic potentials of *unsuccessful* prediction [7] but putting great weight also on the necessity all predictions impose for greater precision and differentiation in defining concepts and for greater attention to the processes of assessment, interpretative or otherwise.* For every prediction that has any meaning at all involves a prior process of assessment, whether conscious or not †; and the study of the processes of clinical and particularly of psychoanalytic assessment is, I think, of such significance for clinical research as to constitute a major investigative goal in and of itself.‡

The Technical Handling of Predictions

In this section, I wish to present our methods for handling the formulation and analysis of our predictions. Our experience over a period of more than ten years has shown them to be well-suited to our purpose. More informal and less time-consuming procedures may be indicated in other psychoanalytic predictive studies with essentially different aims,§ while, at the other extreme, much simpler and yet more rigorous procedures can be applied in fields where both measures (assessment) and theory are truly quantifiable. No matter how informal and exploratory the aims may be, however, there are some obstacles to meaningful prediction common to all attempts to use this method. In repeating and elaborating upon these and other less elementary aspects of the subject, many already touched upon in my previous discussions, I shall make use of a prediction worksheet which we originally drew up in 1949 and then revised and expanded somewhat in 1951 and again in 1955. Table I represents the 1955 revision, with a few comments added to clarify it for the reader.

* Attempts to arrive at meaningful, if only approximate, quantification of appropriate variables through rating scales can provide the same secondary benefits. In our experience these extra dividends are so great that they would justify the large expenditure of time and energy necessary even if the attainment of the direct goal of meaningful quantification should prove illusory. Two limitations should be noted, however. Not all variables are appropriate objects of attempted quantification, conceptually; and even where they are, the amount of "information" lost through ratings makes it imperative to use them not as substitutes for but as complements to qualitative delineation.

† For a discussion of "intuitive" predictions, see p. 16 ff.

‡ Sharing of this conviction by a sufficient number of experienced psychoanalytic clinicians to permit *comparative* studies of the interpretative process would be a necessary condition for maximum exploitation of this interest. Cf. refs. 5 and 63. An encouraging beginning in this direction on an exploratory level is being undertaken as a sub-project of the pregnancy study of G. L. Bibring and her associates.[15]

§ E.g., Escalona,[29] Knapp,[57] E. Kris,[58, 59] M. Kris,[62] Wallerstein and Robbins.[99]

Table I. Prediction Worksheet

I. No forced predictions.

II. Written and dated predictions only. No subsequent editorial revision.

III. Explication of basis or bases of prediction, unless categorized as intuitive. State possible contaminants to best of ability. Where interpretation is basis for prediction explicate interpretations. Interpretative base = double validation problem.

IV. Nature of prediction.
- Intuitive
- Deductive—theoretical
- Inductive
- Correlational
- Actuarial
- Fortunetelling (prophecy)
- Mixtures of above

V. Positive or negative predictions. (Necessary but not sufficient conditions lead to negative prediction.)

VI. Time element in predictions.
- Immediate (horizontal)
- Short term
- Medium term
- Long term
- Postdictions (reconstructions)

VII. Contingency predictions. (If this, then that).

VIII. Independence and interdependence of predictions.

IX. Level of confidence in prediction. Star (*) for low level.

X. Criterion measures: explicate in advance as far as possible.
- Behavioral (including verbal and physiologic behavior).
- Clinical behavioral (symptomatology).
- Interpretative.

Analysis of Results

I. Predictive outcome. ++, +, ±, −, −− State criterion measures actually used.

II. Estimated qualitative significance of outcome in individual case. Analysis of clinical and theoretical significance, if any, of success or failure.

III. Statistical analyses of results, covering *comparisons* of success and failure of predictions, in terms of above variables, within cases, across cases, and in the total population of predictions.

DISCUSSION OF TABLE I

I. *No forced predictions.* This injunction is a reminder that just because it seems possible to make a prediction in a specific area in one or more cases, it does not necessarily follow that the same area can be made the object of meaningful prediction in every child or parent in our sample. This principle is based in part on the simple if regrettable fact that even in our small, intensively studied sample the amount of knowledge from all sources of assessment is a variable, not a constant; that, in fact, it varies over a wide range in both extensity and depth. From the point of view of systematic comparability, this is, of course, a real limitation. More generally, however, even if this were not the case and all assessments had equal breadth, depth, and validity, individual variability in configurations of variables would inevitably force the consideration of unique individual predictions. Our principle merely recognizes the heuristic and theoretical usefulness of these in our present state of knowledge, and encourages their formulation. It in no way fails to acknowledge the scientific importance of systematic comparability across cases when it is available, as it is in many areas.* Finally, and most concretely, freedom not to make predictions tends to decrease the proportion of what I have termed predictions of the fortunetelling variety.[7] Of these, more will be said later.

IIa. *Written and dated predictions only.* This elementary safeguard against self-deception, selective remembering, and gross contamination needs no explanation. It should be stated, however, that adherence to it has resulted in a considerable loss of predictions which, in the rush of research activities, were not written down in time to avoid subsequent contamination by later confirmatory or contradictory evidence. The loss, of course, is only to the predictive parts of our study; the data which could have been, but were not, utilized for uncontaminated predictions remain available for other more usual sorts of investigative use.†

IIb. *No subsequent editorial revision.* This injunction is again the re-

* Quite apart from problems of prediction, justification of this methodologic statement would require a discussion, or better yet a demonstration, of the relative strategic values and the interlocking roles of single case studies and cross case comparisons, whether observational or experimental. Such a discussion of our basic methodologic assumptions would be far too extensive to be appropriate to this chapter. (See ref. 10 for a somewhat more systematic statement of these issues.)

† The same problem of avoidance of contamination, incidentally, applies to the systematic analysis of interpretative processes to which we referred previously. If one wishes to study how inferences are drawn and how they are validated or invalidated, one can scarcely include the validating or invalidating data as part of the process of inference.

sult of our actual experiences. Some of our hurriedly written predictions, particularly in the earlier years of this study, were inadequate both in their degree of explication (see IIIa, p. 14) and in the quality of their theoretical formulation. In trying subsequently to revise them in terms of embarrassing deficiencies in clarity and style, we found it all too easy for subtle reformulations through later knowledge of the cases to enter the picture without immediate conscious awareness of this on our part. On the other hand, it would be restrictively pedantic to omit meaningful reformulation, since the study of what could have been predicted, on what bases, is just as essential to our over-all purposes as is the evaluation of what actually was predicted. Our compromise solution is as follows: any reformulation of a prediction, including statements about what the predictor now thinks he then meant, is treated separately as part of the qualitative analysis of predictive results but does not enter into the evaluation of relative success or failure, which is based exclusively on the original formulation. This is given exactly as written, with occasional clarificatory additions set off from it through the use of brackets, as will be exemplified later.

IIIa. *Explication of basis or bases of prediction, etc.* This is often the most difficult and time-consuming of our requirements, depending on the type and level of prediction being made. Where one is purposely testing a specific and relatively unambiguous proposition of any sort, the task of explication is not a demanding one. Such a proposition may derive directly from published psychopathologic or personality theory or may be formulated for the first time as an inductive or deductive hypothesis. Where, however, one is trying to include many different assessed variables in more complex predictions of normal or pathologic behaviors, the problem becomes more formidable. Although Freud's metapsychology offers us a conceptual framework for multivariable formulations, particularly when supplemented by modern ego-psychological considerations, only a few specific propositions concerning multiple variable determination of specific behaviors are to be found in the literature, chiefly in the field of psychopathology, and most of these are not metapsychologically explicated. In general, then, and with some significant exceptions, predictions of this sort demand new formulations of existing theory or the introduction of some new theory. I emphasize this not to imply that we have been particularly successful to date in this undertaking but, rather, to stress once more the heuristic and elaborative as well as the validating and invalidating functions of prediction in our present state of knowledge. Not that I would be understood to depreciate the importance of validation wherever it is possible, directly or indirectly; or to share the remarkable opinion of some that an interest in validation betrays a lack of clinical level convictions. On the contrary, only the clinical experience and understanding that lead to convictions make it possible to devise meaningful methods of validation and invalidation. It is, rather, the refusal to see or to recognize or to care about the differences between first and second order convictions,[8, 9] and between both of these and demonstrable and therefore communicable knowledge, that impedes progress in psychoanalytic research and understanding, and is in part responsible for its lack of integration with other branches of psychological and biological science.

IIIb. By *predictive contaminants* in this context I do not mean the sort of gross contamination mentioned above. I refer, rather, to possible determinants of a successful prediction which lie outside the inductive or deductive theoretical framework on which the prediction is presumably based, and which, therefore, could partially or wholly destroy whatever validating significance might otherwise be attributed to the success of the prediction.

To give a few examples from the field of current child psychiatric theory: An observer predicts the development of a childhood psychosis in a two year old boy on the basis of his perception of the mother-child relationship, basing this prediction on the theory of the "schizophrenogenic mother," but ignoring the fact, obvious to another observer, that the child is already showing behavior suggestive of a beginning psychotic development. In this case the overt behavior of the child is the predictive contaminant. In a second case, the same prediction is made on the basis of the mother's own severe psychopathology, "immaturity," and affective remoteness, without actual knowledge of the mother-child relationship, but on the assumption that this mother is incapable of any but a pathogenic relationship to her child. In this case the theoretical basis is again that of the "schizophrenogenic mother," but the predictive contaminant is the possible genetic transmission of susceptibilities to psychotic development, however these may be conceptualized in their interaction with experience.[6, 9] Inversely, the mother-child relationship would be a contaminant in a correlational prediction based on a theory of direct genetic transmission as a major factor in childhood psychosis, without individual study of the variability of the mother-child relationships involved, or of the role of the infant in shaping these. Without pursuing this particular theme further here, it is apparent, I believe, that individual predictions on a small number of cases cannot answer questions of this sort, which would require large scale experimental and observational designs for their solution. It is perhaps less apparent, but I believe true nevertheless, that the sort of assessments of innate and experiential parameters necessary for attempts at more complex individual predictions than those given above as constructed paradigmatic illustrations will also be necessary in conceptualizing, designing, and implementing such larger scale experimental studies. (Cf. also predictions #3 and 4 below.)

IIIc. Where the assessment on which a prediction is based is predominantly an interpretative one, i.e., an inference about intrapsychic phenomena drawn from one or more behavioral phenomena, we are in principle faced with a double validation problem: the validation of the interpretation and of the theoretical proposition being investigated.[5] (The same applies, of course, to noninterpretative assessments, but here the reliability and validity of the assessing measures involve questions of a different nature.) This confronts us with some nice problems in the subsequent analysis of predictive results. Thus the failure of a prediction based on explicable theory may be due to faulty theory, or faulty assessment, or both; but a single prediction in a given area of theory can never demonstrate that it *is* both, or which it is. A well-explicated, successful prediction of this sort tends toward partial validation of both theory and interpretative assessment; but, as will be seen when we come to concrete examples, does not necessarily demonstrate the correctness of either, since predictive contaminants and additional intuitive assessments may be involved. Only the careful analysis of each individual prediction followed by the systematic cross-analysis of a large number of individual predictions can, in my opinion, satisfactorily resolve some of the uncertainties inherent in this method.

IV. *Nature of prediction.* Since the meaning of most of the categories listed under this heading is self-evident, and since some of them have been discussed in previous communications,[5, 7] I shall confine myself here to a few points.

a. The term *intuitive prediction* as used here is loosely defined to mean any prediction whose logical basis or bases cannot be explicated by the predictor. I say "loosely" advisedly, since at least four partially overlapping but essentially different phenomena are here subsumed under one category. A "genuine" intuition, as I understand it, is subjectively characterized by the abruptness of its appearance, by the way it forces itself on one without conscious cognitive or volitional activity, and often by an initial "aha" feeling of conviction that the idea, or problem solution, is right. As far as we understand it clinically, it represents a combination of preconscious and unconscious functioning, the mentation being preconscious, the direction it takes often being determined by unconscious fantasies and drive representations.* The history of science is replete with examples of such intuitive problem solutions, sometimes occurring overnight during sleep, sometimes in the midst of quite different daytime activities. Perhaps the best known and most explicit description of such a process of preconscious problem-solving in science was that given by the mathematician Poincaré.[77]

A second sort of "intuition" would better be described as global-impressionistic assessment. It, too, depends somewhat on preconscious functioning, in the sense that a variety of perceptions, some of them subliminal, are combined into an over-all assessment without conscious consideration of their interrelationships. This sort of "intuitive" assessment covers a good deal of what is usually meant by clinical intuition and clinical sensitivity, being involved in such varied phenomena as the famous "diagnostic nose" of the gifted medical clinician, the sensitivity to affect of the psychotherapist, the "intuitive" interpretations of projective techniques, and the global ratings and rankings of a behavioral observer in psychological research. There is no reason to doubt that problem-solving intuitions also occur in these and other areas of clinical psychology and psychiatry, as, for instance, in preconscious integrations of complex data into uniquely illuminating and explanatory inferences (interpretations and reconstructions). Nor is the distinction I am drawing between these two sorts of "intuitions" meant in any way to belittle the values of unusual perceptivities and sensitivities. On the contrary, like most other clinicians I rate these very highly; but beyond that I consider their utilization in systematic clinical research to present us with the difficult and challenging problem of simultaneously treating them both as *tools* of investigation and as *objects* of investigation. Additionally, I would emphasize two points: first, that no matter how highly we may value the intuitive and perceptive aspects of preconscious and unconscious functioning, they cannot do away with the necessity for conscious and logical analytic thinking in psychological and psychoanalytic science any more than in the mathematical and physical sciences, the fields where the intuitive has been best documented and illustrated; second, that sometimes global clinical assessments are not so much a function of preconscious elaboration of overt and subliminal cues, in the positive and productive sense mentioned, as they are reflections of a disinclination for the hard work of conscious explication. To put the same thought more crassly: a tendency to global thinking, with an

* For a somewhat different point of view regarding preconscious functioning, cf. Kubie.[64, 65]

accompanying distaste for quantitative and qualitative differentiation, is not always found to be related to unusual clinical intuitive capacities.

To be sure, it is always possible that an apparently well-explicated interpretation or prediction is actually a rationalization of a preconscious elaboration of other cues than those mentioned. But it is also possible for it to be a rational exposition of theoretically relevant parameters as perceived and "measured." There is no easy and simple way objectively to distinguish between these; but I believe that consistent attempts at detailed explication, including efforts subjectively to describe the processes involved, will help to make meaningful distinction possible.

Of special pertinence to the field of human psychology is a third sort of intuition, which appears to be based on an unusual degree of awareness in oneself of processes which in most people would be unconscious. This phenomenon is seen most clearly in some psychotics, and in a few highly gifted neurotics and "normals." Outstanding and well-known examples in philosophy and literature are Nietzsche, Schopenhauer, and Dostoevski. In severe psychopathology, these unusual self-insights are regularly accompanied by unusual lack of insight and reality testing in other areas. Since they refer specifically to oneself, their validity in terms of estimation of others is largely a function of the universality of the phenomena involved. They clearly lower the threshold of perception of the same phenomena in others, and not necessarily only through projection. Intuitions of this sort, then, while of great value for heuristic psychological science as well as for art and philosophy, have only restricted applicability to the *differential* estimation of psychological parameters in others, i.e., to assessment, in contrast to the first two sorts mentioned.

Finally, there is that sort of "intuition" which is nothing more than a guess, motivated by internal or external pressures to produce something in the way of assessments or interpretations. Good examples of externally motivated guesses can be found in forced ratings, forced predictions, and forced interpretations of tests, in the absence of adequate data on which to base these.

In general it can be stated, I think, that all the varieties of intuition discussed can be right, or they can be wrong. A possible exception to this statement should be made for the self-awareness type of intuition, which is, so to speak, right by definition, and can be wrong only in the sense of being distorted or projected. If the pure guess is right, that is a matter of chance alone. If the creative preconscious problem-solving intuition is partially wrong, we are unlikely to hear about it in that form; but I have had occasion to witness both "right" and "wrong" intuitions of this sort in highly gifted and creative people, in which the "wrongness" could most reasonably be attributed in some instances to distorting effects of unconscious fantasies; in others, however, to insufficient experience in the fields involved to permit accurate preconscious problem-solving.

The pertinence of the foregoing to our particular problem of examining the usefulness and limitations of individual prediction for our purposes is, I think, apparent. It will be exemplified to some degree when we present and discuss some actual predictions from our series, and to a fuller extent in the projected systematic analysis.

b. Omitting entirely any discussion of deductive and inductive theoretical bases for prediction, I shall treat the fields of *correlational* and *actuarial prediction* with some brevity, having handled the latter in more detail in a previous statement.[7] Correlational prediction is what is ordinarily meant by the term prediction in experimental psychological research.* Two or more variables having been hypothesized as being associated, either on theoretical grounds or on the basis of empirical observations, either causally or not, their relationship is then subjected to formal investigation, usually but not necessarily in terms of correlational techniques. If significant positive or negative correlations are consistently found, then variable A is said to be positively or negatively predictive of variable B to such and such an extent; or nonpredictive if very low correlations, approaching zero, are found. The predictability under consideration may be longitudinal in the sense that A is predictive of B, or of the same variable A′, at some later time; or it may be entirely horizontal, in the sense that C is predictive of D at the same moment of time.†

* My use of these terms is my own, of relatively long standing, and is not in entire agreement with other usages in the literature (e.g., ref. 71). In particular, the term *actuarial prediction* is often used in a wider sense than I give to it, to denote any prediction based on previously established statistical relationships between measures of assessment and behaviors.

† Illustrative examples for readers who are not too familiar with this sort of investigation would be studies examining the predictive value of infant test scores for later I.Q. scores;[3, 27] or the predictive value of aptitude tests for academic achievement; or the predictive value of a given objective or projective test, or test battery, for other measures of behavior. In the field of psychopathology proper, the hypothesis that the children of parents judged to be "immature" will show a significantly higher incidence of developmental disturbances and severe psychopathology than will a comparable group of children of more "mature" parents (cf. Pavenstedt and Sander[76]) implies a correlational prediction, independently of other more individualized assessments and predictions which may result from following the cases over time, and without reference to the question of the meaning and validity of the original assessments or the theoretical implications of the hypothesis itself. As one example out of many from our own developmental studies: a specific question under current investigation, whether the time of onset of social smiling is at all predictive of the time of onset of stranger anxiety, can best be handled through correlational techniques.

The values of correlational prediction are as frequently underestimated by the clinician as its limitations are overlooked by the experimentalist and psychometrician. If theoretically based, the demonstration of some degree of predictability by this method leads not only to partial validation of theory but often suggests investigation of other variables in the attempt to increase the level of predictability attained, as can also the negative result of demonstrated *lack* of predictive power. If purely empirically based, the greatest caution is indicated in accepting the validity of correlations which might be due to chance alone, even if high significances are initially obtained; but once validity is clearly established through cross-validation or other procedures, successful correlational predictions of this sort can also lead to valuable heuristic and theoretical gains.

That individual predictions can serve important functions beyond those inherent in the method of correlational prediction is a thesis fundamental to our whole methodology of single case study, predictive and otherwise; * but it is also true that for many questions in psychology and psychopathology, correlational predictions on larger populations are strongly indicated. A major practical obstacle to the utilization of correlational predictions based on psychoanalytic developmental and psychopathologic theory is the amount of time necessary to make valid assessments of the theoretically pertinent variables. For an example of a single variable hypothesis that would in principle be better tested in this manner than by individual predictions, see page 40.

Actuarial prediction, on the other hand, in spite of some superficial resemblances, is essentially different in its nature, and therefore in its uses. In pure culture,[7] it is based exclusively on frequency distributions, in strict homology to life-expectancy tables and other insurance statistics from which the name is derived. Its theoretical basis, then, is not a theory or hypothesis in the particular scientific field involved but, rather, probability theory as such.†

Frequency distributions can, of course, suggest all sorts of investiga-

* Cf. footnote p. 13.

† The distinction here is between probability theory as the theoretical basis of the *prediction* and as the basis of whatever statistical methods are used in evaluating both assessments and predictive results. Meehl's distinction between the validating and the analytic-structural use of statistics [71] is an overlapping but not identical one. For examples of many sorts of statistical predictions representing mixtures of the correlational and actuarial as these terms are used by me here, as well as for its general interest and value, the reader is referred to Meehl's important monograph. A discussion of points of agreement and disagreement with some of the analyses and conclusions of this author, although of real pertinence to our predictive studies in general, would take us too far afield for the limited purposes of this chapter.

tions of relationships between parameters, as witness much productive epidemiologic research of recent years. There is, moreover, no question but that in psychiatry and psychoanalysis we could profitably use more knowledge of the incidence and prevalence of behavioral patterns, including developmental and psychopathologic behaviors, than we actually possess.[5, 6] But *predictions* of the occurrence of phenomena based solely on already well-established actuarial statistics have essentially no direct heuristic or theoretical potential, although the statistics themselves do. Their interest for us in the context of this discussion lies, rather, in their *negative* potential. By this I mean that there is always the danger of unrecognized triviality in an individual prediction which appears to be theoretically or "intuitively" based but which, on an actuarial basis alone, is very likely to be correct. The extreme of triviality in this respect would occur if we should predict the appearance of behavioral or intrapsychic phenomena of near universality without quantitative, qualitative, or sequential parameters being included in the predictions. It is obvious that such a predictive series would automatically be completely successful—and completely meaningless. Parenthetically, the lack of accurate "natural history" knowledge of prevalence and incidence makes the indispensable statistical evaluation of the results of a series of individual predictions such as ours a more difficult task than would be the case if such knowledge were available.

c. I would define *fortunetelling predictions,*[7] or prophecies, as those containing in themselves unspoken predictions of unpredictable significant environmental parameters. The demonstrable importance of many such variables in co-determining behavior constitutes an inherent theoretical limitation to predictability in some areas of human psychology (cf. p. 10), independently of those other limitations due to inadequacies of knowledge, theory, and assessment measures. Clearly, if we wish one of the uses of attempted predictions to be the examination and ultimate improvement of assessment and theory, it is necessary to distinguish between these two sorts of unpredictability and to avoid unrecognized fortunetelling to the greatest possible extent. In practice, however, it is not always easy to make this distinction in certain sorts of medium- and long-term predictions. I have discussed elsewhere two ways of making meaningful long-term predictions which do not involve fortunetelling: the use of contingency predictions; and the formulation of what I have termed negative predictions (see refs. 5, 7, and later discussion below). Here I should like to stress another aspect of the subject. Having repeatedly stated the obvious importance of avoiding predictions of this variety, I should now like to point out, on the basis of subsequent experience, that an over-anxious avoidance of anything that might conceivably involve fortunetelling can be unprofitably restrictive in inhibiting both conscious and preconscious problem-solving. A positive, long-term, noncontingency prediction of future behaviors is *not* fortunetelling under one or more of the following circumstances: when it is theoretically assumed that the particular behavior will be relatively independent of later changes in the environment; or when it is felt that the environmental parameters most pertinent to the predicted behavior can themselves be predicted (e.g., future attitudes and actions of the parents); or when it is predicted that in specific areas the organism will shape the environment itself more than it is shaped by it. (For an example of the second of these assumptions, see predictions #17 and 18; of the third, see #2.)

V. Predictions are ordinarily couched in positive terms; it is predicted that something *will* occur. There is a special and sometimes useful form of prediction which I have called *negative.* It consists essentially of predicting the absence of something on the grounds that conditions necessary for its development or occurrence are absent. A paradigmatic formulation of such a prediction would read: "Of all the *n* subjects under study, only subjects A, B, C, and D, have the possibility of manifesting behavior *x*," which is the same as saying, "E, F, G, etc., will *not* manifest behavior *x*;" hence the term negative. The basis for such a prediction lies in the assumption that we know, or think we know, necessary but not sufficient conditions for the development of a given behavior; which is true, I think, for much of psychoanalytic psychopathology.[5] For an example, see prediction #12.

Negative predictions are also applicable to those instances when one of several conditions, which together are considered necessary *and* sufficient, is itself unpredictable (e.g., an environmental event; cf. p. 21). In this case, however, a positive contingency prediction, if it is possible to formulate one, has greater power as a method, in that it is more likely to be proved true or false.

The advantages and limitations of this method are, I believe, obvious. Its usefulness in a small sample is dependent upon the frequency of occurrence of the phenomenon being predicted. If it is relatively rare, the probability is high that the predictive result will be indeterminate; i.e., the behavior will not occur in either group, and nothing will have been proved or disproved. If, on the other hand, the phenomenon is a frequently occurring one, or if the sample is large, an ordinary experimental design involving correlational prediction is perhaps a more natural way to handle the question of necessary but not sufficient conditions. The advantage of the negative prediction in these circumstances lies solely, but importantly, in the attention it focuses upon possible variable discovery while following a small number of cases continuously and intensively.

A special type of negative prediction in the field of biopsychological relationships is exemplified by Mirsky's propositions concerning the pathogenesis of peptic ulcer and pernicious anemia.[74, 75, 101] Here, formally considered, high and low pepsinogen levels respectively are hypothesized as necessary but not sufficient conditions for the development of these diseases; and predictions of the theoretically based correlational type are then set up for testing the hypothesis. I mention these studies here not only because they represent, in my opinion, some of the best conceptualizations extant in the complex and usually oversimplified field of biopsychological interactions, but also because they well illustrate a point of major significance to psychopathology in general: how innate variables can both shape experience and elicit different responses to similar experiences.*

VI. Assuming that the headings listed under VI, VII, VIII and IX are self-explanatory, I shall conclude this discussion of our predictive worksheet with a few comments about *criterion measures.* Our advice to ourselves to explicate these in advance whenever possible implies, correctly, that it is often not possible, at least for us. It is only in recent years that we have become sufficiently impressed with the advantage of so doing to make consistent, serious efforts in this direction. The values lie partly in areas which I have already discussed: the sharper definition of concepts and the study of the processes of interpretation. Beyond these, however, we are here concerned with the question of different *levels* of *validation* of the predictions themselves. If predictions are couched in terms of overt behaviors, there will eventually be little room for doubt whether they were correct, incorrect, or too poorly formulated to permit a decision. When the criterion measures are matters of clinical judgment and assessment of intrapsychic variables, there is clearly a different level of objectivity involved when this judgment is made by the predictor, with his inevitable investment in having the prediction verified, or by independent judges without knowledge of the prediction. If the criterion assessment necessarily involves depth interpretation, then the independent judges must obviously be trained in psychoanalytic theory and practice. Some of our predictions are of this nature and have to be judged in this manner, interpretatively. I see no reason whatsoever to consider this a methodological weakness. On the contrary, it leads directly to just that study of the

* Cf. ref. 9 and discussions elsewhere in this chapter.

processes of interpretation to which I have repeatedly referred as one major, if secondary, aim of our own investigations, and one which I hope will be increasingly pursued elsewhere also. But having said this, and thereby expressed explicit and emphatic disagreement with those who feel that the study of intrapsychic phenomena has no place in psychological science, it is also necessary to go further than this, in two directions. In the first place, our interest in intrapsychic variables is ultimately concerned with their effects on behavior and with their explanatory and predictive value for behavior, using this term, of course, in its modern sense to include verbal and expressive reports of subjective experience. Secondly, all assessments of intrapsychic variables, correct or incorrect, conscious or "intuitive," are *based* on behaviors in the sense defined, and cannot be based on anything else.* For both of these reasons, then, the attempt to explicate single or multiple behavioral criteria for the validation or invalidation of a prediction concerned with intrapsychic variables seems to me to be strongly indicated. When it is possible, it greatly facilitates objective judgment of success or failure of the prediction, doing away with the necessity for consensual and other questionable criteria of validity. Where it is not possible, our best recourse is the minimal requirement that there be a statement of what criterion measures actually were used in judging the outcome of the prediction, as outlined in Table I.

Some Selected Examples of Predictions

In presenting now a few predictions from our series, I wish to make it clear that there has been no effort to make these in any way either a random or an otherwise representative sample.† The examples have been selected to illustrate some, but not all, of the points I have been discussing. In view of the subject matter of this volume, moreover, they are much more heavily weighted toward psychopathological and away from normal developmental theory than is true of the series as a whole, although examples of predictions based on new hypotheses in the latter field are included, since no normal sequences are without their psychopathological theoretical implications, and vice versa. Two of the children (and their

* Unless, of course, one wishes to invoke extrasensory perception. But, if some or all of these phenomena should ever be demonstrated to be real, they must then have modes of action; and these would be behaviors too.

† The entire series, as stated earlier, is being analyzed individually and across cases. This systematic analysis is far from completed, and must in any case await the opportunity to verify or prove false some of the longer term predictions made.

respective parents) represented, Patty S.* and Tommy T., are, for various reasons, among the best studied in the group.

In summarizing in each case the predictive outcome, if any, and its significance, I shall usually, and regrettably, have to ignore much of the material available to us at the time of prediction and the time of evaluation, and restrict myself to a few findings pertinent to the specific content of the prediction, without reference to the historical facts of the case, or to other assessments, predictions, postdictions, and relationships. I can also not enter here into the all-important question of the reliability and validity of the behavioral and interpretative assessments themselves. It is for these and other reasons that I find it essential to plan on presenting one or more cases at great length. In so doing, it will be possible better to illustrate the limited if indispensable place that predictive attempts have in our over-all methods of study, and also better to exemplify the actual number and levels of assessments entering into them.

In order to lessen the probability of identification of the subjects, the dates on which the predictions were written are omitted, and only the approximate ages of the children at that time given. Parentheses are taken from the original predictions. Any additional material is enclosed in brackets.

#1. Arthur G., "Prenatal. (Mixed deductive-inductive, [with] probably some "intuitive" [aspects]. Medium and long term. Based on prenatal interviews with mother and father to date. See these for explication of interpretations.) [No mention of criterion measures.] If first child is a boy, father's demands upon him will be so great in terms of using him as a "defense" against his own severe castration anxiety, [i.e., excessive demands upon him for "masculinity"], that serious difficulties for the child may confidently be predicted. By this I do not necessarily mean severe pathology, which I do not consider predictable on this basis alone, but clear-cut developmental difficulties which can be specifically related to problems of feminine identification. If first child is a girl, predict [father will show] a panicky resentment toward his wife and baby (short-term). If child is a boy, predict [he] will also run up against mother's strong castrativeness and will be in for a rough time after early infancy. The mother-child relationship during early infancy [time not defined] should be a smooth one."

Predictive outcome: ++ for all parts of the prediction, as evaluated from record up to age of 5 years 9 months. Criterion measures used: results of infant testing, and observation during testing; behavioral observations,

* This girl is the subject of the forthcoming publication referred to earlier.[10] See this for detailed explication of the interpretative bases of some predictions.

impressions, and interpretations of series of play interviews; independent ratings by trained psychological observers, without knowledge of predictions; reports by parents in office interviews; observations and reports during home visits. (See record for content.) Summary of a few findings pertinent to this prediction: (1) Flourishing early infancy, until 10½ months. (2) Excessive timidity late in first year and thereafter. (3) High overt anxiety rating during pre-school period. (4) Characterized as "passive" and clinging by observers. (5) During period between 4½ and 5+ years development of severe "baby talk" speech disturbance, almost unintelligible at times, accompanied by grimacing, which greatly disturbed both parents. (6) Much taking of female (mother's and sisters') roles in play sessions, and in spontaneous play as observed and reported at home. (7) Next younger sister is treated as a "boy" by father, who, for example, plays ball with her rather than with Arthur.

Estimated qualitative significance of outcome: High in several respects, but with definite reservations. I have selected this particular prediction to illustrate several points. In the first place, it is a good example of one that was not too well explicated; in this case, I think, primarily because it was not fully explicable, rather than for technical reasons. In other words, the statement as to the nature of the prediction being "mixed inductive-deductive, with probably some 'intuitive' aspects" overestimated somewhat the formulatable theoretical basis, and correspondingly underestimated the "intuitive." One source of this confusion may have been the complete explicability of the interpretative assessment of the parents.

Four separate predictions are contained in this example, three of them applicable, the fourth, "If the child is a girl, etc.," not. Since they are not interdependent, they should have been formulated separately. The one, that the mother-child relationship in early infancy would be smooth, was based on an appraisal of mother's conscious attitudes and expectations, as well as on inferences about her unconscious needs and fantasies. At this point the whole concept of a child was that of a helpless infant; and it seemed highly probable that this woman, *at this time and for this child,* would feel a strong sense of fulfillment at birth, would thoroughly enjoy the symbiotic and anaclitic aspects of early infancy, but would have greater difficulty and less gratification with an older infant. (I stress the qualification, *"at this time and for this child."* Whenever we feel that we have sufficient data for a valid assessment, we regularly attempt to predict how the mother will respond differentially to different developmental stages in the child; * but, in principle, we consider it fallacious to regard

* Cf. Coleman, Kris and Provence.[19]

the parents' personalities as static, unmodifiable givens, since we regard pregnancy, childbirth, and parenthood as powerful potential sources of development for both parents.* As a concrete example, the prediction in this respect for the third child of this mother was a very different one. In general, the severer the neurotic structure, i.e., the more pathogenic the role of unconscious motivation, and the more powerful the "repetition compulsion," the lower the probability of the occurrence of such adaptive learning leading to change.)

To these assessments was then added the specific factor of strong and behaviorally effective castrativeness in this woman, applicable to the contingency prediction, "If the child is a boy, etc.," with the implication that this would affect the object relationships as soon as the loosening of the symbiotic and anaclitic ties occurred. This assessment of "castrativeness," it should be emphasized, was not in terms of a derived and epithetical way of describing hostile aggressive impulses toward men, but was, rather, a direct interpretation of transparent interview material.† It is obvious to any clinician that such material would usually not be available from a few interviews, but would often require a long period of investigation through psychoanalytic therapy for its reliable and valid estimation. I mention this as one specific example of the sort of lack of systematic comparability across all cases to which I referred earlier.

Another pertinent set of variables entering into this prediction, not mentioned at all in its original written explication, were those dealing with the relationships between the parents, as it was felt they would affect the mother's handling of her conflicts and those of her husband at this time.

The third sub-prediction, that the father would use a male child in the service of defending against his own "severe castration anxiety," was made on a high subjective level of confidence. This implied, to this predictor at any rate, not only dynamic and structural but also topographic ‡ and

* Cf. G. L. Bibring's concept of pregnancy as a "maturational crisis." [15]

† The transparency was due in part to some pertinent overt behavioral data, the publication of which would reveal identities of the subjects to friends and acquaintances locally. These and corresponding data on other subjects are available under appropriate restrictions.

‡ In contrast to some statements and implications in the literature (e.g., A. Freud [35]), I feel strongly that the structural point of view, indispensable as it is, has by no means done away with the necessity for topographic considerations in the explanation of behavior. The overlap between the two, while considerable, is far from a complete one. The need for both does not apply only to clinical theory. On the contrary, if one agrees, as I do, with Rapaport that developmental theory requires the formulation and experi-

economic assessments of this and other aspects of the father's personality. (No comparable genetic data were available at this time.) Specifically, the fear of castration was seen not as an historical residue of a near universal but as a dynamically highly effective, totally unconscious, ubiquitously and repetitively manifested, and guilt-reinforced phenomenon in this man; with resultant expenditure of "large quantities of energy" * in defending against it, and consequent utilization of all possible sources for combating it with less energy expenditure. (In contrast to the mother, the father's pathology was seen as deep-seated and essentially unmodifiable except possibly through long-term therapy.)

If one now asks oneself what clinical or theoretical significance can reasonably, if informally, be attributed to the successful outcome of this particular prediction, pending systematic analysis across areas of prediction and across cases, it is by no means easy to give even a subjectively satisfactory answer. As is the case in a substantial proportion of our successful predictions to date, it raises more questions than it answers, if, indeed, it answers any, by itself, in anything but a tentative and suggestive way. It illustrates the previously mentioned values of attempted predictions in focusing attention on the processes of assessment themselves. Beyond that, it could be said to tend to some undetermined extent to validate the methods of assessment and the pertinence of the constructs being assessed. The methods, however, really require separate demonstration outside the scope of this chapter; while the degree of construct and theory validation offered by a single prediction, no matter how successful, is usually impossible to state objectively in even approximate probability terms. The chief theoretical interest of such a prediction taken alone lies in its theoretical implications rather than in validation. Our prenatal predictions deal in general with the course of pregnancy, the immediate postpartum responses of the mother, and early aspects of the parent-child relationships. The fact that we are willing occasionally to make prenatal predictions about later stages of the child's development, as in this case, implies very strong convictions about the role of experience in general, and specific experiences in particular, in shaping personality development. It does *not* imply a rampant environmentalism which ignores the role of innate factors in the organism, not only in determining differential responses to similar environmental configurations but also

---

mental testing of a psychoanalytically based learning theory,[85, 87] this would differ from current learning theories primarily through the inclusion of both structural and topographic parameters.

* For a discussion of the necessity for, and obstacles to, the meaningful revision and elaboration of psychoanalytic energy theory, see ref. 11.

in strongly shaping the environment itself. In all such prenatal predictions there are potentially important theoretical contaminants in terms of possible preconscious perceptions and expectations of indirect or direct hereditary transmission of some of the parents' biological and primary psychological equipment. Examination of the area and nature of each individual prediction can give us a rough subjective idea of the probability of such contamination in a given case. In the example under discussion this probability seems very low indeed; in others it must be taken quite seriously, as, for example, when a psychotic development is predicted for a child of near psychotic parents (cf. p. 15 above).*

#2. Stephen P., age 4 years. "Predict Stephen will rank among the top two or three cases in our series in 'mental health,' as judged by later independent psychiatric and psychological evaluation. (Long term, theoretical with possible additional 'intuitive' aspects.) Based on: (1) the earliest observations of Stephen as an infant, and his development in the first few months of life; (2) the quality of the early mother-child and later parent-child relationship; (3) the quality of his ego functioning as followed up to this age."

Predictive outcome: Undetermined (±?). No outcome possible yet for this long-term prediction.

Discussion: This is one of a series of such nonspecific and global predictions of eventual "mental health" rankings and ratings of our subjects, in contrast to more specific predictions of symptoms, traits, and test behavior. (The subject of prediction #1 was subsequently, at two years of age, predicted to be among the lowest third of our cases in this respect.) We consider them important to make in spite of the obvious difficulty in explicating simple objective criterion measures for any but the most psychopathologic outcomes. For all other cases we are confronted, as the future independent judges will be, by difficulty in defining mental health in other than negative terms; i.e., the absence of symptoms of mental illness of varying degrees of severity. Much has been written and spoken about this question. In view of space limitations, I cannot appropriately enter here into a review and discussion of either my own or others'

* I cannot here discuss the methodologic and conceptual problems involved in any attempt systematically to study basic and unanswered questions about the differential interactive roles of endowment and experience in the production of behaviors, normal and pathologic. I bring them up merely to emphasize that they are, in my opinion, central to both developmental and psychopathologic theory. Their solution demands, on the psychological level alone, better measures of relatively autonomous as well as nonautonomous ego functions and drive organizations than we as yet possess.[9, 48] It also calls for continuous efforts better to conceptualize and investigate biopsychological relationships.[6, 9, 74]

opinions and speculations in this field. But I think it indicated to state roughly and in gross terms what sort of criteria we do and do not have in mind in making the predictions, independently of whether they do justice to the concept itself, and also independently for the time being of what sort of measures are available for judging the criteria. We do *not* have in mind a simple concept of adjustment as the sole index of mental health, although we obviously cannot leave it out of account either. At the other end of the scale, we also do not mean creativity and productivity, which are certainly important, and, incidentally, far from identical, variables in their own right, and equally certainly can be markedly affected by psychopathology. Since the relationship is both empirically and theoretically far from a simple one, however, we prefer not to equate them with mental health but, rather, to relate them to it in the context of other parameters. What we *do* mean by "mental health" in these global predictions, instead, is (1) the aforementioned negative criterion of absence of significant psychopathology; and (2) the demonstration of maximally effective functioning in various areas within the limitations of endowment and of socioeconomic and other reality restrictions. Following Freud and Erikson [25] in part, we stress particularly the capacity for gratifying object relationships, including a reasonably normal sexuality; the capacity for work, and gratification in work; and the possession of a strong sense of identity, as perhaps the best gross indicators of mental health. None of this, of course, answers questions about measures of these criteria; nor can a purposeful oversimplification of the criteria themselves obscure the need for the assessment of markedly different dynamic, structural, and economic factors underlying such apparently similar behavioral phenomena as could be subsumed, for example, under a judgment of "high work capacity." *

To return to the particular example under discussion: the three reasons originally given for this prediction are specific enough and in themselves plausible enough to constitute an adequate shorthand explication of a predictive base of a theoretical sort. Actually, however, they well illustrate a typical problem in formulating individual predictions on thoroughly studied subjects; and it is for this reason that I have selected this particular "mental health" prediction as an example for discussion. At first glance this looks something like a multiple variable formulation. Perhaps it is. In fact, it probably is to some meaningful extent. But if so,

* I have briefly discussed elsewhere [5] problems raised by different motivational structures underlying similar behaviors, emphasizing the potentialities of finer phenomenologic description for at least differentiating such variables on the overt behavioral level alone. Gill [42] has also touched on this issue, as has Frenkel-Brunswick.[34]

the three variables are almost certainly not independent, but interdependent to an unknown degree. The actual prediction was probably determined much more by our assessment of Stephen's ego functioning and personality functioning in general, at four years of age and previously, than by the other two factors taken alone. It is possible that had we seen him at four years for the first time, and then had the opportunity to study him and his parents thoroughly, we would have felt free to make the same prediction; but it would have been without the first-hand knowledge of the rate and smoothness of his development that entered into the assessment. On many formally assessed and rated and ranked variables, Stephen had consistently ranked at or near the top of our group. Among these I shall mention: warmth and discrimination in object relations, reality testing, active mastery of the environment (a rating on which we set particular store as one early behavioral measure of "ego strength"), early identification with a masculine father, free expression of nonhostile aggression,* free but well-controlled expression of "smaller amounts" of hostile aggression, relatively low behavioral and inferred anxiety levels, good capacity for cognitive problem-solving for his age, and outstanding problem solving in "critical periods" of libidinal and object-relation development.

As one part of this picture at four years we noted the fact that the early mother-child relationship had been assessed on an equally high level. This mother with this child received the highest over-all assessment of the mother-child relationship during the first eighteen months of any "couple" in our series, in terms both of over-all qualitative statements and of nine specific ratings of the qualities of the mother-child relationship which we routinely make at intervals of about two months. Apart from its high level, this series of ratings was distinguished from those on other highly rated mother-child relationships in our group by its relative constancy over time, in contrast to the much more usual fluctuations of some of the ratings during different developmental stages of infancy.

There is surely no reason to doubt that there was a close connection between what we saw in infancy and at four years, nor that the relationship was in part a causal one; i.e., that the mother's handling of the infant contributed significantly to the sort of functioning we observed later. But we are far from certain as to the extent and limitations of this contribu-

* This concept of ours, not in general use, should be distinguished from Hartmann's "neutralized" aggression, in that its implications for both energy theory and developmental theory are different; in some respects, in fact, opposite. For future discussion of this, see ref. 11.

tion, just as we do not know to what extent the outstandingly superior neonatal equipment of this infant, listed as one of the three predictive bases, contributed to the excellence of the relationship between him and his mother. (This mother, parenthetically, is an intellectually and culturally quite limited woman who, except in her role as a mother, did not have a strong personal appeal to any of the observers and raters. Because of her relative lack of interest in the psychological part of the Child Research Council program, and a slightly shy and anxious distaste for being interviewed, we had less verbal information from and about her prenatally than is true of most of our parents. She was nonetheless assessed on a high level as regards the "mental health" criteria mentioned earlier. With the two younger siblings of Stephen, the mother-child relationship was also rated highly; but somewhat less so with the middle sibling, a brother, than with the other two. This second child was less outstanding neonatally than was Stephen, and his development was less smooth, particularly in terms of preverbal communication. In the second half of the second year, concomitant with a gradual but definite decrease in the rated qualities of this mother-child interaction, a speech disturbance was manifested, which has not yet entirely disappeared at three and a half years.)

To get back to our three partially interdependent predictive bases: we surely would not have felt free to make a long-term "mental health" prediction on the basis of the early mother-child relationship alone, at least not in such a positive sense, although short-term predictions in terms of developmental theory were confidently made. I stress this fact because of the frequency with which at present everything in the way of severe psychopathology is attributed in some child psychiatric circles to experiences in the first year or so of life, disregarding both innate variables and later childhood experience. On the level of convictions based on clinical experience and reinforced by the results of experimental observations on human infants,[90, 97] as well as controlled animal experimentation,[4, 14, 89] there can be no question of the importance of early experience in shaping personality. But a statement of this degree of generality commits itself to practically nothing in terms of theoretical explanation or prediction, nor does it take into account the very great differences between different sorts of experiences, and their timing in terms of the maturation of perceptive and other cognitive apparatuses. Questions of this sort in respect to both normal and deviant development again cannot be systematically exemplified or discussed within the space limitations of this chapter, although they constitute a major part of our own and others' investigative interest. Continuing, rather, on this global and undifferentiated level of discussion, our present thinking on the subject of the early mother-child relationship as a pathogenetic factor can roughly be formulated as follows: (1) An outstandingly "good" mother-child relationship during infancy, as defined in binary terms, is possibly a guarantee against the most severe psychotic manifestations of childhood and later, not only because a variety of experiences with mother provide the matrix for the whole of development and serve as the prototype of object relations in general, but possibly also because the very existence of such a relationship as defined is an index that the innate equipment and learning capacity of the child is not such as to make a psychotic outcome probable. (2) It in no way, however, guarantees against significant degrees of psychopathology, the necessary antecedent conditions for which [6] may occur as the result of later experiences (cf. prediction #1). (3) Inversely, a "bad" mother-child relationship in infancy undoubtedly contributes significantly to psychopathology, through the experiences and even more through the *lack* of experiences implicit in it. (An important variety of "bad" is represented by the literal absence of a mother, as studied by Spitz,[90] Spitz and Wolf,[97] Goldfarb,[43, 44] Bowlby,[16] and others.) In addition to this immediate experimental aspect, it can also, under certain circumstances and in analogy to what we said above, serve as an indicator of innate deficiencies in the infant, and also as a possible predictor of future pathogenic experiences with the mother. (4) Although some of the deleterious effects of absent or "bad" mothering in infancy may well be partially irreversible, and we personally are inclined on theoretical grounds to think that they are, there is as good as no empirical evidence to demonstrate this. We have a great deal of evidence, on the other hand, to show that there can be very "bad" early mother-child relationships the observable effects of which are in part reversible through surrogate objects or through adaptive changes in the mother.

Finally, it should be stated that we do not consider this prediction for this particular child to be of the fortunetelling variety. The explication, to have been more complete, should have contained a sub-prediction to the effect that the parents' handling of this boy during the oncoming oedipal conflicts as well as later would continue to meet his most important needs and to help him in necessary problem-solving. Beyond this, the prediction implied the proposition that short of such drastic environmental changes as the early death of one or both parents, Stephen would significantly shape his own environment and experiences (cf. the discussion on p. 22) and had already attained the capacity to profit from being confronted with moderately difficult problems. This highly individualized proposition can, of course, be wrong. If so, the failure of our prediction would, I think, be fully as instructive as its success.

Our provisional confidence in this prediction has been heightened rather than lowered by what has occurred in the meantime. Stephen is now in his seventh year. Some months after this prediction was formulated, while still in his fifth year, a baby sister was born. To an even greater extent than had been anticipated (and in part predicted), Stephen found himself confronted with more difficult problems than he had encountered up to this point. As we assessed what was going on at the time, his sister not only appeared (correctly) to be a much more serious rival for his mother's love and attention than his younger brother had been, but also provided him with a classic reinforcement of his budding castration anxiety within the framework of a normal and rapidly developing oedipal situation. In order not to make a case history out of a single prediction, it suffices to say that for the past four months Stephen has given every evidence of having solved this problem too. His functioning in all the respects mentioned earlier is again, after a period of relative disturbance, on the same high level for his age that it was previously.

As further, and in some ways contrasting, examples of early psychopathological predictions based on qualities of the parents, of the infant, and of the mother-child relationship, I present the following:

#3. Sammy R., age 5 months. "Predict marked pathological behaviors will be seen soon in this infant. Unable to specify beyond what is already present. Based on assessment of highly unusual mother-child relationship, with father and grandparents as inadequate surrogates. Symptoms may be somatic or behavioral or both. Major [predictive] base is that handling of child, [deleted to avoid identification], constitutes to our perception a true affect deprivation." [Was not certain of this until recent observation and interview; found relationship initially difficult to assess.] "Short term, theoretical and clinical-inductive, contaminated [by beginning behavioral pathology already present]. Criterion measures: behavioral."

Predictive outcome: ++ Criterion measures used: observation of behaviors, markedly lowered scores on developmental testing.

Significance of successful outcome: For reasons of discretion, I am not able to describe here the particular behaviors involved, nor the details of mother's handling, both of which would reveal identities of the subjects to themselves and their acquaintances.* Most of the theoretical and clinical interest of this assessment and prediction is thereby lost. What remains is a nonspecific example of some short-term pathologic effects of experience

* Cf. footnote p. 27.

on an infant who, as far as we could judge by our neonatal and early postnatal assessments, did not himself contribute significantly to the disturbed relationship or the later symptoms through innate deficiencies or abnormalities in his equipment or its maturation.

My chief purpose in bringing up this prediction, however, is that it serves as a necessary introduction to another made five months later on the same child.

#4. Sammy R., age 10 months. "Predict that Sammy will *not* develop an autistic psychosis in childhood. Based on social responses of the infant to mother and to the examiners (see records of observations and test behaviors). Medium term, inductive, negative of a special sort." (Another prediction made simultaneously to the effect that Sammy would rank among the lowest four or five cases in our series in later "mental health" assessment will not be discussed or explicated here.)

Predictive outcome: Undetermined (±?).

Discussion: This prediction is meant to test, insofar as it can, a highly specific psychopathological hypothesis concerning the etiology of early infantile autism, first described and investigated, and more recently followed up, by Kanner,[54-56] and also studied as part of the area of childhood psychosis by Mahler,[69, 70] Despert,[21] Rank and her associates,[79, 80] Weil,[100] and others. The personalities of both parents, especially the mother, as well as their way of life, correspond classically to the descriptions of the parents of such children in the literature. In fact, a visiting child psychologist with some experience in this area who observed Sammy with his mother several times, and also had access to his record, was so struck by this fact that she flatly predicted that he *would* develop an autistic syndrome. For the purpose of testing the hypothesis of a purely experiential etiology of this disorder, it makes no difference whether the prediction is expressed in positive or negative terms. My reason for formulating it negatively is simply to express my opinion that neither the parents' personalities nor the resulting affect deprivation are sufficient conditions to produce this behavior (cf. the discussion by Kanner in ref. 56 and by Mahler in ref. 70). Specifically, this infant, while manifesting marked behavioral pathology, seemed to us a very unlikely candidate for the development of what Kanner has termed the two primary symptoms of infantile autism, extreme self-isolation and "obsessive insistence on sameness," to judge by his manner of responding to people and to experimental test items.

A formal logical analysis of a prediction of this sort raises some points of interest. Although reports of infantile autism are becoming increasingly frequent, its (unknown) incidence is undoubtedly low, and the "actuarial" expectation of its occurrence in a small group of children of "normal" parents presumably very low indeed. Therefore, ignoring its theoretical base, the a priori probability of predictive success (no psychosis) is very high, and the significance of success in terms of an over-all concept of "predictability" correspondingly low. Inversely, the success of a positive prediction (psychosis) would be accorded high significance on the same grounds. These considerations would actually apply in practice to "intuitive" predictions without a theoretical base: an "intuition" that a child of ten months would *not* develop an autistic psychosis would, if proved true, hardly constitute evidence of an intuitive capacity in the predictor; but we would begin to take notice if he successfully predicted that such a psychosis would, in fact, occur, even if he were completely unable to explicate the methods of assessment or the theoretical base. When, however, as in this case, we are attempting to test a specific, largely inductive hypothesis, the situation is in principle quite different. Purely logically, the question of incidence does not arise if the theory is that of a necessary and sufficient condition (if A, then B). Under these circumstances, a low incidence of B merely implies a low incidence of A also; and a single exception is enough to disprove the hypothesis. Actually, of course, no such formalistic rigor is applicable to the thesis of a predominantly experiential etiology of infantile autism, if for no other reason than the impossibility of demonstrating that $A_1 = A$; that is, that the affect deprivation arising from this mother-child relationship is effectively the same as in cases where infantile autism does occur. Clinically, then, if our prediction is successful, we would estimate its invalidating significance for the experiential hypothesis to lie somewhere between the extremes of very low and very high just outlined. A series of such predictions would be necessary for a more convincing invalidation.

We temporarily leave the field of pathology per se for that of developmental psychology in general.

#5. Bobby F., six months. "Predict that Bobby will show strong eight-months anxiety. (Short term, theoretical.) Based on present and past use of sensory modalities, with particularly strong visual and tactual components, relatively low kinesthetic. [See below for explication of this base.]"

Predictive outcome: — and + (To be treated as a minus for statistical purposes.) Bobby showed relatively little fear of strangers at any time with mother present. (Average rating of "stranger anxiety" from seven to eighteen months was two on a five-point scale, with highest rating three.) From about twelve months on, however, he showed very high "separation anxiety" on actual separation from mother, both observationally in experimental separation, and at home, according to her reports, whether strangers or relative strangers were present, or whether he was left alone.

Estimated significance of partially unsuccessful outcome: High in terms of clarification of concepts and improvement of assessment methods. Moderately high heuristically.

Discussion: This prediction was made jointly by one of my associates and myself at a time when we were struggling (as we still are in most respects) to make some systematic sense out of relationships between sensory-motor behavior in infancy and some facets of later psychological functioning. Along with others,[13, 29, 72, 76a, 76b, 102] I had long been convinced, on both empiric and theoretical grounds, that important relationships of this sort do exist. Among these, my own chief speculative interest had focused on the idea, arrived at through a rather devious route involving perceptive aspects of the Rorschach test in relation to clinical diagnosis,[12] that differences in sensory-motor behaviors were partially predictive of later *choice of defense;* in interaction, of course, with experience also. The relationship was conceived as being associative rather than causal, with the sensory-motor behaviors being viewed as indices of biological interindividual variability in modes of reaction. I had refrained from publication of these speculations in the hope that I could acquire enough empiric data to give substance to them. At present, although our observations have strengthened the conviction that there is validity to this idea, I am still not in a position to demonstrate convincingly the existence or nature of these relationships. To help in reaching this goal, they also have been made the basis of a number of relatively long-term predictions, which will not be presented or discussed here.

At the same time, however, we also became interested in a shorter term, more delimited, and possibly more direct relationship between the use of sensory modalities in early infancy and certain fears and anxieties occurring toward the end of the first year of life, including the so-called eight-months anxiety (Spitz [91, 95]). Our chief interest in these anxiety phenomena arises from what we consider to be their central importance to developmental theory as indicators of structural change due to maturation and learning, and of shifts in libidinal and aggressive object cathexes; and we are in full agreement with Spitz [92, 95] in his over-all estimation of their genesis and significance. We also agree with this author as well as with earlier observations of Bühler and her associates [17, 18, 53] as to the general timing of anxious responses to strangers in the age range from approximately seven to eleven months, occasionally earlier. Our empiric findings as to the phenomenology of eight-months anxiety, however, are not in full agreement with Spitz's; as for instance, when he states that in his experience infants in their mothers' arms or laps at this age very rarely show anxiety at the stranger's approach.[92] The fact that our experience is a different one has also, along with other somewhat divergent findings and points of view, led us to a somewhat different conceptualization of this whole complex of phenomena, although our basic theoretical orientation toward it is in most respects closer to his than to that of Szekely [98] or of Meili.[72] At any rate, we find it necessary and profitable to distinguish between two differently operationally defined assessments, that of "stranger anxiety," and of "infantile separation anxiety." Not that these are independent; on the contrary, we think they are both to a large extent reflections of the same thing: fear of object loss. But we think also that the different ratios that we find between them, which occur even in our relatively small sample in all possible combinations (i.e., both high, both low, one high with one low), denote important variability in response to this basic fear. This, in turn, reflects on the dynamic level different configurations of other forces, such as aggression toward mother, and fear of it, on the one hand; and fear of the intruder who comes between infant and mother on the other.* Genetically, this surely implies different experiences, and possibly also innate or at least constitutional variability. Finally, and more speculatively at present, we also think that these differences may have partial (correlational) predictive value for the future course of anxiety development; that is, for the eventual predominance of castration or other mutilation fears, or of fear of loss of love. In view of the importance of these basic fears for psychopathologic developments, *extreme* degrees of infantile separation anxiety and stranger anxiety should have some differential predictive potential for psychopathology. Empirically, so far, this seems to be the case. But it must be emphasized most emphatically that these are normal developmental phenomena, whose complete absence would be highly pathological, representing either severe maturational deficit or the essential absence of a mother-child relationship.

It would not be appropriate to extend this discussion further at this time, nor to discuss our methods of assessment of these variables. I have brought up this much only for the purpose of illustrating the usefulness of an unsuccessful prediction, and to make understandable the explication of its theoretical base. Had it read, "Predict strong manifestations of infantile separation anxiety," it would have been correct. Had it gone further and added, "because of difficulty in restituting the absent mother," it would have been illuminating as well as correct. For the theory in

* Cf. Lewin's concept of father as the awakener.[67, 68]

question, as we now see it, has less to do with the genesis of fear of object loss than with variability in means of dealing with it. The hypothesis in its original form was not ours but Katherine Wolf's.* In conversations with her, at a time when we were engaged in joint work on each other's cases, she suggested that the infant who relates to his mother predominantly through vision is more prone to severe "eight-months anxiety" than is one who makes greater use of other senses for this purpose.[102] This observation was consonant with our own impressions from a less extensive experience, as well as with some theoretical considerations arising from our exploratory studies in sensory-motor behavior in general. Specifically, we find it useful to distinguish in our ratings, based on observation and experimentation, the relative predominance (for age) of visual, tactual, auditory, and kinesthetic modalities in (1) physiologic tension reduction in earliest infancy and later ("quieting"); (2) relating positively to mother and other drive objects; and (3) exploring the world of inanimate objects. These are rated separately from (4) over-all sensory responsivity, and (5) the important area of hypersensitivity (Bergman and Escalona [13]). Our present formulation of Wolf's hypothesis would read: infants who have predominantly (for their age) used the visual modality for (1) and (2) above will have much greater difficulty in restituting the absent mother † in the period of infantile separation anxiety than will those who have used the kinesthetic; with tactual and auditory modalities assigned an intermediate place in the order named. Accordingly, the manifestations of this anxiety will be more severe and more prolonged.

* The illness and early death of this investigator, before she was able to organize and publish the findings and ideas arising from her work of recent years at the Yale University Child Study Center, represents a real loss to the field of infant study. Her extensive experience with infants, prior to and during her productive collaboration with Spitz,[96, 97] in combination with her own observational and theoretical gifts, gave her an unusual potential for teaching as well as for investigation. I and my associate and collaborator Katherine Tennes would like to take this opportunity to acknowledge our debt to her in sharpening and broadening our own observational efforts.

† This does not allude, of course, to the assumed hallucinatory wish fulfillments of early infancy (Freud [36, 38]). Although the plausibility and explanatory value of this construct are high, its existence, its timing, and the sensory modalities involved are essentially unknown, but not necessarily unknowable. Behavioral observation, in conjunction with physiologic assessments, has some promise in this respect, in spite of the misleading ease with which such observations as those of mouthing and sucking movements in sleep and near sleep can be adduced as evidences of wish fulfillment. In my opinion, much more rigorous experimentation is needed to justify this conclusion. It would be of some interest to relate the use of sensory modalities in infancy to later childhood and adult dream modalities, as well as to varieties of hallucinations and illusions in psychopathologic states.

The plausibility of this "out of sight, out of mind" hypothesis is, I think, apparent. I shall not enter here into its further theoretical implications if it should be confirmed, as seems likely on the basis of the results of subsequent predictions on other cases. We should reasonably soon have enough cases at both the visual and kinesthetic-auditory ends of the scale to permit statistical validation or invalidation, which will undoubtedly be necessary in view of the complexity and multiple determination of the phenomena involved. Bobby F. represents the extreme visual case in our series so far, in terms of assessments beginning as early as three weeks of age.

I shall next present a few predictions made on one of our best studied and understood subjects, selected from a total of twenty-one, some of them interdependent, made on this child to date. In so doing, I shall have to refrain from the temptation to give a picture of the clinical and theoretical coherence in the interrelationships between the various assessments and predictions. It is hoped that it will later be possible to publish this and other cases at sufficient length, with appropriate but undistorting protection of the subjects' anonymity. In the meantime, my purpose here is again solely to illustrate and discuss some of the areas covered in our predictive series.

#6. Tommy T., age 6 months. "Predict [a.] behavioral evidence of anal retention during period of bowel training [and immediately thereafter] and [b.] development of retentive derivatives in adult personality. (Medium term and long term.) Based on hypothesis of "vectors" or "modes" being already evidenced in part in early play of infant with toys and other inanimate objects, and being partially predictive of behavior and experiences in toilet training."

This awkwardly formulated prediction was a revision of one made ten days earlier, during and immediately following an observation of this infant, which read: "There was much 'holding onto,' little 'getting' and little 'giving' [assessed, of course, for this age, in which overt 'giving' as such does not yet occur]. On this basis, a prediction of anal retentive trends is of some theoretical interest."

Predictive outcome: for a. +. Criterion measures used: reports from mother and nurses; also independent interpretations of play interviews by others; for b. Undetermined (±?), (but at present expect it to be a minus. For discussion of this, see below).

Estimated qualitative significance of successful outcome for a.: Restricted as far as the hypothesis itself is concerned; high in terms of its potential for further investigation of some important theoretical issues.

Discussion: This prediction, of limited theoretical and clinical significance in itself, nonetheless raises several points of methodologic and particularly of theoretical interest. In the first place, it is in a different category than any we have presented in that it is a purely "investigative" prediction rather than a validating or invalidating one. It aims at testing an hypothesis about which the investigator had no particular clinical conviction one way or the other when it was formulated but which appeared to be of interest and importance both in itself and as a model. Accordingly, in the subsequent handling of our predictive results as a whole, its success or failure cannot be included in statistics concerned with the validity of assessments, constructs, or established theory.

The specific hypothesis advanced could, taken alone, better be tested experimentally on a larger group than through individual predictions, since both independent and dependent variables could, in principle at least, be adequately assessed without repeated and intensive study. In fact, I doubt that it can be proved or disproved in a small sample, although our results to date tend to support it. We can already state with certainty that it (the infantile "holding" vector as defined) is not a *necessary* condition for anal retention; i.e., the latter can occur in children who showed no signs of strong "holding" tendencies in infancy. The experienced psychoanalytic clinician will correctly relate such behavior to variables in object relationships, drives, and defensive functions. In other words, strongly anal retentive behavior at this age (1½ to 2 years) usually expresses *conflict* about the mother or mother substitutes in terms of emotions, attitudes and drives.* But the validity of this statement does not, in itself, preclude the possibility that the use of this particular means of expression may imply already existing retentive trends. Our data show, as stated, that this is not always the case, that it is not a necessary condition. Whether or not it is a *sufficient* condition is not yet clearly demonstrable from our material. If it were, this might mean that the experiences of early infancy leading to the relative predominance of "holding

* That the conflicts are anything but uniform in the configurations of forces involved is exemplified on the simplest level by the great variability found in the relative degree of participation of anxiety about bodily loss, on the one hand, and negativistic aggression toward the mother, on the other. Libidinization of the retention adds a new and different dynamic of major importance (see later).

A nice illustration of a still different dynamic configuration is given by recent observations of a late toilet-trained, two year old child of a mother who works part-time. This girl's early infantile "vectors" were strongly "giving" and "throwing away" ones, with minimal "holding onto." At two years there was a period of several months during which she would retain both urine and feces in the mother's absence, but immediately upon her return would offer her the "gift" of going to the toilet and evacuating. That this behavior clearly served other purposes also does not alter the compelling picture of a retention for the purpose of "giving."

onto" behavior in middle infancy would find their later counterparts in experiences during the period of toilet training; or that innate factors in the infant organism would themselves shape both the holding behavior and the object relationships during toilet training; or that both sorts of factors interact. Our data to date suggest that this "vector" is *not* a sufficient condition for anal retention, but, rather, a highly contributory one; although it may turn out to be sufficient for initial but transitory manifestations of this phenomenon.*

Although the term "vector" derives from Alexander's [2] usage, the conceptualization behind the hypothesis is essentially different from his,† and more closely allied to that of Erikson's "modes." [22, 25] What is new here is the attempt: (1) to assess the relative predominance of such modes in infancy; (2) to examine to what extent they are predictive of later infantile behaviors; and (3) to trace their interaction with subsequent experience in the development of stable personality traits.

Of greater pertinence to established psychoanalytic theory is the second half of this prediction, that anal retentive derivatives would be seen in the subject's adult personality. Tommy developed a rather strong retention of feces during toilet training and up to two and a half years of age. A detailed interpretative assessment of his functioning at that time, based on a series of richly informative play sessions, as well as on other sources of information, led to a series of statements about him, of which the following few are most pertinent to our present discussion. (These are presented here in highly condensed and deleted form, omitting entirely the explication of the interpretations.)

1. Tommy is entering into a somewhat premature phallic stage, with maternal seduction as one major contributing factor.
2. Early and late oral fixations are marked, and serve as loci for frequent partial regressions under stress. Fear of object loss as the result of oral-aggressive and phallic-aggressive fantasies is the chief stress at this time.
3. In spite of the existing (but subsiding) anal retention, there is little evidence

* The hypothesis states nothing as to the genesis of the "infantile holding vector" itself, whether predominantly innate or experiential or interactive. This essentially different though related question requires for its investigation the comparative assessment of neonatal and postnatal motor behavior; of feeding behavior; of the use of the mouth for exploring, grasping, retaining, and getting rid of; and of the development of object relationships and affectivity. It is a good example of the typical complexity involved in empiric investigations of such problems, as well as of the necessity in developmental research for intensive, small sample, individual studies along with experimental approaches on larger populations.

† Cf. Fenichel [32] for a thoughtful and telling critique of Alexander's vector concepts in so far as they apply to neurotic conflict.

of libidinization of anal functions, and no evidence of significant anal fixation points.

4. Urethral interests are intense, both in an active, aggressive, libidinal, "normal little boy" sense and also as passive fantasies and as sources of anxiety about hostility to parents and parent surrogates, and about the nature of parental sexual activity (urinary intercourse and conception fantasies).

5. Postdict important urinary and urethral erotic components in the recent episodes of night waking and disturbance in Tommy; components which were not elicited in recent interviews with mother.

6. In the last play session there is interpretative evidence that the retention of urine is assuming important meanings for Tommy; and "it is predicted that within a short time there will be clear-cut behavioral urinary retention, taking over from the anal zone." (Predictive result one and two months later was + +.)

7. In spite of severe anxiety manifestations and temporary deeply regressive responses to them, Tommy's zest, curiosity, capacity for enjoyment, resiliency, active mastery (with help) of his anxiety and of very great problems in object relationships, reality testing, cognitive problem-solving capacity, and other ego functions are assessed at moderately high to very high levels.

To return now to our prediction of anal retentive derivatives, the specific theoretical issue involved can be posed as follows: is strong libidinization (or "aggressivization") of a pregenital function, narcissistically or in terms of object relationships, but sufficient to make for a fixation at that point, a necessary condition for the appearance of stable derivative traits in later personality? * If not, which we must consider as a possibility if we take seriously our task of validation and clarification, then a strong "infantile vector" leading to later specific pregenital behaviors would be significantly predictive of such traits. If, however, it is the meaningful *use* of such modes for impulse gratification and for attempted solutions of original and derivative conflicts which results in such pregenital substitute formations as stable precipitates in personality, then we would expect at best a correlational rather than an individual predictability from early "vectors." †

Although, technically speaking, we cannot yet mark the second part of our prediction as clearly wrong (— —), since it is stated in terms of adult personality traits, I feel sure at this point that it will turn out to be incorrect. This (assumed) predictive failure speaks strongly, I think, for

* The same question can be further elaborated in terms of energy theory, particularly as regards cathexis, counter cathexis, and neutralization. I shall omit consideration of this point of view here, as being more appropriate for a subsequent communication.[11]

† It hardly needs to be pointed out that I am here referring only to pregenital substitute formations and not to other sorts of personality traits, some of which may well derive from the interaction of genes with universal rather than with variable experiences.

the second of our alternatives; for the psychoanalytic thesis that impulse gratifications or conflicts about them in the context of object relationships are essential for stable pregenital derivatives in personality. Tommy is now in his fifth year and shows none of the classic anal derivative traits.[1, 37, 72] Even more than the anal retention, the rather extraordinarily severe urinary retention was of short duration, and completely disappeared as a symptom. Outstanding at present is his extreme demandingness in a classically oral sense, with an insatiable demand for gifts, both for their own sake and as a demonstration of love from the donors. In this sense, possession is important but not at all for the sake of keeping, his motto in this respect being: to get and to have, not "to have and to hold."

In connection with the *lack* of anal fixations in this child, another unsuccessful prediction, made at the time of this over-all assessment along with a number of successful ones, is of some interest.

#7. Tommy T., age 2½ years. *"Predict development of slight [transitory] stuttering soon. (Short term. Intuitive, quasi-theoretical, and possibly contaminated. Measures: purely behavioral.) Quasi-theoretical basis derives from handling of aggression in this session, the present status of the mother-child relationship, and the age of the child."

Predictive outcome: — —. No stuttering whatsoever was observed or reported.

Estimated theoretical significance of unsuccessful outcome: Limited as regards theory of stuttering, in view of the tenuous nature of the predictive base. High in some other respects (see discussion below).

Discussion: This prediction, somewhat trivial in itself as compared to others on this child, was made mentally during the course of observing the play session referred to above. I bring it up, among other reasons, to illustrate how a "genuine" intuition can be wrong. For, at the time it first occurred to me, while watching and listening to Tommy, it had all the elements of a genuine intuition as defined earlier (p. 16). It came suddenly and involuntarily, it had no immediate conscious base, and it was accompanied by a subjective feeling of conviction that the idea was a valid one. A few days later, while writing up the impressions, interpretations, and predictions based on this session, this conviction had been almost entirely dissipated. Unlike some other times when an apparently intuitive assessment or prediction could subsequently be rationally explicated in a convincing manner, the rather feeble theoretical base which occurred to me here was so unsatisfactory that I termed it quasi-theoretical, and starred (*) the prediction to indicate a low level of confidence. Certainly, it was not based on classic psychoanalytic theory of stuttering, which emphasizes anal fixation as a primary factor in this disorder. Since I believe it is correct, however, to distinguish between transitory stuttering as an inhibition and chronic stuttering as a pregenital conversion neurosis (cf. Fenichel [32]); since inhibited aggression and conflict about aggressive utterances are basic to both; and since oral fixations as well as problems in communication with mother * and father are, in my experience, particularly common in early transitory stuttering at this age; the theoretical base given was not without some substance, all these factors applying strongly to Tommy. Nevertheless, although they might suffice for a negative prediction, they could not possibly be considered a sufficient base for a positive one. In looking around for a reason for my initial feeling of confidence, then, it seemed possible that the prediction was not intuitive at all in the "genuine" sense but, rather, that it was contaminated by an unnoticed perception of some actual verbal behavioral cues; hence the phrase "possibly contaminated." Subsequent careful relistening to the tape, both by myself and others, failed to reveal any evidence of beginning stuttering or any other speech disorder.

What actually happened to Tommy's speech is, I think, of considerable interest. As stated, no stuttering occurred. But within a few weeks, Tommy developed a marked, though entirely transitory, lisp which had never been observed earlier. We have noted above his strong oral fixations and his tendency to temporary regression under stress. The pertinence of these to lisping is obvious and needs no belaboring, nor are they too illuminating in explaining why the lisping occurred at this particular point. Of somewhat greater interest is the fact that the use of the tongue in lisping is in some children very much like the use of the tongue in sucking and mouthing at the breast; and that Tommy's deepest regressive responses to anxiety were characterized by his assumption of a hypotonically immobile sitting posture which was startingly similar to that passively assumed by him in early infancy while being cradled in his mother's or nurse's arms and lap for feeding.†

On a clinical level, however, my chief interest in the failure of the prediction of stuttering, and the unpredicted development of lisping, lies in the fact that it afforded a new insight into the genesis of at least one

* Is this the reason why "m" sounds are the most difficult for some stutterers? I am unable to find objective data in the literature about the frequency of this and other consonants ("f", "s", "sh", "b", etc.) as special foci of stuttering as compared to a more generalized undifferentiated sort; but on a clinical level I know that there are some stutterers in whom this focalization around one or only a few consonants is outstanding.

† This was independently noted by one of my associates and by me.

case of transitory lisping as a symptom, and perhaps of some other cases also. Relatively unimportant and trivial as the phenomenon itself is, I think the specific dynamic involved sufficiently intriguing to wish to bring it up here. Remembering the urinary retention and the urethral erotic fantasies as they were involved in Tommy's disturbed relationships with his parents at this time, it occurred to me some months later that the avoidance of the sibilant "s" sound might have been motivated by its urinary connotations. This idea being reinforced by my knowledge that the term "piss" rather than "pee-pee" was Tommy's customary usage, I inquired whether the parents or nurse had earlier used the hissing "s-s-s" to encourage his urination, as is so frequently the case. The answer was affirmative. And the lisping disappeared along with the urinary retention.

Finally, there remains the question of a good intuition gone wrong. Having brought at this prediction in such a clinical and informal fashion, I should not withhold a bit of personal information from the reader. In my earlier discussion of intuition, I mentioned both the facilitating and distorting effects of unconscious fantasies on preconscious thinking. I think them well illustrated here—the writer was first a lisper and then a stutterer as a young child.

#8. Tommy T., age 2½ years. "(Theoretical. Medium term and probably long term.) Predict that separation anxiety [fear of object loss and loss of love] and its derivative manifestations will be relatively higher than castration fear and its derivatives, with clear evidences of both. (Measures=subsequent ratings in future years; differentiation of the two series on the Rorschach;* independent judgments by psychoanalytic clinicians of future interview data; eventually, hopefully, psychoanalysis.) The bases for this prediction, explicated in detail elsewhere, are drawn only in part from the data of this session; in part they come from knowledge of the parents, and their expected response to and handling of Tommy's

* The lack of well-demonstrated reliability and validity of the Rorschach test raises pertinent questions about its use as a criterion measure for intrapsychic variables. The reason why I feel justified in so using it here is that I believe I have good clinical evidence of its validity for this particular differentiation, based on experience with both adults and children. These data have not yet been systematically analyzed for the adults, and only in part for the children. For a brief discussion of the Rorschach measures involved, see Ricciuti [88] and references cited there.

I am omitting as inappropriate for this presentation examples of a whole class of predictions specifically concerned with the relationships between psychological test data and clinical assessments, aiming at concurrent and predictive validation or invalidation of one or the other or both.[20, 88] Adequate discussion of the complex issues of reliability and validity involved,[20] as they apply to the many different sorts of predictions we make, would take us so far from the field of clinical psychopathology and would demand so many examples for their concrete illustration that I am confining their mention to this footnote and planning on their presentation elsewhere.

emerging phallic interests [i.e., it is predicted that they will not strongly reinforce his already beginning castration anxiety] as interpreted from this interview; in still another part they derive from much earlier data on separation and stranger anxiety."

Predictive outcome: Undetermined (±?) for the long term. + for the medium term; but the independent criterion measures outlined are not yet available, nor is the Rorschach differentiation. Additionally, the medium-term prediction was actually meant for somewhat later in his development than his present age (in his fifth year). To date, Tommy's ratings on dynamically effective castration anxiety are moderately high; on dynamically effective fear of object loss and fear of loss of love they are much higher. (Cf. the discussion of prediction #7.)

Discussion: I shall not bring up the detailed explication mentioned above, since to do so would necessitate a lengthy summary of Tommy's record. Nor can we reasonably comment on the significance of the somewhat prematurely defined outcome, particularly in view of the lack of satisfactorily independent criterion measures up to this time. I wish, rather, to discuss two assumptions implied in the making of this prediction, irrespective of base or outcome; the one methodologic, the other theoretical.

The methodologic assumption is that it is possible and meaningful to compare the "amounts" of anxieties of different sorts, an assumption which is by no means self-evidently true but requires empirical demonstration. Our experience to date with ratings based on interpretations of behavior, and then used as bases for predictions, gives us reason to believe that semi-quantification of this sort is not only useful, in the sense of forcing sharper definition of concepts and of the processes of interpretative assessment, but is also valid, within limits.*

Our second implied assumption requires a brief theoretical digression for its discussion. The formulation of the prediction suggests that we consider these anxieties to be relatively independent of each other. In this connection, one restricted aspect of the psychoanalytic theory of anxiety is pertinent. I refer to the frequently made statement[35, 40, 41, 78] that castration anxiety is a special form of separation anxiety, deriving in part from it, in part from the biologic fact of being a male, in part from specific experiences; that it is a variety of fear of object loss. This type of theo-

* It should not, of course, be confused with true quantification. Nor can the use of nonparametric methods of statistical analysis, valuable and important as these are in dealing with unknown distributions, succeed in the magical task of making accurate measures out of inaccurate ones, as occasionally seems to be assumed by some of the more enthusiastic and less understanding users of these techniques.

retical statement is one of a large class of integrating considerations which play a prominent role in psychoanalytic literature, particularly in Freud but elsewhere also. In general, they are useful in trying to give speculative theoretical coherence to regularly occurring sequences of phenomena, in "explaining" near universals on the basis of antecedent universals. Concretely, in this instance, the thesis means that since separation from the breast or bottle, separation from mother, and separation from parts of one's own body, i.e., feces, universally occur, the resultant "readiness" for object loss is fertile ground for the development of fear of castration, and perhaps helps explain its frequency. Thus stated, the thesis is entirely plausible, and entirely untestable. The latter fact does not deprive it of usefulness, coherence, and possible explanatory value. Nor is my statement meant to imply that this sort of speculation is "bad" theory.* It implies, rather, that it must be distinguished from theorizing involving propositions which are either testable in themselves or lead to derived hypotheses which are testable. If, now, one treats separation anxiety and castration anxiety as variables rather than as universals, one can ask the question: will experiences leading to heightened separation anxiety tend to increase the degree of "readiness" for object loss, and will this, in turn, increase the probability of heightened castration anxiety? If so, then high and low separation anxiety should be correlationally predictive, to some degree, of high and low castration anxiety. Put this way, the proposition becomes a testable one. Its refutation, however, would not invalidate the original thesis, as stated, but merely restrict its scope. For it should be noted that the derived hypothesis in this case is *not* a necessary logical deduction from the general thesis but only a possible extension of it, one which, if true, would increase the scientific usefulness of the original conceptualization. One could equally well "derive" the proposition that the degree of readiness for object loss is immaterial; that it is universally present to a sufficient extent to provide a necessary or contributory invariant condition for the development of castration anxiety; and that the *degrees* of the latter are a function of other experiential and innate variables than those most directly involved in the development of fear of object loss.

* Although anathema to the pure logical positivists, untestable hypotheses are accorded an honorable place in scientific theorizing, not only by some philosophers of science but also by many creative scientists themselves. (Cf. e.g., Poincaré, *Science and Hypothesis, Foundations of Science,* loc. cit.[77].) Josiah Royce called them "devices of the understanding whereby we give conceptual unity to certain types of phenomenal facts which come to us in a discrete form and in a confused variety," an excellent description, I think, of some aspects of psychological and psychoanalytic theory at present.

The clinically well-demonstrated role of experience in co-determining the degrees of dynamically and behaviorally effective castration anxiety in the male means that if we wish to translate these theoretical considerations into an empirical investigation of our derived hypothesis, we would expect at best a rather low positive correlation between measures of the two variables. Our data to date give, in fact, low positive correlations between ratings of *infantile* separation anxiety and later ratings of castration anxiety; but the number of boys whom we have been able to follow long enough and intensively enough to make such ratings with any confidence in, and intrinsic evidence of, validity is so small (seven) as to make it impossible to judge whether these are real or chance relationships.* Thus, the hypothesis is neither proved nor disproved by our data. We have here an excellent illustration of what I mentioned earlier: how the amount of time required to achieve reliable and valid assessments of some psychoanalytic variables restricts our population size to a point where the applicability of correlational and other statistical techniques to problems where they are most needed is itself restricted.†

* The correlation coefficient obtained was +.34. With an n of only 7, there is an even chance that the true correlation approximates zero; i.e., that there is no demonstrable relationship between the variables; and it could even turn out to be a negative relationship, as far as the evaluation of these data alone is concerned. Lest the psychometrically sophisticated reader question the appropriateness of running any correlations at all on so small a group, I would mention that some of the correlations between other variables have been high enough so that even for this very small n the significances have been at the .01 level and better. These will not be discussed here, except to say that the question of whether such very high positive correlations are not in part due to circular contamination of the ratings through theoretical bias is a justified and important one. This is one of the many reasons, in fact, why we consider prediction to be an indispensable complement to other methods of investigation in the field of psychoanalytic personality theory.

† Our present "intensive" group, defined as having been studied since before birth and still being followed regularly, consists of 23 children, 13 girls and 10 boys. Of these, 8 girls and 7 boys are from 4 to 11 years old, the remaining 5 girls and 3 boys being in the age range from 1 to 2½ years. Although some of the latter will presumably continue to be followed intensively later, their inclusion in this group was largely for the sake of adding cases to our infancy studies as such. In addition, 15 children, 7 girls and 8 boys, who used to be in the intensive series, are no longer followed regularly by us, but are available for occasional study; and 5 others, 2 girls and 3 boys, who had been in our intensive series for varying periods of time, have left Denver.

The issue of sampling bias, both in the original selection and in connection with families dropping out of or being dropped from our intensive series, while clearly of importance, will not be discussed here. Nor shall I describe our larger non-intensive group, since only a few individual predictions have been formulated for members of this population.

#9. Tommy T., 2¾ years. ** "("Theoretical." Long term.) Because of the degree of mastery shown [in play sessions and in real life situations], particularly the mastery of strong anxiety, it is predicted that "ego strength" will be high, and good adjustment will occur under expectable stresses [expected to be quite severe in the immediate future], with moderate neurotic structure. (The two stars indicate a very low level of confidence in [the long-term aspects of] this prediction, although the bases for it, the mastery and potential "ego strength," are in themselves given on a high level of confidence [cf. the assessments on pp. ......, under prediction #6]. It is actually, on a theoretical basis, much too early in this child's development to make any such global predictions rationally, since the contingencies cannot be well enough predicted, and therefore the prediction verges on the fortunetelling variety. The reason it is made at all is to reflect my own conviction of the great importance of these variables for adjustment [and mental health] rather than to test any well-formulated theory.)"

Predictive outcome: Undetermined (±?). But Tommy has shown evidence of successful problem solutions to date. Cf. the discussion of prediction #11.

Discussion: Perhaps the chief interest in this prediction, in spite of the low level of confidence with which it was made, lies in the fact that it was formulated at a time when Tommy was in a period of rather severe disturbance, characterized clinically by extreme difficulties in going to sleep, and long periods of wakefulness and crying during the night, during which he would demand constant attention from one or both parents. During the day he appeared to his parents and other observers to be in relatively much better shape, playing well with his playmates and showing much of the zest and curiosity that were characteristic of him. We took this as one more example of that resiliency in Tommy to which we had previously repeatedly referred. The genetic and dynamic bases for the night disturbances were well understood by this time and were in consonance with a series of interpretations and predictions made three months earlier, but not presented here. On a social level, Tommy's night-time behavior was becoming a major problem to both parents, who found it impossible to get enough sleep for themselves. They broached the question of therapy for Tommy, but at the last moment decided against it for the time being.

There was ample experiential reason for Tommy's disturbed state. As a neonate and in early infancy he was rated high on many aspects of his innate equipment. Beyond that, his first year had been a relatively favorable one, but the second year had brought with it a number of difficulties in his relationships to mother and to surrogate mother figures.

Technically, the prediction was too vaguely formulated in terms of the sentence "good adjustment will occur . . . with moderate neurotic structure." What was meant was that by our criteria of "mental health" Tommy will rank fairly high in our group, but that there will be clear evidence of neurotic anxiety and neurotic symptoms, which will not be severely incapacitating. (Cf. #11.)

#10. Tommy T., 2¾ years. "(Theoretical. Partly negative. Long term.) It is predicted that whatever psychopathology develops will be neurotic-depressive, or anxiety-hysterical with compulsive trends, and will not be primarily compulsive, nor schizophrenic, nor psychotic-depressive. (Detailed explication elsewhere.) (Measures: clinical and clinical psychological.)"

Predictive outcome: Undetermined (±?).

Discussion: This is one of a small series of deductive psychopathologic theoretical predictions formulated in both positive and negative terms and containing, therefore, multiple sub-predictions. The detailed theoretical explication is too long to enter into here, and cannot be condensed without losing its cogency.* I present this example here only to illustrate this particular predictive form.

#11(9b). Tommy T., age 4 years, 8 months. "The 2¾ year old global mental health prediction on this boy (#9) is repeated here on a much higher level of confidence, on the basis of what has since occurred. After a very stormy period, Tommy has shown what we assess as a predominantly healthy development. His handling of hostility is freer and at the same time better controlled, nonhostile aggression is more utilizable, and he is able to admit his anxieties more readily and to tolerate them better, as well as to show continued evidence of his ability to master them actively under most circumstances. Object relationships are markedly improved. His early Oedipus seems on the way to satisfactory resolution, with predominantly masculine identifications. There remain, on the negative side, his continued high level of fear of loss of love, his excessive demandingness [cf. the discussion of prediction #6], and his tendency to easy though temporary regression to strongly fixated oral points."

Specifically, it is predicted that Tommy will rank toward the bottom of the upper third of our series in later independent "mental health" assessments.

#12. Charlie R., 6+ years. "(Deductive-theoretical. Long term. Negative.) It is predicted that of all the boys under study in our intensive series, none will develop sexual perversion in the form of genital exhibitionism or of fetishism with the exception of Charlie R., who may develop one of these perversions. (Based on the combination in Charlie, and lack of this combination in the others, of extreme castration anxiety and a convinced belief in the female phallus,

* It is available for reference.

with relative lack of repression of these for his age; * extreme fear of mother, with marked and strongly inhibited hostility toward her and his sister; nevertheless, strong erotic arousal by women (cf. play sessions); shyness, especially with women; distorted identifications, with prediction of faulty supergo functioning, and high social anxiety; uneven ego development to date, history of relative lack of success in real life problem-solving to date, poor synthetic capacity, reality testing slightly impaired, but nothing in cognitive behavior that would lead me to predict a psychotic development. (For genetic data supplementing this horizontal assessment at the present age of six years plus, and necessary for a better explication of this base, see the record.) Measures: clinical and, questionably, clinical psychological." [See discussion below.]

Predictive outcome: Undetermined (±?); and will probably remain so. See discussion below.

Discussion: This is an example of a negative prediction as defined earlier on p. 22. (Prediction #4 was also negative, but was of a different type, formulated for an individual only and not for a group.) Although technically a well-formulated prediction, it is in some respects a "bad" one. In the first place, since overt perversions of this sort are rare, as far as we know, the chances that none of the subjects will develop one are high; therefore, predictive success is very probable, and its significance would be correspondingly low. (Cf. my discussion of this, p. 22, as one of the limitations of negative predictions of phenomena whose incidence is low.) Beyond this, however, there is another weakness inherent in the question of criterion measures, or rather in the probability of their being applicable. It might well be the case that one or the other of the subjects would develop an overt perversion but that we would never know of it, since it is unrealistic to assume that we or our successors will be able to follow all our cases through young adulthood in sufficient clinical detail to know for certain whether or not a disorder of this sort is in fact present. This restriction does not apply to most of our negative psychopathological

* The inclusion in this base of relative lack of repression of castration anxiety and of the belief in the female phallus stems from my own past experience in the study of a very small group of genital exhibitionists, where I found, contrary to statements in the literature,[32] that conscious memories of fear of castration and of belief in the female phallus were present in several cases. These subjects were not analyzed, but it may be assumed that these memories served, in part at least, as screens for other repressed material. I have had no personal experience with fetishism as a primary perversion (as contrasted with the frequency of fetishistic components in the sexual life of many neurotic and essentially "normal" men); and consequently cannot say empirically whether the same holds true for some of these cases. On theoretical grounds, I would be inclined to consider it somewhat less likely, in view of the more complex and less primitive nature of fetishistic perversion.

predictions, since psychosis, for example, or overt behavioral traits, or specific test behaviors, cannot well be hidden in the same sense.

Further discussion of this prediction will follow shortly, after I mention a second version, made at the same time on the same child.

#13. Charlie R., 6+ years. "(Deductive-theoretical. Possibly "intuitive" also. Long term. Positive.) It is predicted that this boy will show strong perverse components in his adult sexuality. This statement is not meant in such a way as to be considered verified by the future demonstration of slightly perverse elements in foreplay. It predicts, rather, that one or another sexual perversion, exclusive of overt homosexuality, such as genital exhibitionism, fetishism, sadism, masochism, etc., will play a prominent part in sexual arousal and discharge, though not necessarily to the extent that normal sexual intercourse will not occur, as in the "pure" perversions. Thus, it will require for its verification or invalidation a situation where such knowledge will be available. This does not seem unlikely in the case of this boy, for whom we have previously predicted (at 3¾ years), in global mental health terms, that he will rank among the lowest three cases in our total series (i.e., of 23 intensives plus 15 previous intensives still available). This prediction is based on the same assessments as those listed in the accompanying negative prediction. The exclusion of overt homosexuality, which was implied but not stated there, is based on the strong erotic arousal by women as well as on the nature of his oedipal development, which involved little inverted homosexual attachment to father in spite of strong feminine identifications [with his mother and sister].

Predictive outcome: Undetermined (±?).

Discussion: This prediction is less specific than the previous one, and in principle, therefore, of somewhat less potential theoretical and heuristic value. Its actual value is probably higher, however, since there is more chance of its being proved correct or incorrect; although here too the possibility of no definitive outcome is an appreciable one. It might well be asked, therefore, why we make such predictions at all; why we do not confine our predictive attempts to areas where the probabilities are high that outcomes will be clearly positive or negative. The answer is simple. We feel that we would lose a large number of predictions of potential value if we took considerations of this sort into account while making the predictions. Initially, then, we do not let ourselves be concerned with the criterion measures as such, or with the probabilities of being able to apply them. We think that to do so would impair the conscious or preconscious processes of associating to the material which are the essence of some clinical predictions, as contrasted with those based on relatively simple and well-explicated hypotheses and measures (cf. # 3, #5, and the bulk of our short-term developmental predictions not being presented here);

processes which determine what, if anything, we are going to predict in a given case at a given time. Later on, in writing up the predictions as soon as possible, we are of course concerned with these matters, and we could at that point exclude such predictions from our series; but as we see it, there would be nothing gained and much lost if we did so. For apart from the values of the assessment processes themselves, to which we have repeatedly referred, we think the gain from even a small proportion of determined outcomes in predictions of this sort well worth the time "wasted" in formulating and explicating a larger number whose outcomes presumably never will be clearly determined.

In this connection, I should like to use this pair of predictions to illustrate the discrepancies which occasionally arise between the initial mental act of formulating a prediction and the way it subsequently appears in the written formulation. In most of our predictions there is no such discrepancy; the content of the written version is essentially the same as what was initially thought of during an observation of an infant or child, or an interview with a parent, or while subsequently listening to a tape or studying the written record. In this case, however, as in some others, the original version was different. While observing a play session with this child from behind the one-way screen, I was again impressed, as I had been in the past, by an unusual quality in his relationship to the play interviewer, which I noted as "a highly excited fusion of hostility and libido in this anxious child." If this had led to the idea of the possible development of perverse sadism in this boy, it would have seemed entirely plausible. Instead, the thought occurred to me suddenly, and with some conviction, "This boy will be a perverse exhibitionist." In trying, a few hours later, to examine the possible bases for this intuition, I reviewed the factors mentioned above in the explication of the predictive base, most of which had been assessed earlier in one form or another. Taken together, they seemed on a rational level to represent some necessary and contributory, but probably not sufficient, conditions for the development of perverse sexuality; with the extreme castration anxiety and the belief in the female phallus corresponding to accepted and well-established clinical psychopathologic theory,[32] and some of the other assessments mentioned being more on the level of important contributory factors. None of them seemed to justify the specific choice of exhibitionism as such, however, although the prominence of the female phallus concept in this child's fantasy expression did point more toward exhibitionism or fetishism than toward some other perversions. In looking further for some preconscious or unconscious determinant of the choice of exhibitionism, we could exclude anything unusual in his overt behavior in this respect as a younger child. As far as we know from the rather limited types of information obtainable from the parents in this case, as well as from our own observations, actual genital exhibitionism as a young pre-school age boy in no way exceeded the usual behavior of this sort. If anything, it may have been less than we ordinarily find, which would be compatible with but not necessarily supportive of the hypothesized dynamic configuration; but at any rate almost surely did not enter into the predictive "intuition." I was finally able to recover for myself one clinical observation which may have been responsible for the "fortunetelling" specificity of this original mentally made but unwritten prediction: an episode in which the child flourished a gun in front of the interviewer's eyes in a manner which could have suggested exhibitionism as such and not just the obvious mixture of aggressive and libidinal excitement mentioned in my observational notes, and which had been noted in previous sessions as well. If this were the case, it might be considered to constitute a partial predictive contaminant to the theoretical base; on the other hand, it could also be true that awareness of the components of the theoretical base would be necessary for the perception of this episode as exhibitionistic or otherwise perverse. In any case, being dissatisfied with the theoretical justification for a positive prediction of exhibitionism as such, I compromised on the two predictions I have presented: the one negative, adding fetishism to exhibitionism because of the well-demonstrated importance of the female phallus concept in this disorder, where it is even more regularly found than in exhibitionism; the other a positive prediction of one of several perversions as the outcome in this case, based on the presence of necessary and, as I see them, highly contributory conditions. Since we do not know *sufficient* conditions for the development of the overt perversions, the positive prediction, made on a high level of confidence, must be considered as partly "intuitive" also, in the sense of a clinical "feel" for a perverse quality already apparent in this child. Finally, the second example contains a specific negative sub-prediction excluding the development of overt homosexuality.

In summary, assuming that positive or negative outcomes to these predictions can eventually be obtained, I would estimate their significances as follows:

1. A successful outcome of the negative prediction #12 would have very little meaning, for the reasons discussed above, unless Charlie should develop one of these two perversions, in which case the theoretical signifi-

cance would be high. Because of the possible behavioral contamination discussed, the theoretical significance would be even higher in the case of fetishism than of exhibitionism.

2. An unsuccessful outcome for this prediction (i.e., development of one of these perversions in one of the other subjects) would have definite, partially invalidating significance, and probably heuristic value also.

3. A successful outcome for prediction #13 would have considerable significance for partial validation of the bases given as necessary or contributory factors, and might even lead a little closer to the goal of knowing necessary and sufficient conditions. A restricting factor here is the uncertain nature of the "intuitive" element involved. Otherwise the low a priori probability of the prediction being correct by chance alone would give it a higher significance than can be attributed to most single predictions. (Cf. prediction #18.)

4. An unsuccessful outcome of this prediction would be harder to evaluate for its significance. Since the theoretical bases given are not claimed by anyone to be sufficient, there would be no invalidation of established theory. Since I formulated it as a positive prediction on a high level of confidence, however, there must either be a "private" theory involved that the additional factors formulated do, in fact, constitute sufficient conditions, or the prediction is based in part on preconsciously perceived and formulated cues. In the first instance, predictive failure would invalidate the hypothesis that these factors are sufficient; in the second, it would be another example of the fallibility of clinical intuition.

The following examples illustrate an effort to change the criterion measure of a predicted intrapsychic variable from an interpretative to a behavioral one.

#14a. Mary D., 3 years, 10 months. "Predict that Mary's strong coprophagic impulses will persist as part of her unconscious motivational system. [No criterion measures given.] (Mixed deductive-inductive theoretical. Long-term.) Based on interpretation of coprophagic impulses at 2–11, [followed shortly by] direct behavioral and verbal verification of this interpretation; and [the sub-prediction of] the utilization of this impulse in the service of revenge on mother, and as restitution of the fantasied loss of a penis." [The base must have included also an implied sub-prediction about the immediate future of the parent-child relationships, as well as previous assessments of orality and anality in this child, which were not stated here but elsewhere.]

A few months later, in reviewing this prediction, I was struck by the probable difficulty in future attempts to verify it or prove it false, since it seemed unlikely, for various reasons, that this child and her family would be among our intensively studied cases. Even if they were, a valid interpretative assessment of unconscious coprophagic impulses might be difficult to obtain at a later age except in a setting of psychoanalytic therapy, which was not anticipated in this case as an eventuality likely to occur. Nor was there any reason on the basis of our relatively limited knowledge of this child to expect a psychotic development; if there had been, we would have co-predicted overt coprophagia as a prominent symptom. For these reasons, as well as on the general principle of preferring to give overt behavioral criteria for intrapsychic variables whenever possible, it seemed advisable to attempt to delineate such criteria for this particular case. The following secondary prediction was therefore formulated.

#14b. Mary D., 4 years, 2 months. "Predict that Mary will show throughout her development, but particularly later on [when the coprophagic impulses have undergone repression], marked peculiarities in her food preferences and dislikes, either in terms of an extreme avoidance of strong, smelly foods or an extreme liking for them. (Cf. previous [assessment and] prediction of coprophagia.)" [For probable contamination see discussion below.]

Predictive outcome: + + to date (early adolescence). Mary has been characterized by the nutritionist at the Child Research Council as one of the most "unusual" eaters in a large series of cases followed by her. She has rejected many ordinary foods in favor of unusual combinations of strong tasting and smelling ingredients (details omitted). Recently, there have been periods when these have been given up, followed by other periods of "orgies" of eating them.

Estimated significance of successful outcome: Fairly high. See discussion below.

Discussion: This prediction was not one of those aimed at the validation of an interpretative assessment, which had already been achieved prior to the formulation of the prediction. Although we are not concerning ourselves in this presentation with the non-predictive validation of interpretative and behavioral assessments, a major topic in itself, I think it perhaps justified to make an exception in this one instance and give the assessment data themselves, in view of their extreme simplicity as compared to the usually much more complex problems of inference involved.

During a richly informative play session at 2–11, in which Mary had been forbidden to paint by her mother because she had come home from the last session with paint on her clothes, the play had initially centered largely around toileting the family dolls. After repeated requests to paint had been refused, Mary turned to clay play, asking the interviewer to make her a variety of objects, with which she acted out some specific aggressive and phallic fantasies. She then told a story about a boy, Jimmy, who broke a bird bath.

Interviewer: "What happened when Jimmy broke it?"

Mary: "Mother looked. Jimmy told his mother, 'I'm sorry'."

Int.: "What did his mother do?"

Mary: "She whipped him."

She was manipulating a small ball of clay, and held it up to her mouth at this point.

Mary: "I'm going to eat it. Why am I going to eat it?"

Int.: "Is it because you want to taste it, and see what it tastes like?"

Mary: "Let's play ball."

Some time later, during the administration of a test, Mary interrupted, and said with a note of stubborn defiance in her voice that she didn't want to do that. Told she didn't have to, she got up, went to the other side of the room, crouched down against the wall, said "I'm busy, I'm going to study," and resumed play with the clay.

Mary: "You're going to be a little girl, and I'm going to be Mrs. X. (you). You're going to be Mary."

Int.: "All right, we'll change places."

She took the piece of clay, pushed it into the play toilet, and asked the interviewer to flush it down.

Int.: "What am I flushing down?"

Mary: "Tinkle and grunt. Let's eat the grunt."

She picked up the clay from the play toilet and offered it to the interviewer.

Int.: "It's all right if you want to taste it."

Mary bit down on the piece of clay, made a face, and said, "I have to spit it out."

Parenthetically, the difficulty as well as the fascination involved in attempts at exhaustive interview analysis from an over-all developmental point of view are well illustrated by the fact that even in this very small excerpt from one out of many play sessions, there are a large number of questions to be asked and inferences to be drawn about defensive mechanisms and other ego functions, as well as about object relations and drive organization at this point in her life. I cannot discuss these here, nor are they necessary for the understanding of this specific and restricted prediction. What is necessary to clarify again is the fact that the prediction, although *based* on the assessment of strong coprophagic impulses, was not concerned with their existence but, rather, with their persistence as a dynamically effective force. What was predicted was that they would find resonance and utilization in the service of object relations, of aggressive and libidinal drive discharge, and of anxiety control; and would therefore be unconsciously maintained rather than resolved. Such a formulation implies symptom formation, or derivative trait formation. The reported conflict in recent times about her special eating habits, with periods of "abstinence" followed by reversion to the old pattern, suggests that symptom is a better word than trait in this case. But the distinction does not seem too important here, particularly since we have not followed the psychological development of this girl in recent years sufficiently closely to estimate the role of this behavior in her psychic economy at the present time, or to assess what personality traits best describe her.

I return now to the second prediction, with its translation of an implied interpretative criterion measure into a behavioral one. A letdown is in store for any reader who may have felt, in common with the author, a certain quality of elegance in the success of this effort; in a not too elegant area, to be sure. In reviewing the case very recently, for the purpose of this publication, I discovered from the nutritionist's records that Mary was already eating some of the unusual foods at the time the prediction was written. This had not been stated in the written report presented at staff conference at that time. Moreover, the form of the prediction itself does not betray an awareness of this fact, since it outlines alternative outcomes in terms of extremes. Subjectively, also, it is easy to recall the feeling of pleasure I experienced in finding such a simple behavioral criterion, instead of the tortuous efforts usually involved in trying to list multiple behavioral criteria for predicted intrapsychic constellations. It is possible, then, that there was no contamination, that I had never heard any discussion of the subject. On inquiry, however, it turns out that several other staff members had heard such discussions, and the possibility must therefore be seriously considered that I utilized this knowledge in the formulation without any conscious awareness of it. If so, it illustrates nicely the limitations of subjective attempts at recognizing some forms of contamination.*

In concluding this section with a few predictions selected for their psychopathologic interest from a much larger number made on what is probably our best studied case to date,† I would emphasize that far from being representative of our predictive series as a whole, some of them are unique

* The perceptive reader will note that the damage involved is more to narcissism than to science, that even if this knowledge had been consciously made use of in formulating the "translation," the significance of the successful predictive outcome would in no way be impaired. Unless, of course, someone wishes to advance the proposition that Mary's interest in eating feces was because they reminded her of the foods she so much enjoyed! I have occasionally heard arguments no better than this advanced against some clinical psychoanalytic findings and hypotheses.

† Cf. p. 25, and footnote there.

as regards detail, specificity, and the level of confidence with which they were made. Not to make this clear might well give a false impression of where we stand at present in our predictive attempts. The fact that the parents of this child were particularly good informants, that their own histories and personalities were well understood, and that the child revealed an unusual amount about herself in play sessions and interviews as well as in projective and objective testing undoubtedly contributed heavily to this character of uniqueness. But it does not necessarily follow that these quantitative factors would be sufficient in all cases to achieve this degree of predictability; it is probable, I think, that a combination in the mother of rather severely repetitive psychopathology with many ego strengths was also responsible.

#15. Patty S., age 3 months. "Predict that Mrs. S. will identify Patty with her [own] younger sister to such an extent that much of her attitudes and behavior toward her will be directly traceable to this factor. (This prediction was made earlier mentally, but not written down until today.) Short, medium, and probably long term. [Theoretical. No criterion measures given.] Based on interview material with Mrs. S., for which see record [i.e., on detailed knowledge of the history and meanings of Mrs. S's relationship to her ambivalently regarded but largely hated younger sister].

Predictive outcome: + +. Confirmed on various interpretative levels repeatedly. For most recent and strongest validation, see discussion below.

Estimated significance of successful outcome: High in several respects. See discussion below.

Discussion: This prediction was reformulated about three years later in a more satisfactory form than the rather vague statement given above, emphasizing the predominantly hostile components in the mother's "identification" * of Patty with her younger sister, which were clearly implied but not clearly stated in this original hasty formulation. By that time the prediction was already considered as interpretatively validated in its short- and medium-term implications, and the chief interest lay in an interdependent prediction (not counted separately for statistical purposes) that Patty's adolescence would intensify the negative meanings of this unconscious connection for the mother. This second prediction, in turn, was based on further knowledge of Mrs. S.'s relationship with her sister, obtained in the course of interviews about some of her own problems and not in any direct connection with Patty. It turned out that the low point of this relationship occurred when Mrs. S. was about seventeen and her

* The quotation marks around this word are intended to distinguish this usage from "true" identifications, since different mechanisms are involved.

sister was just entering puberty. (The details explaining this must be omitted for the usual reasons of discretion.) At no time was there any verbalization about this "identification" of sister and Patty.

To illustrate what I mean by *different levels of interpretative validation,* I present an excerpt from a taped interview with Mrs. S. some years later, when Patty herself was entering into a very early adolescence and was in a disturbed and unhappy state (see #17 and #18):

Mrs. S.: "I've been thinking a lot about Patty, and I didn't know what —eh . . . this would be today . . . but I thought—eh—of the possibilities of . . . well—(sighs)—I mean either we would—talk straight—about her, or . . . I can—uh—see a great deal—about me that—that results in Patty, but I don't know—which way, I mean I . . ."

J. D. B.: "By talking straight about her you mean—"

Mrs. S.: "Yeah, the symptoms."

J. D. B.: "Talking *only* about her?"

Mrs. S.: "The behavior, the handling. . . . There's a very marked—thing—that started developing . . . hmm—I became aware of it early this summer—but uh—Patty's—Patty's problems—started long before I became aware of this.—Uh . . . whether this feel—feeling group, or this group of feelings has been active—before or not I don't know, but I'm sure that it was.—And—uh—I mean it has nothing to do with the immediate outbreak of symptoms, but this summer I found that I couldn't say my sister's name. I said Patty all the time. And I continue to—" etc.

The implications of the success of this prediction for psychopathological and personality theory cannot be fully discussed or demonstrated here, since that would involve a detailed case study of the mother. Unresolved early conflicts in this woman had led to unusually strong "repetition compulsions;" and the prediction consisted essentially of the assessment of these in the context of a rather thorough knowledge of her past and present functioning in general, permitting the inclusion of structural, topographic, genetic, and economic parameters along with the more usual dynamic considerations. This mother is a gifted person, with many strengths and abilities. Throughout her life she had had a series of overt and sharp conflicts with family, friends, and acquaintances, almost all of which were transparently motivated by repetitive attempts to solve unsolved infantile and adolescent problems. The prediction, then, was further based on the sub-prediction that marriage and motherhood, initially at least, would *not* serve as a maturational factor for this woman, but, rather, would offer new and intensified opportunities for inappropriate and unsuccessful attempts at problem-solving. Further than this I cannot go at present, beyond the parenthetical comment that the last few years have in fact seen some significant changes occurring in this young woman, including important shifts in her relationship to Patty.

More generally, this prediction points up a recognized but perhaps somewhat underestimated factor in parent-child relationships. We have been impressed with the frequency with which we have found in our cases that a parent's handling of a child is importantly co-determined by the unconscious "identification" of the child with an appropriately aged and sexed sibling. In no other case did this factor have quite the repetitive dynamic force found to exist in this one; but in several others it achieved a substantial degree of effectiveness in shaping, and in part warping, the mother-child relationship. In correctly attributing an even greater significance to parents' basic identifications of themselves with their own parents, and of their children with themselves, with, in the pathologic case, the resultant attempts to work through their own unsolved problems on their children (cf. #16), there has been, I think, some tendency to overlook the importance of this secondary and essentially different sort of "identification" of a child with a younger parental sibling.

#16. Patty S., age 3 months. "Predict that Mrs. S's identification of Patty with herself will be in large part projective, i.e., that she will attribute to Patty many things in herself that she doesn't like, and few that she does. At the same time she will be able to derive narcissistic pleasure from Patty whenever she perceives her positively." [This hurriedly written and badly formulated prediction, based on interview material, and written at the same time as #15 above, was also based on observations of the mother-child interaction during the first three months of Patty's life. It thus represents a mixture of theoretical, clinical-inductive, and "intuitive" which it is difficult to evaluate adequately in retrospect, and which, of course, should have been stated at the time. In the terms in which it was written, it calls for both interpretative and behavioral criterion measures.]

Predictive outcome: +. Verified interpretatively, behaviorally, and verbally throughout the record. Cf. particularly the summaries of interviews with Mrs. S.

Estimated significance of successful outcome: Moderately high only in view of unclear nature of predictive bases. (Would be high if it had been formulated something like the following, for which there was ample material available: The fact that Mrs. S. will derive narcissistic as well as maternal object-libidinal gratifications from Patty, together with the fact that she will project negatives onto her, together with the fact that she will "identify" her strongly with her hated younger sister, as well as treat her as she felt she herself was treated by her mother, in conjunction with a strong conscious wish to do just the opposite for her—all this leads to an over-all prediction of an unusually ambivalent and particularly erratic mother-child relationship. Actually, a statement very much like this, only in greater detail, exists in the records, but it is made at a later age (2¾ years) and cannot be considered to be even an informal prediction, but, rather, an explanation of what already had been observed in Mrs. S.'s behavior with Patty.)

#17. Patty S., age 6¾ years. "With the onset of adolescence, i.e., pre-puberty, predict severe neurotic (possibly depressive) symptoms. (Theoretical. Medium-term.) Based on the degree and nature of [the] underlying conflicts; [my] conviction that the defenses (which will be relatively successfully maintained during an unusually clear-cut latency*) are not stable enough to hold up under [the predicted] stresses of adolescence; [my] knowledge of mother's own adolescence, plus her identification [of herself] with Patty, plus her "identification" of Patty with [her own] younger sister, all leading to [a sub-prediction of] increased strain on the mother-child relationship at that time; and on classical psychoanalytic theory of recrudescence of oedipal and pre-oedipal libidinal conflict in adolescence."

Predictive outcome: + +. Criterion measures used: purely clinical-behavioral. Like her mother, Patty had a very early adolescence. She developed severe symptoms which led to her entering treatment.

Estimated significance of successful outcome: High in several respects. Will be discussed jointly with #18.

#18. Patty S., age 6¾ years. "Predict chief *symptomatology* of adolescent psychopathology will be based on separation fears rather than [on] mutilation, with probable depressive component (see previous prediction [#17] and earlier assessments and predictions [about ego functions, penis envy and its handling, castration resentment, mutilation anxiety, oral fixations, and fear of loss of love]). Theoretical [and intuitive?]. Based on mother's overt hostility and Patty's strongly inhibited counterhostility; earlier reactions to separation (but cf. low level of infantile separation anxiety); strong oral fixations; sub-prediction that libidinal arousal will be [unconsciously] associated with repressed early seductions, leading to fear of loss of mother's love, reinforced by actual [predicted] loss of love."

Predictive outcome: + +. Criterion measures used: clinical-behavioral, reports of parents and others, data from (taped) interviews with Patty. Outbreak of symptoms at onset of very early adolescence, one year before the menarche. Overt symptoms were: depressed mood, much weeping, whininess, tearful demands that mother not leave her alone at all, com-

* The material in parentheses is from another prediction about Patty's latency, not being presented here.

plaint of "a funny feeling" when she did, some transient hair and finger sucking, verbalized concerns about possible early death of parents or possible divorce of parents (both highly unlikely contingencies in reality), and many other "separation" fantasies. Other pertinent material elicited: marked turning away from and ignoring of father; only moderate concern about oncoming menstruation; some concern verbalized about what happens to women in the hospital when they have babies; no other conscious anxiety about mutilation; strong interpretative evidence of mutilation anxiety in dreams and fantasies.

Estimated significance of successful outcome: High in several respects. See discussion below.

Discussion: The outcome of these two interlocking but not interdependent predictions raises a number of questions of interest. The first of these, which should precede the discussion of the others, is whether we can reasonably estimate their "significance," using this term here in its statistical sense to mean the probability that the success was not due to chance alone. There can be no doubt that one of the limitations of informal, nonsystematic clinical investigation, to which we owe so much in our field, lies in the tendency to remember successes and forget or ignore failures in diagnosis, prognosis, interpretation, and reconstruction. This is limiting not only because of the obvious objection that certain successes may indeed be due to chance alone, but even more importantly because it deprives us of the opportunity to learn theoretically and methodologically from the failures. It would be of value, then, from both points of view, to have comparable predictions on other cases. We have none. I called attention earlier in this chapter (p. 13) to the regrettable but unavoidable lack of systematic comparability in some areas of prediction in our series, and can now use these examples to illustrate different meanings of the rather cliché phrase, "unique configurations of variables." Everybody being unique in some respects, it is clearly the task of psychological science to recognize but not be stultified by this fact, to discover and formulate laws which account for individual and group variability as well as for invariants and universals. The uniqueness of these predictions in our series, then, does not derive from the fact that Patty and her mother and father are unique, since this is true of every child and every parent; but rather, as stated earlier, from a specific and unusual combination of pathology, strengths, and partial insights in the mother, with certain motivations in both parents which led to their being unusually good informants. The probabilities of finding this combination in a relatively small series are presumably small; and in this sense it is reasonable to say that it was a matter of chance that these predictions could be formulated at all. Once formulated, however, with a high level of confidence in their theoretical base, the question of the "significance" of their successful outcome is an entirely different matter. In spite of the lack of systematic comparability with other predictions, it is theoretically possible to subject the probability of these outcomes being due to chance to a statistical treatment, through examination of the frequency with which this sort of disturbance, with this timing and these symptoms, has occurred in our small intensive series and our much larger, nonintensive longitudinal group. In the absence of really good actuarial (epidemiologic) data, reservations are in order as to the exact meaning of the high significances obtained through these comparisons. Of more statistical significance is the fact that I have never seen or read of a case much like this one, in spite of the relative frequency of adolescent disturbances as such. Even with ideal epidemiologic data, however, there would be no way to express statistically the added "significance" inherent in the success of a theoretically based and self-consistent prediction as compared to one that is purely empirically based. I believe I have made it clear in this chapter and elsewhere that I in no way share the feeling of many clinicians that statistics have little applicability to human psychological investigations, that they must fail to do justice to the subtle complexities of human nature. I think such opinions reveal a misunderstanding of the varied uses of statistical methods and their essential indispensability, correctly used, for the analysis of qualitative, semi-quantitative, and truly quantitative measures alike. To be sure, the misuse of statistics is so prevalent as to give some apparent justification to these misinformed and, in some cases, phobic attitudes. On the other hand, while competent psychometricians are aware of the sort of limitation I referred to earlier, and of others as well, the frequency with which these are overlooked in the psychological literature in the name of "tough-minded" and "objective" science betrays, I think, an equivalent "tender-mindedness" about numbers.

Assuming, then, that we are justified in this case in estimating the probability of the predictive success being due to chance alone as negligibly small, and assuming further that no gross or subtle predictive contamination was involved, we are now in a position to examine further the bases of the predictions and see what conclusions can reasonably be drawn from them. Again, I do not wish to present a case history, but only enough of it to clarify the bases for these particular predictions, to enable the reader to transcribe the inevitable "shorthand notes" of a hurriedly written prediction into a clinically and theoretically coherent statement of what was meant.

Patty's infancy was in part a stormy and difficult but, above all, an uneven one. The mother-child relationship (see prediction #16) was highly erratic but by no means cold or empty. Extreme permissiveness alternated with occasional unreasonable demands; periods of closeness and involvement were followed by withdrawal from the child on the part of the mother; the whole being complicated by a major surrogate role played by a nurse, who combined great affection for Patty with an extremely rigorous and meticulous approach to feeding, toilet training, and discipline in general, and later assumed for her the figure of an ambivalently loved but highly dangerous and threatening witch. As in all such cases, oral fixations and disturbances were prominent, but I shall not delineate them in detail here. I also omit, as not immediately pertinent or necessary for our purposes, the important question of what Patty as an organism brought to these relationships. Following the very early development of intense phallic preoccupations, with frequent overt clitoral masturbation (21–23 months) and much questioning about sex differences, Patty was sent to a nursery school at two years of age, where she was by far the youngest in a group of three and four year olds. Our evidence was entirely clear at the time, and was so noted, that she perceived this as a desertion by mother, as an object loss, and as a punishment for her libidinal expression. From that time on, for the next few years, she became increasingly sensitive to separation from mother, in contrast to the earlier very low degree of infantile separation anxiety, which we had considered to be a reflection of disturbances in the early mother-child relationship. Attempts at weaning were resisted, and Patty continued on the bottle until four years of age, insisting also, particularly on the way to and from school, in clutching her "nanny" (as with many children, a particular blanket). Mother felt guilty about sending her to school so early, and tried hard to be closer to her. There occurred at 26 months an incident in which Patty, sitting on mother's lap "loving" her, drew her mother's hand toward her own genitals, touched them with it for a moment, and then attempted to reach toward mother's genital region. The latter, who, as interpreted by us, was searching with some desperation for a closer relationship than she had yet achieved with Patty, was able to stop the procedure at this point, but had initially acted as though paralyzed. She responded to the incident, inevitably, with strong feelings of guilt that she had seduced Patty into this behavior, became somewhat depressed, and withdrew more from the child. Hospitalization for tonsillectomy at 2–9 reinforced the connection for Patty between mutilation and separation. (Her earliest and most vivid screen memory during therapeutic interviews much later was of looking out of the hospital window at mother, who was waving goodbye.) From 2½ to 6, in addition to many positive aspects of her development, her anxiety level was a fluctuating one, but over-all very high for our series, with many orally tinged mutilation (castration) and primal scene nightmares ("the tractor bited me"), and a fascinating series of verbalized fears, ranging chronologically from fear of the dark (2–5), fear of waking up and finding herself not at home (2–9), overt fears of desertion (3–2), fears of adults and of the Gingerbread Man (3–3) (cf. 40), fear of going to sleep as such (3–6), and fear of airplanes and people shooting and killing (3–9) to overtly expressed fear of genital injury in the dark (4–0) and of flushing the toilet (4–1). From 5–0 until after 6 there developed strong fears of being hurt, particularly of blood and of stinging insects, with the constant use of band-aids for slight cuts; then fears of being put in jail for killing and stealing, fears of burglars, and fears about childbirth (5–3); at 5–8 more expression of fears of desertion, with an increase in the number and severity of nightmares; at 6 severe nightmares about dying and smothering. By 6–8, one month before these predictions were formulated, there had been no nightmares for several months, the verbal and overt behavioral expressions of fear of injury and of blood had markedly decreased, and a variety of minor compulsive rituals had made their appearance. Patty's eventual response to her intense castration preoccupations (denial of absence of penis, later acceptance with strong castration resentment, attacks on father's genitals, fantasies of having literally been castrated, a high degree of penis envy) was an exquisitely feminine narcissistic one, co-determined in this case, I feel sure, as I think it is in many others, by a strong biological "femininity" as well as by rewards from father and others for her general charm and attractiveness. A true but highly conflictful oedipal attachment to father was complicated both by his "mothering" during periods of estrangement from mother from infancy on and by the carry-over of the much stronger pre-oedipal libidinal attachment to mother. Strong hostile aggressive impulses toward both parents, whose complex determination need not be reviewed here, underwent progressive behavioral inhibition during this period without significant inner resolution, although, like the anxiety, it fluctuated in partial consonance with mother's attitudes and behaviors. We interpreted the strong inhibition as being primarily determined by fear of desertion and loss of love. The hostility found its most typical and constant expression between 6 and 6¾ in an almost complete rejection of the intellectual and esthetic values of the parents, in an active anti-intellectualism and Philistinism in choice of interests and friends, combined with a partly affected but partly genuine boredom rarely seen at this age. (Both the boredom and the Philistinism were markedly intensified during the unusually clear-cut latency period referred to earlier.) Accident proneness was also noted.

Although this summary would be entirely inadequate if we wished here to discuss Patty from an over-all developmental point of view, and equally so if we wished to use her case for its contribution to the theory of anxiety, pre-oedipal development, superego functions, aggression, etc., etc.,* it should suffice for our restricted purposes of exemplifying a predictive base in somewhat greater detail than hitherto. Clearly, there is no way of proving, either to the reader or to myself, that other factors than those just reviewed were not also utilized "intuitively" in formulating these predictions, which at first glance seem to verge on fortunetelling. It seems, in fact, entirely possible that they were. But this in no way obliterates the important differences between a prediction in which a base, thought to be sufficient, subsequently seems so also; one where, on the contrary, the consciously explicated base later seems clearly inadequate; and one where there was essentially no explication. All can be useful, as I have tried to demonstrate, but in different ways and to different degrees.

We can condense what seem to be the necessary and sufficient conditions for these predictions as follows:

(1) The erratic and uneven mother-child relationship from birth on, with mother reliving much of her own unhappy childhood and adolescence on and through Patty, partly through identification with her own mother (#16).

(2) The strong oral fixations.

(3) Mother's specific and repetitive "identification" of Patty with her own younger sister, with the ebb and flow of overt hostility toward Patty reflecting in a close to unbelievable literalness the corresponding ages of maximum conflict with and guilt about this sister, permitting the prediction that Patty's early adolescent development would intensify mother's hostile withdrawal from her (#17).

(4) Patty's being sent to nursery school at a very early age, following excessive masturbation for that age; her perception of this as punishment for sexuality through desertion and loss of love; mother's guilt about having sent her, with attempts at greater closeness; the "seduction;" more guilt and further withdrawal in a depressed state; the hospitalization for tonsillectomy.

(5) Later, deep repression of pre-oedipal and oedipal phallic sexuality; strong identification with mother along with major efforts to be as different as possible; much conscious but increasingly inhibited hostility to both parents, with increased fear of loss of love from mother.

(6) All these leading to the prediction that the arousal of libidinal impulses in early adolescence would result in: (a) greater fear of loss of love, reinforced by increased hostility, and finding resonance with an actual

* Cf. ref. 10 for some of these considerations.

withdrawal of love by mother, with regressive activation of previous child-like fears of desertion; and (b) the deepening of the repression of all the material centering around the castration complex itself. Hence the prediction of depression and overt separation anxiety symptoms.

As just stated, we are in no position to consider here the contributions of this case and these predictions to a large number of important theoretical issues, the discussion of which must be reserved for elsewhere. One major area of clinical psychoanalytic theory is so obviously involved in what I have presented of the case, however, that I cannot refrain from a brief comment. I refer to that aspect of the theory of anxiety that deals with the development and structure of phobias, infantile and adult.[30, 40, 41, 67] Passing over the implications of Patty's unusually rich repertory of phobic manifestations between 2½ and 6, including the absence of true zoophobias, I would pose two questions only: why was Patty's adolescent symptomatology so free of adult-like anxiety-hysterical phobic displacements, and of overt anxiety in general? For she did not become panicky when mother left her, but depressed, with some feelings of unreality and almost of depersonalization (the "funny feeling"). Meaningful answers to these questions clearly demand, I think, a thorough metapsychological analysis of the case; and I have not given the reader enough data for this purpose, though perhaps enough to permit reasonable speculation about some of the important genetic, dynamic, economic, structural, and topographic factors at play. To these I would add, in regard to the first of our questions, this further consideration: Patty's very early adolescence found her much more advanced physiologically than psychologically. Beyond that, certain aspects of her cognitive functioning were relatively poorly developed even for her age; not autonomously, I might add, but as the direct and predictable result of experience. I refer to her conceptual thinking, and imply that this too plays a role in symptom formation: a thesis which I shall not develop further here.

Finally, and on a more general level, I should like to give special emphasis to the *experiential* aspect of this series of predictions about Patty. Throughout this chapter I have repeatedly stressed the importance I attribute to innate variables in their interaction with experience, and in their capacity to help shape experiences, as contrasted with the pure environmentalism of much present-day learning theory and "dynamic" psychopathological theory. In so doing, there is always the danger of being misunderstood as minimizing the importance of experiential variables in normal and pathologic personality development; as considering them as secondary or even epiphenomenal to innate biologically determined factors in personality; even of being associated with the old *homunculus* type of hereditary personality theory, which is again finding its modern proponents. There is by this time sufficient experimental and clinical evidence to demonstrate the obvious conclusively: that both sorts of factors, innate and experiential, are significantly involved in all behavior. What is of interest is how to conceptualize and investigate the different kinds and degrees of interaction between them.[6, 9] These predictions were largely based on observed and predicted experiences; and their successful outcome, assuming the absence of unrecognized predictive contaminants, constitutes impressive evidence that some experiences, particularly if repetitively reinforced, can be of over-riding importance in effecting some behaviors.

One is reminded of Freud's complementary series concept.[41] Although his conceptualizations of the nature of the relationships between the constitutional and the experiential, and between the biological and the psychological, were necessarily different from those which seem most strategic to pursue today, the basic thesis advanced in this concept appears at present to be as well supported by clinical experience, and as much neglected in most etiologic investigations, as it was when he first formulated it.

Concluding Remarks

In view of the amount of repetition which I have permitted myself in the foregoing pages, I do not think it necessary to summarize systematically all the points I have tried to cover. The limitations, not only of predictability but of the individual predictive method as we use it, are, I think, obvious; and some of them have been illustrated. We believe these to be outweighed by the advantages we have discussed. Among these, the necessity imposed by predictive attempts for sharper definition and differentiation of concepts as well as for the study of the processes of assessment, particularly interpretative assessment, have been emphasized, but only in small part exemplified. We have illustrated to a somewhat greater extent the potential values of successful and unsuccessful predictions for variable discovery, and for the validation, invalidation, and clarification of theory.

In heavily weighting the selection of our examples toward psychopathology, we have also biased them toward the long-term variety. In so doing, we have given only a few examples of short-term developmental predictions, which constitute a large proportion of the predictions we make; and we have entirely excluded examples of the horizontal variety, aiming primarily at validation of method rather than of theory. This concentration on clinical theory has also weighted our sample somewhat in the direction of the "intuitive," in the various senses defined.

Major emphasis has been placed in this presentation on the method of individual prediction itself, on its technical pitfalls and what we have found to be useful in trying to avoid them. We do not wish, however, to leave the impression that we think less rigorous predictive procedures have no place in clinical investigation. On the contrary, I think that the very act of putting convictions, and particularly *etiologic* convictions, to any sort of individual or correlational predictive test, no matter how unrigorous, is in itself worthwhile, provided only that elementary precautions against self-deception are maintained.

Any theoretically minded psychoanalytic or psychiatric clinician who sets himself the task of formulating explicated predictions will be confronted with the problem of how to reconcile the complexity and variability of human functioning, as he sees it convincingly in his everyday work, with the relative simplicity of scientific formulation. For there is no doubt, in my opinion, that scientific progress often requires simplification, and that this holds particularly for work in complex systems. Psychoanalytic theory itself is an excellent example, historically, of necessary and productive simplification relative to the actual complexities of the system under study. So was Newtonian physics. What was once useful simplification becomes one sort of over-simplification at a later stage in the development of science. Modern psychoanalytic ego psychology, for example, while itself undoubtedly a simplification, has served the function of preventing psychoanalysis from becoming an over-simplified theoretical system, in this special sense of the word. Better integration of data and concepts from the behavioral and biological sciences with psychoanalytic theory will in the future, I feel sure, serve the same function.

The distinction between productive simplification and grossly distorting over-simplification of another sort is of particular pertinence to psychoanalytic investigation. Many of the attempts at experimental validation of some aspects of psychoanalytic theory have been criticized, and rightly so,[5] as being so over-simplified as to have essentially no meaning in terms of the theories they have attempted to test. I do not think any other judgment is possible for many of these investigations. But we cannot indefinitely reject any and all attempts at experimental psychoanalytic research and at the same time do nothing to help in the clarification and simplification necessary for meaningful rigorous investigation. It may be noted in this connection that there are some who take a pessimistic point of view about the possibility of systematic research in our field, on the ground that things are too complex ever to permit the necessary simplification, yet have no hesitation in "explaining" these complex phenomena with the utmost simplicity and authority.

Although the distinction between simplification and over-simplification, then, is clearly of major importance in all fields of psychological and biological investigation, it is not an easy one to draw in advance. On a conceptual level one could say, for example, that formulations which ignore parameters known to be relevant are over-simplified [9] and that those which include everything that conceivably *could* be relevant are over-complex, both constituting poor bases for investigative work. But this a priori definition, plausible and in a sense true as it is, is itself over-simplified. The fact is that many creative scientists, Freud among them, have purposely and productively ignored variables known, to others at least, to be relevant. It is perhaps one of the marks of the genius in science that he somehow knows what to ignore for the time being; that he is so often right, and sometimes wrong, on insufficient evidence. For the rest of us, the definition of the difference between simplification and over-simplification is in the last analysis an empiric and circular one: the sort of simplification that leads to progress is the right sort; otherwise, it is over-simplification.

I feel sure that some colleagues will consider a number of my theoretical formulations to be over-simplified, while others will feel, on the contrary, that they are far too complex to be scientifically useful, in addition to being too subjective and too often "intuitive." While rejecting both these points of view insofar as they represent generalizations about scientific method, I accept and share them in part as specific criticisms. Some of what I have presented is, inevitably, deficient in one or the other of these directions. Whether or not the global, long-term mental health predictions in particular are over-simplified will have to await empiric demonstration in the future. If they prove so to be, as seems entirely possible, we shall none the less have learned from them. And with this *apologia,* I conclude.

Bibliography

1. Abraham, K.: Contributions to the theory of the anal character. Internat. J. Psycho-Analysis *4:* 400–418, 1923.

2. Alexander, F.: The logic of emotions and its dynamic background. Internat. J. Psycho-Analysis *16:* 399–413, 1935.

3. Bayley, N.: Consistency and variability in the growth of intelligence from birth to eighteen years. J. Genet. Psychol. *75:* 165–196, 1949.

4. Beach, F. A., and Jaynes, J.: Effects of early experience upon the behavior of animals. Psychol. Bull. *51:* 239–263, 1954.

5. Benjamin, J. D.: Methodological considerations in the validation and elaboration of psychoanalytical personality theory. Am. J. Orthopsychiat. *20:* 139–156, 1950.

6. ———: Directions and problems in psychiatric research. Psychosom. Med. *14:* 1–9, 1952.

7. ———: Discussion of Kubie, L. S.: Psychoanalysis as a basic science. *In* Alexander, F., and Ross, H.: 20 Years of Psychoanalysis. New York, Norton, 1953.

8. ———: Knowledge, Conviction, and Ignorance. Unpublished address delivered at the meeting of the National Association for Mental Health, Indianapolis, 1954.

9. ———: Some considerations in biological research in schizophrenia. Psychosom. Med.: *20:* 427–445, 1958.

10. ———: From Infancy to Adolescence. The History of One Child. In preparation.

11. ———: Psychoanalytic Theory and Clinical Psychoanalysis. In preparation.

12. ———, and Ebaugh, F. G.: The diagnostic validity of the Rorschach test. Am. J. Psychiat. *94:* 1163–1176, 1938.

13. Bergman, P., and Escalona, S. K.: Unusual sensitivities in very young children. Psychoanalyt. Study of the Child *3–4:* 333–352, 1949.

14. Bernstein, L.: The effects of variations in handling upon learning and retention. J. Comp. Physiol. Psychol. *50:* 162–167, 1957.

15. Bibring, G. L.: Personal communication, 1957.

16. Bowlby, J.: Maternal care and mental health. Bull. World Health Organ. *3:* 355–533, 1951.

17. Bühler, C.: The First Year of Life. New York, Day, 1930.

18. ———, Hetzer, H., and Mabel, F.: Die Affektwirksamkeit von Fremdheitseindrücken im ersten Lebensjahr. Ztschr. f. Psychol. u. Physiol. d. Sinnesorg. *107:* 30–49, 1928.

19. Coleman, R. W., Kris, E., and Provence, S.: The study of variations of early parental attitudes. Psychoanalyt. Study of the Child *8:* 20–47, 1953.

20. Cronbach, L. J., and Meehl, P. E.: Construct validity in psychological tests. Psychol. Bull. *52:* 281–302, 1955.

21. Despert, J. L.: Some considerations relating to the genesis of autistic behavior in children. Am. J. Orthopsychiat. *21:* 335–350, 1951.

22. Erikson, E. H.: Configurations in play—clinical notes. Psychoanalyt. Quart. *6:* 139–214, 1937.

23. Erikson, E. H.: Problems of infancy and early childhood. Cyclopedia of Medicine, Surgery and Specialties *12:* 714–730, 1940.

24. Erikson, E. H.: Childhood and tradition in two American Indian tribes. *In* Kluckhohn, C., and Murray, H.: Personality in Nature, Society and Culture. New York, Knopf, 1948, pp. 176–203.

25. ———: Childhood and Society. New York, Norton, 1950.

26. ———: The problem of ego identity. J. Am. Psychoanalyt. A. *4:* 56–121, 1956.

27. Escalona, S.: The use of infant tests for predictive purposes. Bull. Menninger Clin. *14:* 117–128, 1950.

28. ———: Problems in psycho-analytic research. Internat. J. Psycho-Analysis *33:* 1–11, 1952.

29. ———, and others: Early phases of personality development: A non-normative study of infant behavior. Monogr. Soc. Res. in Child Development *17:* 1–72, 1952.

30. ———, and Heider, G.: Prediction and Outcome. A Study in Child Development. To be published 1959.

31. Fenichel, O.: Remarks on the common phobias. Psychoanalyt. Quart. *13:* 313–326, 1944.

32. ———: The Psychoanalytic Theory of Neurosis. New York, Norton, 1945.

33. French, T. M.: Discussion of Kubie, L. S.: Psychoanalysis as a basic science. *In* Alexander, F., and Ross, H.: 20 Years of Psychoanalysis. New York, Norton, 1953.

34. Frenkel-Brunswick, E.: Motivation and behavior. Genet. Psychol. Monogr. *26:* 121–265, 1942.

35. Freud, A.: The Ego and the Mechanisms of Defense (1936). New York, International Universities Press, 1946.

36. Freud, S.: The Interpretation of Dreams (1900). New York, The Macmillan Co., 1931.

37. ———: Character and anal eroticism (1908). *In* Collected Papers, vol. II. London, Hogarth, 1946.

38. ———: Formulations regarding the two principles in mental functioning (1911). *In* Collected Papers, vol. IV. London, Hogarth, 1946.

39. ———: Introductory Lectures to Psychoanalysis (1916). London, G. Allen and Unwin, 1922.

40. ———: The Problem of Anxiety (1926). New York, Norton, 1936.

41. ———: New Introductory Lectures on Psychoanalysis (1933). New York, Norton, 1933.

42. Gill, M.: The present state of psychoanalytic theory. J. Abnorm. & Social Psychol. In press. Cited by Rapaport, D., footnote 87.

43. Goldfarb, W.: Psychological deprivation in infancy and subsequent adjustment. Am. J. Orthopsychiat. *15:* 247–255, 1945.

44. Goldfarb, W.: Emotional and intellectual consequences of psychologic deprivation in infancy: A revaluation. *In* Hoch, P. H., and Zubin, J.: Psychopathology of Childhood. New York, Grune & Stratton, 1955.

45. Hartmann, H.: Ich-Psychologie und Anpassungsproblem. Internat. Ztschr. f. Psychoanal. u. Imago *24:* 62–135, 1939. Translated by Rapaport, D.: Ego Psychology and the Problem of Adaptation. New York, International Universities Press, 1958.

46. ———: Comments on the psychoanalytic theory of instinctual drives. Psychoanalyt. Quart. *17:* 368–388, 1948.

47. ———: Comments on the psychoanalytic theory of the ego. Psychoanalyt. Study of the Child *5:* 74–96, 1950.

48. ———: Contribution to the metapsychology of schizophrenia. Ibid. *8:* 177–198, 1953.

49. Hartmann, H., and Kris, E.: The genetic approach in psychoanalysis. Psychoanalyt. Study of the Child *1:* 11–30, 1945.

50. ———, ———, and Loewenstein, R. M.: Comments on the formation of psychic structure. Ibid. *2:* 11–38, 1946.

51. ———, ———, and ———: Notes on the theory of aggression. Ibid. *3–4:* 9–36, 1949.

52. ———, ———, and ———: The function of theory in psychoanalysis. *In* Loewenstein, R. M.: Drives, Affects, Behavior. New York, International Universities Press, 1953.

53. Hetzer, H., and Wolf, K. M.: Babytests. Eine Testserie für das erste Lebensjahr. Ztschr. Psychol. & Physiol. d. Sinnesorg. *107:* 62–104, 1928.

54. Kanner, L.: Autistic disturbances of affective contact. Nervous Child *2:* 217–250, 1943.

55. ———: To what extent is early infantile autism determined by constitutional inadequacies? *In* Association for Research in Nervous and Mental Disease. Research Publications Vol. 33: Genetics and the Inheritance of Integrated Neurological and Psychiatric Patterns. Baltimore, The Williams & Wilkins Company, 1954.

56. ———, and Eisenberg, L.: Notes on the follow-up studies of autistic children. *In* Hoch, P. H., and Zubin, J.: Psychopathology of Childhood. New York, Grune & Stratton, 1955.

57. Knapp, P.: Personal communication, 1958.

58. Kris, E.: Notes on the development and on some current problems of psychoanalytic child psychology. Psychoanalyt. Study of the Child *5:* 24–46, 1950.

59. ———: Psychoanalytic Explorations in Art. New York, International Universities Press, 1952.

60. ———: Neutralization and sublimation: observations on young children. Psychoanalyt. Study of the Child *10:* 30–46, 1955.

61. ———: The recovery of childhood memories in psychoanalysis. Ibid. *11:* 54–88, 1956.

62. Kris, M.: The use of prediction in a longitudinal study. Ibid. *12:* 175–189, 1957.

63. Kubie, L. S.: Psychoanalysis as a basic science. *In* Alexander, F., and Ross, H.: 20 Years of Psychoanalysis. New York, Norton, 1953.

64. ———: Neurotic Distortion of the Creative Process. Lawrence, University of Kansas Press, 1958.

65. ———: A re-examination of the significance of the preconscious in human mentation. Paper read at the December 1957 meeting of the American Psychoanalytic Association. To be published.

66. Lewin, B. D.: The Psychoanalysis of Elation. New York, Norton, 1950.

67. ———: Phobic symptoms and dream interpretation. Psychoanalyt. Quart. *21:* 295–322, 1952.

68. ———: The forgetting of dreams. *In* Loewenstein, R. M.: Drives, Affects, Behavior. New York, International Universities Press, 1953.

69. Mahler, M. S.: On child psychosis and schizophrenia: Autistic and symbiotic infantile psychoses. Psychoanalyt. Study of the Child *7:* 286–305, 1952.

70. ———: Discussion of Kanner and Eisenberg (56). *In* Hoch, P. H., and Zubin, J.: Psychopathology of Childhood. New York, Grune & Stratton, 1955.

71. Meehl, P. E.: Clinical vs. Statistical Prediction: Minneapolis, University of Minnesota Press, 1954.

72. Meili, R.: Anfänge der Charakterentwicklung. Bern & Stuttgart, Huber, 1957.

73. Menninger, W. C.: Characterologic and symptomatic expressions related to the anal phase of psychosexual development. Psychoanalyt. Quart. *12:* 161–193, 1943.

74. Mirsky, I. A.: Psychoanalysis and the biological sciences. *In* Alexander, F., and Ross, H.: 20 Years of Psychoanalysis. New York, Norton, 1953.

75. ———, Futterman, P., and Kaplan, S.: Blood plasma pepsinogen: II. The activity of the plasma from "normal" subjects, patients with duodenal ulcer, and patients with pernicious anemia. J. Lab. & Clin. Med. *40:* 188–199, 1952.

76. Pavenstedt, E., and Sander, L. W.: Personal communication, 1955.

76a. Piaget, J.: The Origins of Intelligence in Children. New York, International Universities Press, 1952.

76b. ———: The Construction of Reality in the Child. New York, Basic Books, 1954.

77. Poincaré, H.: Mathematical creation. *In* Foundations of Science. Translated by Halsted, C. B., Lancaster, Science Press, 1946. Also *in* Newman, J. R.: The World of Mathematics. Vol. 4. New York, Simon & Schuster, 1956, pp. 2041–2050.

78. Rangell, L.: On the psychoanalytic theory of anxiety. J. Am. Psychoanalyt. A. *3:* 389–414, 1955.

79. Rank, B.: Adaptation of the psychoanalytic technique for the treatment of young children with atypical development. Am. J. Orthopsychiat. *19:* 130–139, 1949.

80. ———, and Macnaughton, D.: A clinical contribution to early ego development. Psychoanalyt. Study of the Child *5:* 53–65, 1950.

81. Rapaport, D.: On the psycho-analytic theory of thinking. Internat. J. Psycho-Analysis *31:* 161–170, 1950.

82. ———: The autonomy of the ego. Bull. Menninger Clin. *15:* 113–123, 1951.

83. ———: Organization and Pathology of Thought. New York, Columbia University Press, 1951.

84. ———: On the psycho-analytic theory of affects. Internat. J. Psycho-Analysis *34:* 177–198, 1953.

85. ———: Psychoanalysis and developmental psychology. Unpublished address at Clark University, Sept. 21, 1957.

86. ———: The theory of ego-autonomy: A generalization. Bull. Menninger Clin. *22:* 13–35, 1958.

87. ———: The structure of psychoanalytic theory (a systematizing attempt). *In* Koch, S.: Psychology: A Study of a Science, Vol. 3. New York, McGraw-Hill. In press.

88. Ricciuti, H. N.: Use of the Rorschach test in longitudinal studies of personality development. J. Projective Techniques *20:* 256–260, 1956.

89. Ruegamer, W. R., Bernstein, L., and Benjamin, J. D.: Growth, food utilization and thyroid activity in the albino rat as a function of extra handling. Science *120:* 184–185, 1954.

90. Spitz, R. A.: Hospitalism. An inquiry into the genesis of psychiatric conditions in early childhood. Psychoanalyt. Study of the Child *1:* 53–74, 1945.

91. ———: Anxiety in infancy: a study of its manifestations in the first year of life. Internat. J. Psycho-Analysis *31:* 138–143, 1950.

92. ———: A note on the extrapolation of ethological findings. Internat. J. Psycho-Analysis *36:* 162–165, 1955.

93. Spitz, R. A.: The primal cavity: A contribution to the genesis of perception and its role for psychoanalytic theory. Psychoanalyt. Study of the Child *10:* 215–240, 1955.

94. ———: No and Yes. On the Genesis of Human Communication. New York, International Universities Press, 1957.

95. ———: A Genetic Field Theory of Ego Formation and its Implications for Psychopathology. Annual Freud Lecture, 1958. To be published by International Universities Press.

96. ———, and Wolf, K. M.: The smiling response: A contribution to the ontogenesis of social relations. Genet. Psychol. Monogr. *34:* 57–125, 1946.

97. ———, and ———: Anaclitic depression. An inquiry into the genesis of psychiatric conditions in early childhood, II. Psychoanalyt. Study of the Child *2:* 313–342, 1946.

98. Szekely, L.: Biological remarks on fears originating in early childhood. Internat. J. Psycho-Analysis *35:* 57–67, 1954.

99. Wallerstein, R. S., and Robbins, L. L.: The psychotherapy research project of the Menninger Foundation. Bull. Menninger Clin. *20:* 239–262, 1956.

100. Weil, A. P.: Clinical data and dynamic considerations in certain cases of childhood schizophrenia. Am. J. Orthopsychiat. *23:* 518–529, 1953.

101. Weiner, H., Thaler, M., Reiser, M. F., and Mirsky, I. A.: Etiology of duodenal ulcer. I. Relation of specific psychological characteristics to rate of gastric secretion (serum pepsinogen). Psychosom. Med. *19:* 1–10, 1957.

102. Wolf, K. M.: Personal communications, 1952–1954.

103. Wolff, P. H.: Observations on newborn infants. In preparation.

3

Some Aspects of the Neurophysiology of the Newborn and Their Implications for Child Development*

By JULIUS B. RICHMOND and EARLE L. LIPTON

THE CLINICIAN who works with children is necessarily concerned with the development of object relations, the ego, personality, and social and cultural patterns of adaptation. For a deeper understanding of these developmental phenomena it becomes necessary to learn more of the building blocks out of which they are formed. The study of the development of relationships in the human infant should logically carry us back to embryonic and fetal subjects, but since this is not feasible, we have concerned ourselves mainly with newborn infants.

Because of the infant's incapacity to communicate at a verbal level, psychologically oriented studies of the newborn infant are relatively few. Indeed, studies of newborn infants can only be *oriented* psychologically, since data collection must necessarily be physiologic (including motor behavior) or biochemical. The problem of conceptualizing what is transpiring within the infant psychologically can lead to adultomorphic speculations on which theoretical formulations are then based. Because of the limitations of our knowledge concerning infant development, efforts should be expended toward the accumulation of data on which more effective theoretical formulations may be based. It is hoped, however, that as new formulations develop they will be modest and in keeping with the data rather than premature elaborations from the data. It is anticipated that direct observations of infants will obviate the need to rely on speculations derived from retrospective data from older children and adults.

In considering early infant development, it is helpful to visualize a model which incorporates various levels of communication between parents and infant. If we view a hierarchy of communications which

* Studies presented in this paper were supported in part by a grant from the Ford Foundation.

influence parent-infant interaction, we may see the social and cultural backgrounds of the parents as having determined the feelings of the parents (their individual psychology) in relationship to the infant. The communication to the infant, in terms of how he is fed, clothed, fondled, and diapered, is physiologic. This relationship may be represented diagrammatically as follows:

Social and cultural factors	← →	Feelings toward infant (individual psychology of parents)	→ ←	Physiologic transaction with infant (feeding, clothing, diapering, activity, etc.)

The complexity of nonverbal forms of communication leaves us without a functional language for describing parent-infant interaction.[45] This complexity has been indicated by Benedek[4] in her statement that, "Growth, neurophysiologic maturation and psychosexual development are intrinsically interwoven processes." Thus, at various ages, depending upon the state of neurophysiologic maturation, the process of communication will vary. The development of object relationships, for example, is facilitated by visual maturation.

Knowledge of newborn neurophysiology can be helpful in several ways: (1) it may provide us with more understanding of constitutional differences at birth; (2) it may provide us with data concerning inter-individual differences at birth which may be related to developmental patterns in the growing organism; and (3) it may provide us with basic data concerning the physiology of emotional development. In this connection, Engel[13] has indicated: "Indeed, the inescapable fact is that there is as yet no physiology of the mother-infant symbiotic unit, or of object relationship. Nothing is known of the physiology of separation, grief, and depression; other than embryology, there is no real comparative physiology of growth and development; the physiology of moods and affects is incomplete; there is no physiology of love, and only meager knowledge of sexual processes, erotic phenomena, and sexuality. Yet, much evidence suggests that such processes are concerned in intimate but obscure ways with the development of a wide variety of somatic changes, including pathologic changes."

In order to facilitate a better understanding of the physiology of emotions, it is essential that we have adequate data concerning the newborn in order that these data may serve as a baseline for further studies and for the development of theory. Our presentation will concern itself, therefore, with significant data available concerning the central and autonomic nervous systems of the newborn infant. If these data help in the formulation of theory, they will have served their purpose.

CNS Immaturity at Birth

The brain of the human newborn infant is comparatively large, but it is histologically and biochemically quite immature. Its weight of 300 to 350 grams is nearly that of adult primates (chimpanzee, 350 grams; gorilla, 450 grams; orangutan, 240 grams). Within two years the brain weight nearly trebles, and by six years of age 95 per cent of the mature weight (1200–1300 grams) has been attained. Since water content decreases after birth, future comparative studies should include data on solid tissue weight.

Conel's [10] studies of the cerebral cortex of the young infant have provided us with more information on the development of the cortex than we have concerning other parts of the brain. The inner cellular layers of the cortex are the more advanced at birth; this is particularly true of the anterior and posterior central gyrus areas. In the motor cortex the most advanced areas are those which control neck and shoulder movements. Progressive complex arborization of dendritic processes during the first few months of life was found with no evidence of a quantitative cellular increase. Thus, cellular endowment is fixed at birth, but complex morphologic changes continue for a long period. Since it is now generally accepted that neurons are connected in a network and not merely in a linear series, and that nerve impulses pass about the connections in a circular, more or less continuing fashion, the potential significance of this growing arborization for the development of the infant may be appreciated.[16] Certainly, the pediatrician is well aware of the disorganizing effects of central nervous system infections and other insults on the orderly pattern of development.

The relative slowness of the maturation of the central nervous system may well be a leading factor in man's ultimate developmental attainments. The extreme flexibility of his thought processes appears to evolve through prolonged scanning of the environment with simultaneous and subsequent integration through complex processes of association. Hebb [19] has stated that "the process of perceptual learning must be thought of as establishing a control of association-area activity by sensory events. The larger the association areas, both absolutely and relative to the size of the sensory projection areas, the slower the establishment of such a control must be and the less rigid and complex its final form." This would tend to explain the rapid early learning in lower species and the slower primary learning in man.

Myelin first appears in the fetus at four months gestation, and there is subsequently a progressive appearance of the material in certain tracts of the cord. The motor root fibers precede the dorsal roots in this regard. The principal fiber tracts of the brain stem and spinal cord are myelinated at birth but little or no myelin is found in the cortex. In fact there is little in the cerebral hemispheres until six to nine months of age, and pyramidal tract myelinization is not completed until five to six years of age.[1, 26]

In the past, attempts have been made to correlate the initial functional activity of the nervous system with the appearance of myelin, synaptic thresholds, development of neurofibrillae, and other phenomena. It has been established that neurons can convey impulses prior to myelinization. Conel[10] has avoided making any such correlations, for it would appear that the relationships among many of these, in addition to biochemical factors, interacting in complex fashion are responsible for the development of neural function.

After early embryonic life, mammals show essentially no regenerative capacity in the central nervous system.[22] Experimental insults to the developing neural crest of lower species result in irreversible damage to central and peripheral neural structures. In this manner, Yntema and Hammond[47] have demonstrated the derivation and migration of gastrointestinal ganglion cells from neural crest tissue. Once the enzyme systems presumed to be responsible for the capacity for regeneration in some inframammalian species have been definitely established, we may hope for comparable data concerning the time at which embryonic nerve tissue loses this capacity.

Advances in the field of enzyme chemistry have resulted in many studies of the developing nervous system in animals. Cholinesterase, acetylcholine and porphyrin concentration in various sites has been tentatively correlated by some authors with function and with neural differentiation.[27, 42] Few studies have been performed on human tissue in varying stages of development. Richter's excellent review[39] indicates the directions which such work might take as a result of provocative animal studies. Studies of the rat and guinea pig show critical periods of histologic, enzyme and electrical activity change. These occur in the prenatal period of the guinea pig and postnatally in the rat, which is considerably less mature at birth.

During the first four years of life it is estimated that more than one half the total body oxygen consumption is by the brain.[39] This may be correlated with the rapidity of growth during these early years. It appears that enzyme systems concerned with glucose oxidation first appear in lower centers during fetal life. These energy supplying mechanisms continue to increase after birth. Anaerobic glycolysis, still present in the newborn, may account for the greater ability to withstand hypoxic insults as compared to the adult.[26]

The enzyme systems change as the "metabolism of growth" is replaced by the "metabolism of function." [39] The adult brain has a much reduced capacity to synthesize or utilize proteins and lipids and is almost wholly dependent upon carbohydrate. This factor plus the rapidly developing blood-brain barrier allows for relatively greater homeostasis in the brain than any other organ.

Environmental Influence on Structure and Function

From available evidence it would appear that the neonate brain has certain advantages in its relatively immature and less differentiated state. There has been considerable clinical speculation that the relative infrequency of cerebral palsy and other neurologic disorders as a consequence of hypoxia and other insults is due to the immature brain's capacity to recuperate with a minimum of residual damage and to the facility with which other brain areas compensate for any loss of function which may occur.[25, 26]

Experimentally, environmental stimulation appears to have some effect upon ultimate structure and function under normal circumstances of development. Langworthy's studies [30] in kittens revealed that myelinization may be significantly influenced by neuronal function. The optic nerve of the eye blindfolded from birth histologically manifested less myelinization than that of the contralateral, stimulated eye. In similar fashion, LeGros Clark [9] demonstrated a failure of development of certain retinal cells in animals restricted to an environment of blue light from birth.

Rao [36] found that vascularity of the visual cortex was decreased by the removal of eyes in neonate rats. Apparently, human premature infants whose eyes have been exposed to light since birth show more mature optic nerve development than full-term infants of an equivalent age at the time of death.[25] These types of studies seem to give support to the contention that even after the fetal stage, environmental stimulation (or lack thereof) can modify developing structure in the central nervous system.

Evidence of the importance of afferent impulses in influencing function comes from the stimulating work of Weiss.[3] Motor neurons, separated from their associated muscles by section of their axons, give rise to less selective impulses. If regeneration occurs into a different muscle, the neuronal discharges become less general and diffuse and subsequently take on characteristics determined by the new muscle. Thus, a muscle exercises an effect upon its associated motor neurons that determines their central selectivity.

Central afferent connections may play a vital role in the early generalized behavior of the organism. Specificity of response and inhibition of mass activity may well relate to increasing afferent impulses. Barron indicates that: ". . . in ontogeny, the arrival of afferents within the neuronal field of the limb efferents is associated—in the sheep, for example—with the dissociation of the limb from activity patterns of the trunk initiated through stimulation of the maxillary division of the trigeminal." [3]

Hebb's experiments [20] suggest that early sensory stimulation (or at least relationships with others) is needed for the development of the ability to learn later from experience. Puppies raised in solitary confinement had little capacity to avoid painful stimuli after repeated exposure, unlike control animals raised in the usual environment. Their responses were inappropriate, unorganized and panicky. Spitz [45] compares this with the later learning difficulty observed in children who had experienced affect-deprivation in infancy.

Studies of the postoperative recovery of sight in cases of congenital blindness (cataract) indicate that despite the presence of considerable development in other aspects of behavior, the first visual learning is extremely inefficient and often amazingly difficult and delayed.[19] This is confirmed by Riesen's studies [37] of chimpanzees reared in darkness who could not for a long period discriminate even the moving, white-clad attendant from any other part of their environment. Less integration is apparently required in insects or rats reared in darkness since they discriminate visually with little if any delay under such experimental circumstances. This further illustrates the relatively more rapid primary learning in lower species referred to by Hebb,[19] who observed that "the human baby takes six months, the chimpanzee four months, before making a clear distinction visually between friend and enemy. Evidently, this is a period of learning as well as of maturation, not just a matter of waiting until certain neural structures are fully grown, with learning then at a typical adult rate."

Neonate Capacity for Sensation and Response

The onset of motor behavior is at eight weeks gestation in the human fetus. Patterned responses to tactile stimulation occur first, followed at nine and a half weeks by unprovoked spontaneous movements.[23] By fourteen weeks most of the neonate reflexes are at least represented. After this, movements are less stereotyped and responses become more specifically related to the areas stimulated. Proprioception, taste, olfaction, audition and vision are potentially functional senses prior to birth according to studies in premature infants.[8]

The problem of whether findings in the fetus so tested really represent the true fetal state has been expressed by Barcroft. He stated that hypoxia in the extrauterine state may account for some of the responses and activities observed. Data from these observations have served as the basis for discussions which debate whether behavior develops through individuation of partial patterns from an initial total pattern, as proposed by Coghill, or through the progressive integration of initial simple reflexes as suggested by Windle. Barron,[3] in an incisive discussion, has integrated these views on the basis of current neurophysiologic principles; the reader is referred to his paper for elucidation.

The newborn reacts to light but little is known about the ability to differentiate stimuli in terms of wave length, complexity of form, etc. As with audition, responses depend upon intensity and duration. There is evidence of visual fixation on objects and pursuit movements.[18] Such observations demonstrate a "certain amount of ability to orient in the environment and to localize the sources of excitation." [35]

Pitch discrimination has not been definitely established on the basis of behavioral response. Short intense stimuli produce lid reflexes, autonomic changes and gross muscular responses. Decreasing response occurs with repetition. Tones of greater intensity and duration tend to decrease motor activity. Response to sound varies according to the physiologic state of the infant, with little reactivity during nursing. These observations have been utilized as a gross test for hearing in the newborn infant.[38]

Infants react vigorously to various odors and seem to indicate "pleasure" by sucking and licking and "displeasure" by grimacing, head turning, etc. The neonate differentiates certain taste qualities; sucking with a sugar stimulus, stopping when salt or bitter stimuli are presented.

Reactions to pressure, pain and thermal stimuli have been studied but little is known of differential sensitivity of various cutaneous areas. Thermal stimuli often produce local responses, though extreme cold often leads to withdrawal movements while warmth may lead to movement toward the stimulus. The authors' studies of heart rate and skin temperature responses to the stimulation of various skin areas are described later. Many additional observations of neonate sensitivity and neuromuscular behavior are to be found in Pratt's review,[35] the observations of Gesell, McGraw, and many other workers.[17, 33]

Despite this evidence of considerable sensitivity to external stimuli, Carmichael [8] believes "it is the internal stimuli which account for most of the mobility of the infant." It is our general impression, however, that under usual home and nursery conditions the neonate probably is responding to external stimuli a much larger proportion of the time than has been stated in the past. Some of our experimental data which follow tend to support our view.

Autonomic Function

Our interest in children with disorders commonly designated as psychosomatic (ulcerative colitis, peptic ulcer, asthma, eczema) has led us to an inquiry into the genesis of the psychophysiologic disturbance in these children.[34] Our present state of knowledge does not permit us to define the precise contributions of constitutional predisposition which may influence organ involvement, or environmental factors which may be implicated in specific organ response. This is, of course, the "nature vs. nurture" controversy; no attempt is made to provide a solution of this problem, for we feel that we are concerned with the interaction of these forces rather than the priority of one over the other.

For a better understanding, data are necessary which will contribute toward some clarification of these problems. An editorial in *Psychosomatic Medicine* summarized the current developments in this field as follows: "Earlier studies devoted to a kind of descriptive typology seem now oversimplified. They have given way to more carefully contrived and controlled experimental ones and to the accumulation of more soundly tested data. This is a healthy development that should lead, in time, to much needed theoretical formulations in this complicated field where interacting forces of many kinds are at work." [11]

In an effort to define constitutional factors more clearly, we have felt the need to investigate the "functional constitution," of the individual in terms of autonomic reactivity in the early life of the infant. We have, therefore, directed our attention to such studies in new born infants. The problems concerned with autonomic studies generally and this age group specifically are formidable. The studies to be presented, therefore, while lacking in direct application to clinical work, are essential for the elaboration of theory and as building blocks on which long-term observations of children may be based.

It is significant to emphasize that these studies are important not alone for a better understanding of "psychosomatic disorders" but are also basic to learning more of the development of cortico-autonomic relationships.

These relationships have implications for an understanding of the physiology of emotions, particularly if the physiologic data can be correlated with psychological interaction of parents and child. Studies of patterns of response in early life should ultimately offer a better understanding of the genesis of the physiology of anxiety, anger, and other emotional states. This has implications for the child's development of concepts concerning his relationship to his body as an object, emerging ego patterns, and personality development.

Because of the relative lack of information concerning autonomic function in the neonate, we have found it necessary to study its general characteristics. This has led to many methodologic problems both in the laboratory and in the analysis of data which can be dealt with only briefly in this presentation. For more extended discussion, the reader is referred to a recent paper.[31] Our data are derived from a population of newborn infants in order to discern general patterns of autonomic reactivity as well as the variations within the individual.

General Characteristics of Neonate Autonomic Activity

In one of our experiments, 32 infants were studied in a constant temperature environment.[32] Each was stimulated with thirteen different stimuli applied in the same order. These consisted of one minute of (1) tactile stimulation (to and fro) of the lips, abdomen, genitalia and anus; (2) air jet of constant velocity on the same areas; (3) cold (25°C) and warm (45°C) immersion of the foot and ankle; (4) sudden lowering of the body to elicit a startle reflex; and (5) restraint of both arms, and all extremities. Heart rate, recorded on an EKG, was measured for one minute periods before and during stimulation. Skin temperature studies were performed simultaneously.

Relationship between Prestimulus Level and Response. The heart rate change with stimulation showed an inverse relationship to the prestimulus rate in this population data. Greatest increments in rate occurred at the lower prestimulus levels (FIG. 1). This is a confirmation of the observations of Lacey and Wilder which have been labeled: "the law of initial values." [28] Presumably this represents a homeostatic control of the autonomic nervous system by means of feedback or self-regulatory mechanisms. Examples of this in individuals are seen in figures 2 and 3 where heart rate and respiration responses are charted.

These data emphasize that in studies of the autonomic nervous system it is essential to know the state of the organism prior to stimulation in order to interpret the response appropriately.

Differential Responses to Varying Stimuli. Figure 1 shows the correlations, all of which are statistically significant, between heart rate, prestimulus level, and algebraic change in rate. Cold immersion produced greater responses than air on the abdomen, and air on the anal region gave less reaction. Thus, one observes that the reactions are not "all or none" and that seemingly identical stimuli applied to different body sites produce different orders of response. Stroking of the abdomen similarly was more productive of increase in rate than stroking the anus. In fact,

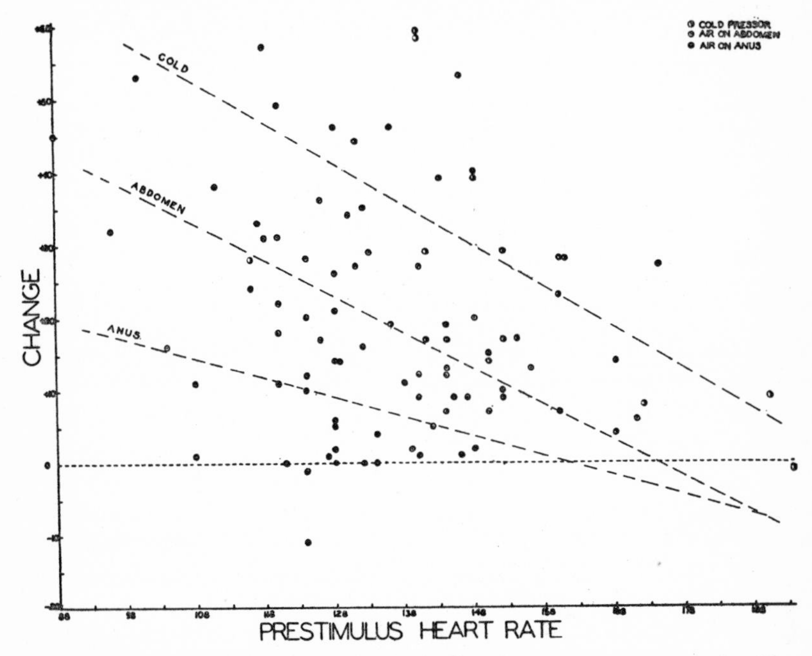

FIG. 1. Scatter and regression lines including heart rate responses by 32 neonates to three stimuli. All correlations are significant at the .01 level. Note the inverse relationships between prestimulus rate and change in rate.

the latter stimulus often resulted in a slowing of the heart rate. We are not yet in a position to explain these differences neurophysiologically.

Influence of Internal State upon Reactivity. In a subsequent study, repeated stimuli were presented to each of ten neonates before and after feedings during their first five days of life.[31] Here we found not only that tactile stimulation of the oral mucosa produced greater heart rate response than similar stimulation of the abdominal skin, but that both heart rate level and algebraic change in rate were greater when the infant was presumably hungry. These findings emphasize that mild stimuli which simulate daily life experiences of the newborn infant are productive of responses.

The neonate is responsive to his external environment when apparently asleep (FIG. 4) and may be especially reactive when irritable and apparently hungry. However, there are occasional periods during sleep, during intense rage-like behavior, during the "resting states" described subsequently, and during feeding when responsivity is minimal or lacking.

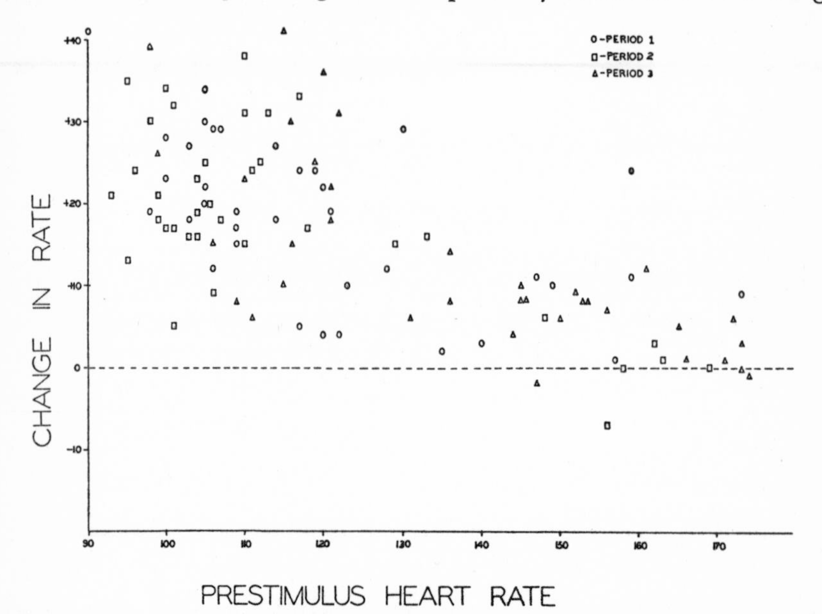

FIG. 2. Scattergram of heart rate responses by a neonate on two successive days. Stimulus was a jet of air under constant pressure for a 5 second period. Prestimulus rate is an average of the previous 5 seconds; stimulus rate was defined as the rate during the fifth second of stimulation. An inverse relationship appears.

We have few data during these refractory-like states. We are in the process of studying other autonomic functions to determine whether the organism is generally or differentially refractory to stimuli during these periods (FIG. 5).

Relationships between Somatic and Visceral Responses. We have found a high correlation between change in motor activity (when quantified by Brownfield's technique [7]) and change in heart rate. Sometimes, however, as when sucking, the infants' heart rate may increase although overt muscular activity other than sucking ceases.

In these studies, we have observed a rise in heart rate, and a change in depth and rate of respiration, often occurring within less than one second after a motor response. These data are presented in figure 4 in which EEG leads demonstrate the artefacts due to motor change.

We do not present these findings in terms of cause and effect but only note the remarkable association of somatic and autonomic responses. This may be of importance in those studies in which we seek to determine the autonomic concomitants of emotion. Engel, Reichsmann, and Segal[14] noted, for instance, that highest gastric acid secretion occurred when

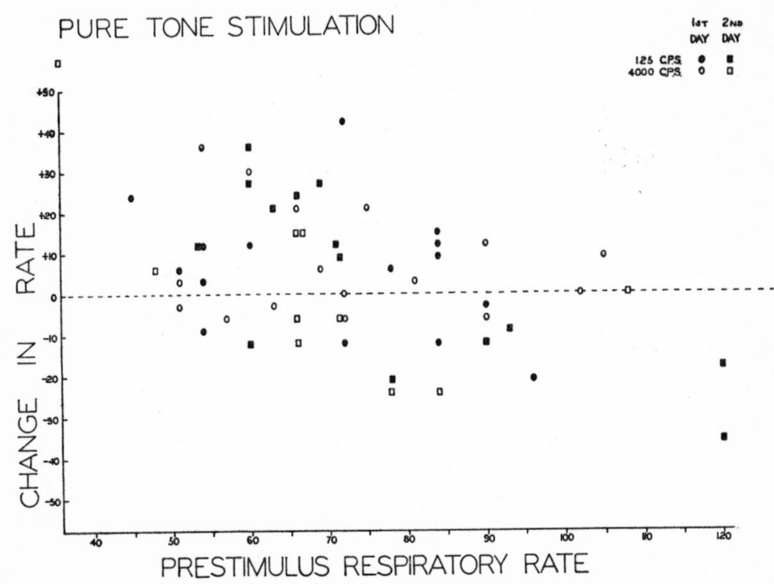

FIG. 3. Scattergram of respiratory responses by a neonate on two successive days. Stimuli consisted of pure tones of 125 and 4000 cycles per second. Rates were recorded as the average rate during 5 seconds prestimulation and the 5 seconds of stimulation.

the infant Monica, actively participated with her external environment (as in contentment, joy, irritation or rage) and often showed greatest muscular activity. They cautiously stated: "Whether the increased gastric secretion may be merely part of a general increase in the physiologic activity of the body and not have the specific meaning we have proposed cannot be settled from a consideration of the data of this study." They subsequently stated that these physiologic observations are "the biologic anlage of processes that may later have psychologic expression."

From these studies of a neonate population we may conclude the following: (1) that responses vary according to the stimulus, (2) that responses vary according to the state of the infant prior to stimulation, (3) there would appear to be a considerable degree of sensitivity to mild stimuli such as minimal touch of mucous membrane and skin areas, and (4) there appears to be a close relationship between autonomic and neuromuscular responses.

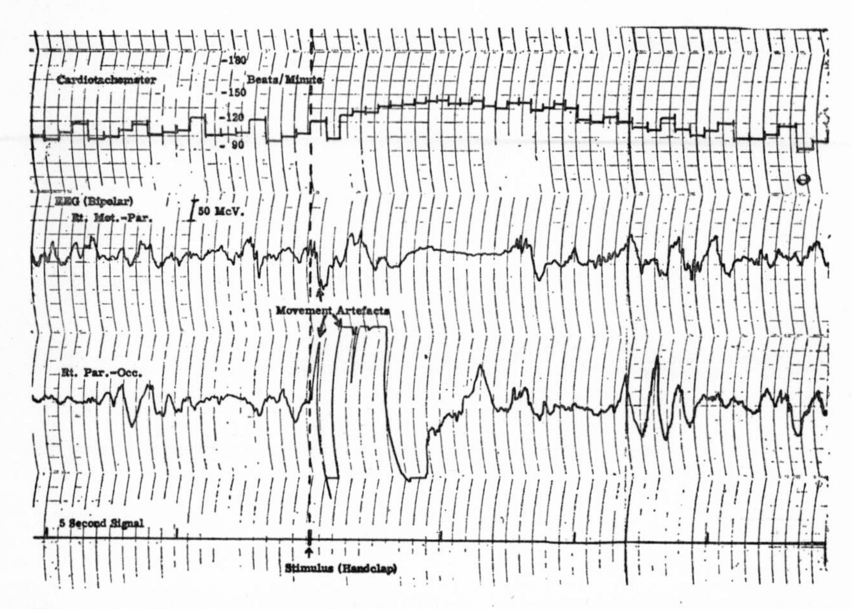

FIG. 4. Cardiotachometer and EEG changes after a sound stimulus (handclap) during sleep. Marked sinus arrhythmia (not found in all newborn records) disappears as the rate increases to 144 beats per minute and reappears later. Motor response is immediate; arousal pattern follows stimulus by 3–4 seconds, and heart rate increases within 1–2 seconds.

DIFFERENCES BETWEEN NEONATES

Much of past work has delineated responses of newborn populations with little in the way of comparing individual infants. The more recent studies of Fries,[15] Brownfield,[7] and Graham et al.,[18] seem to indicate differences between infants in spontaneous activity and in response to stimulation.

Brownfield,[7] observing and sampling motor activity during the first week in the hospital nursery, derived spontaneous activity scores from 100 infants. These showed a symmetric distribution. Quiet babies slept more, showed almost the same activity when awake but less vocalizing than the active babies. The latter were especially vocal, active and awake before feedings. There was a correlation between spontaneous activity and activity in response to an auditory stimulus.

Her conclusion that this may mean the quiet baby has less sensitivity to hunger and other stimuli must be tempered by the knowledge that

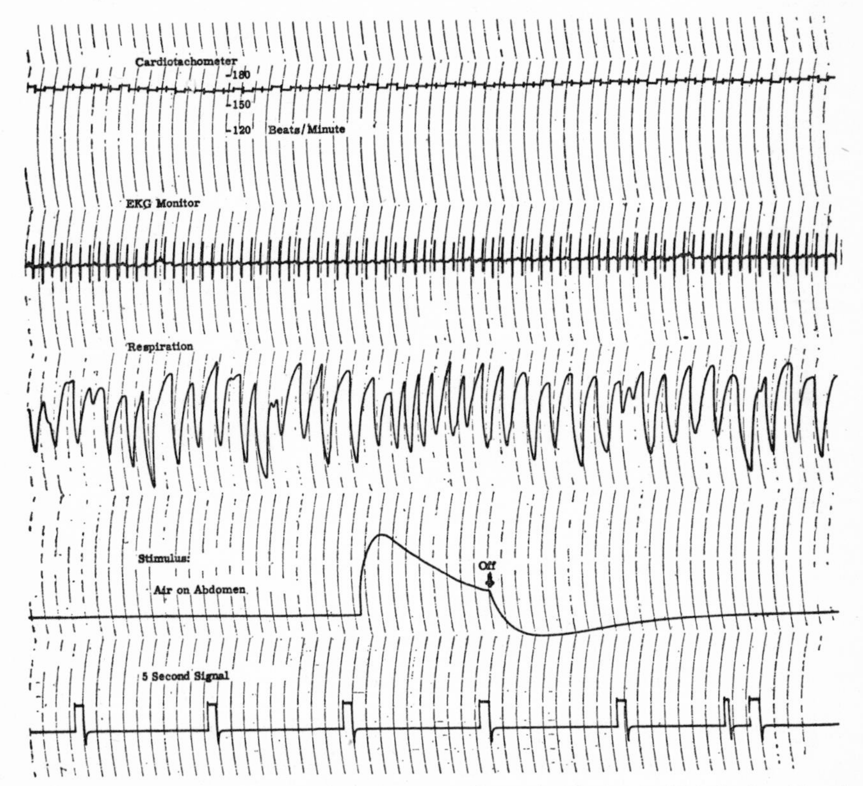

FIG. 5. Immediate respiratory response after stimulation with air jet. Respiratory rate averaged 72 per minute prestimulus and 96 per minute during stimulation. Note that motor behavior, crying, and heart rate did not change during stimulation.

babies vary considerably in caloric needs and in ability to nurse; and similarly, mothers vary in their ability to provide proper stimulation and breast milk. Quiet babies may be more satiated during these early days. Other physiologic factors will be discerned and taken into account as studies of this nature are continued in the future.

Differences in Range of Heart Rate. A striking example of differences between neonates was the findings in our recent study of nonidentical female twins who were quite mature at birth though both were just under five pounds. One twin was usually very quiet and inactive while the other was generally vocal and active, particularly prior to feedings. Their ranges of heart rate before and during stimulation were quite different, with little overlap (FIG. 6). They were repeatedly tested before and after feedings during the experiment described previously.

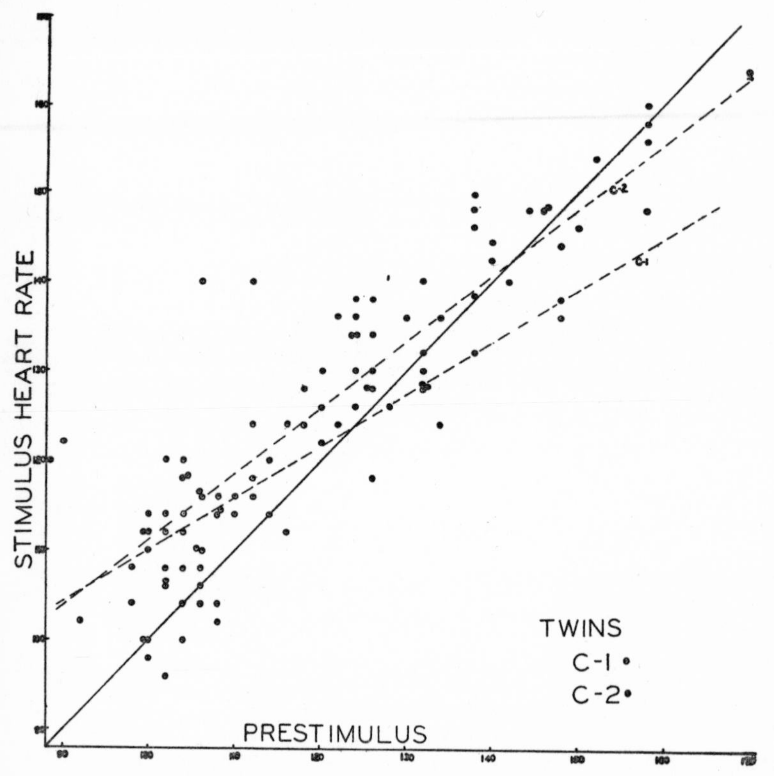

FIG. 6. Nonidentical twins tested on repeated days before and after feedings. Both prestimulus and stimulus heart rate ranges are considerably different. The dotted lines are the regression lines although the correlations are not entirely rectilinear.

The mother, who had had three previous children, spontaneously commented upon the distinct differences between these twins. She repeated these observations three months later when the more active baby was still the most vocal at feeding time while the other remained relatively quiet and "complacent." Comparative longitudinal studies of behavior seem to have documented the clinician's long awareness that infants are considerably different at birth [46] and mothers' observations that subsequent fetuses often show differences in motility in utero.

The different heart rate ranges of the 32 infants described previously are seen in FIG. 7.[32] Our subsequent studies have demonstrated that repeated observations of individual neonates show considerable variations in rate from period to period but that, over-all, distinct interindividual

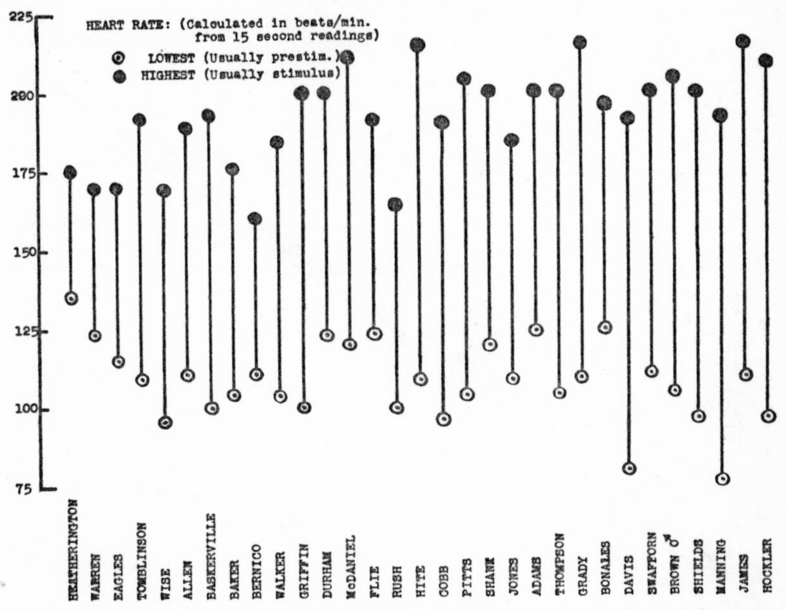

FIG. 7. Ranges of heart rate noted in newborns tested under comparable conditions. Extreme rates, below 80 or above 200 beats per minute, had rarely before been noted in normal newborns. Highest rates usually accompanied the cold immersion test.

differences in mean heart rate are striking, as in the twins referred to above.

Differences in Response Patterns. When the regression lines for ten individual neonates are plotted showing the relationship between prestimulus and stimulus heart rate, one observes different slopes (FIG. 8). This indicates that some infants show greater responses at their lower ranges of prestimulus heart rate than others. We found, as did Bridger and Reiser,[6] that the points (prestimulus levels) at which no response to stimulation usually resulted also differed. We also found less predictable responses and thus greater scatter and lower correlations in some individuals. These observations may prove of value in testing for interindividual differences in autonomic reactivity. We are currently studying individual infants in terms of their total response patterns at various levels of prestimulus activity to ascertain more interrelationships. The relationship between stimulus-induced response and prestimulus level is not always described best as a linear correlation. Unfortunately, we are not yet prepared to

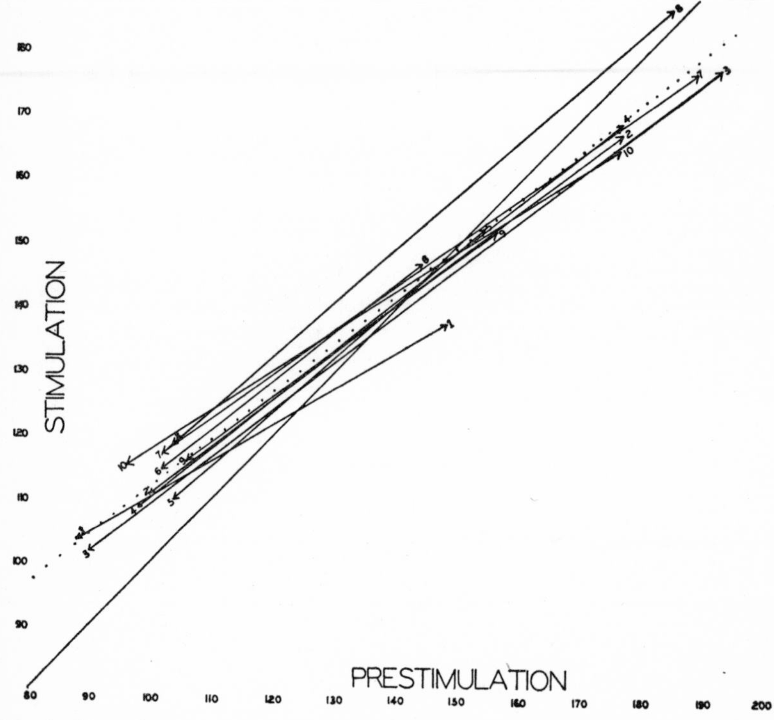

FIG. 8. Assuming a rectilinear relationship between prestimulus and stimulus heart rates during tactile stimulation, these are the regression lines for each of 10 infants. The dotted line is the common regression for this population; the long solid line is the "no change" line (where both rates are identical). Slopes and scatters were considerably different.

amplify these statements since data for the solutions to these problems are not yet available.

We have been impressed by the changes in motor and autonomic activity that may immediately follow cessation of stimulation. These may correlate with the "OFF" electroencephalographic changes described by Ellingson [12] at the end of photic stimulation, since we have sometimes observed only a poststimulus cardiac change with this particular stimulus. Some infants appear to continue to react to a stimulus for a long period after it has stopped; others return rather quickly to the prestimulus level. A striking example of this persistence of response is seen in figure 9. For a

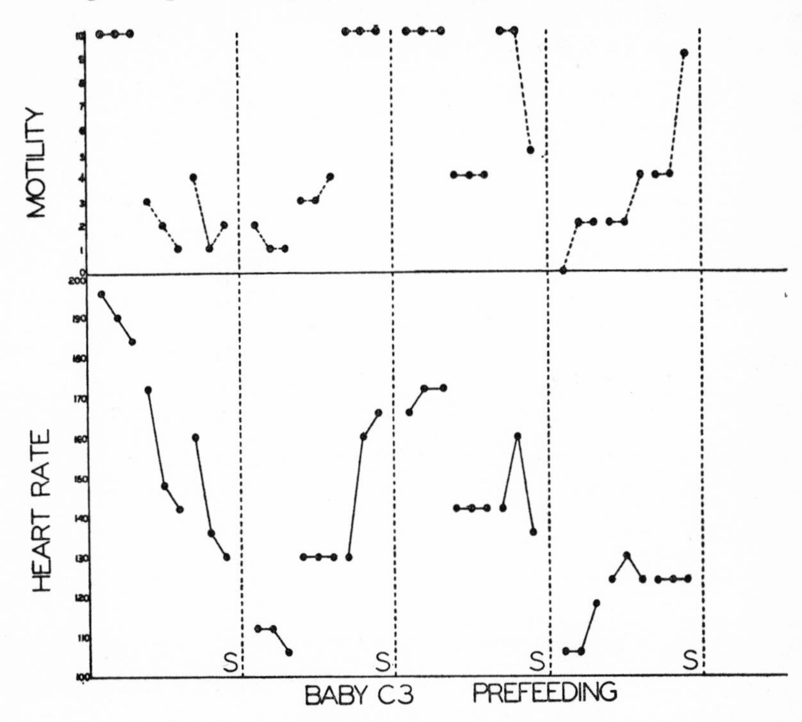

FIG. 9. The upper dotted lines represent motor activity; the lower solid lines, the simultaneous heart rate activity. Each box represents one 90 second test period and the figure shows a sequence of consecutive tests. Each point is a 10 second score and the clusters of three readings represent prestimulus, stimulus and poststimulus periods. An interval of about one minute occurred between tests. Letters at the bottom represent the stimulus (L=lips; A=abdomen; S=nipple, sucking). A "see-saw" pattern is noted; direction of response relates to prestimulus state and the changed state appears to persist until the next trial.

complete understanding of homeostatic response patterns, observations should go beyond the period of stimulation—a commonly neglected source of data.

Studies have purported to demonstrate that individuals manifest different patterns of autonomic end organ reactivity. In order to deal with this problem adequately it would be necessary to have considered prestimulus values, which few investigators have done. We believe that the autonomic endowment in this regard can be described in the newborn period if one preserves an approach which accounts for the prestimulus state of the organism. Such observations will provide further measures of interindividual differences and, in longitudinal studies of child development, permit more appropriate interpretation of data.

Sleep and the Neonate Electroencephalogram

Because of their basically rhythmic patterns, sleep and the electroencephalographic patterns in the newborn are considered together. The electroencephalogram also provides a useful method for the study of sleep and cortical activity. That inherent rhythmic biologic patterns are based on a series of time units was postulated by Sherrington as early as 1906.[43]

It has been found that during sleep the newborn is generally less reactive to stimuli and manifests least motility. Unfortunately, criteria of sleep in the newborn are tenuous. The EEG may show a sleep pattern even when the eyes remain open.[12]

Aserinsky and Kleitman [2] found cyclic motility during sleep, each complete cycle lasting for 50 to 60 minutes. The average quiescent period during each cycle was 23 minutes. Infants slept for a duration of one or two cycles during the day and five or more at night, often awakening when apparently hungry. This work, which infers an inherent central nervous system rhythm, needs confirmation and elaboration.

We have observed brief periods of at most several minutes' duration when, often after a period of crying and mass activity, the infant suddenly seemed dormant though his eyes remained open. Very minimal motor and questionable heart rate responses occurred when stimulation was given at these times. It may be that this refractory state served to interrupt a state of considerable energy expenditure and allowed for temporary conservation. Similar "resting states" have been described in animal studies. It will be interesting to see whether these correspond to the periods in which "sleep" EEG records have been obtained while the eyes remained open.

Infant and adult electroencephalograms are similar during sleep. Slow frequency waves of high amplitude tend to mask the smaller waves, but there are a large variety of amplitudes and frequencies in the newborn record. The marked fluctuations of electrical activity and varying dominance of different frequencies makes studies of maturation of cortical activity extremely difficult.

Investigators have found little sustained rhythmic activity after birth. Most activity occurs in the Rolandic region, with frequent asynchrony between hemispheres. Sleep and awake patterns are discernible, the latter showing low voltage during activity, as in adults.

A flattening of the EEG occurs during sleep in response to sound stimulation. This is the "arousal" response recorded first in older individuals and related to afferent discharges of the reticular formation. Ellingson found that only 54 per cent of the 52 neonates showed this response and that it was not a consistent one.

We have confirmed this observation and also the finding of occasional spontaneous "arousal" patterns after movement during sleep. In some preliminary studies we have observed cardiac and respiratory changes simultaneous with the EEG response (FIG. 10), but these occasionally occurred independent of the arousal pattern. We anticipate more consistent EEG responses as we explore stimuli beyond the usual handclap or loud voice.

Ellingson[12] obtained EEG responses to photic stimulation but found a long latent period which increases with repeated stimulation. However, if after a long series of tests the flash frequency was changed (e.g., from 30 to 40 f./sec.), the latent period decreased, thus inferring an accommodative rather than a fatigue mechanism. At two or more flashes per second, responses often occurred only at the beginning of stimulation and immediately after the stimulus was discontinued.

Cortical EEG responses to light are found in the human on the first day of life but not in rabbits or cats. The human infant also has more myelinization of visual pathways at birth. Ellingson relates the latency of cortical response to slow transmission in the optic nerve which has a smaller diameter and thus slower conduction velocity than the adult. This concept was derived from work which demonstrated a linear relationship between conduction velocity and fiber diameter. Retinal immaturity and delayed synaptic transmission may also be responsible, but little information is available in regard to these factors.

Most workers agree that the above described EEG findings of inconsistent amplitudes and frequencies with little rhythmic activity and long latency with stimulation are indicative of cortical immaturity. As with other physiologic variables, there appear to be variations between neonates, suggesting once again different degrees of maturation at birth. Correlations between these studies and autonomic reactivity will prove to be interesting experimental ventures. The Laceys' report[29] of rhythmic patterns of cardiac function and the cortical integration of these patterns in older subjects is worthy of exploration in this age period. This approach may provide fundamental data for the better understanding of the growing relationship between psychological (or cortical) processes and physiologic (or autonomic) function.

PARENT-INFANT INTERACTION

Although long-term longitudinal studies of child development have been under way in a number of settings, relatively little data is available concerning the relationship between parents and their newborn infant. Clinical studies by various interdisciplinary groups are underway which

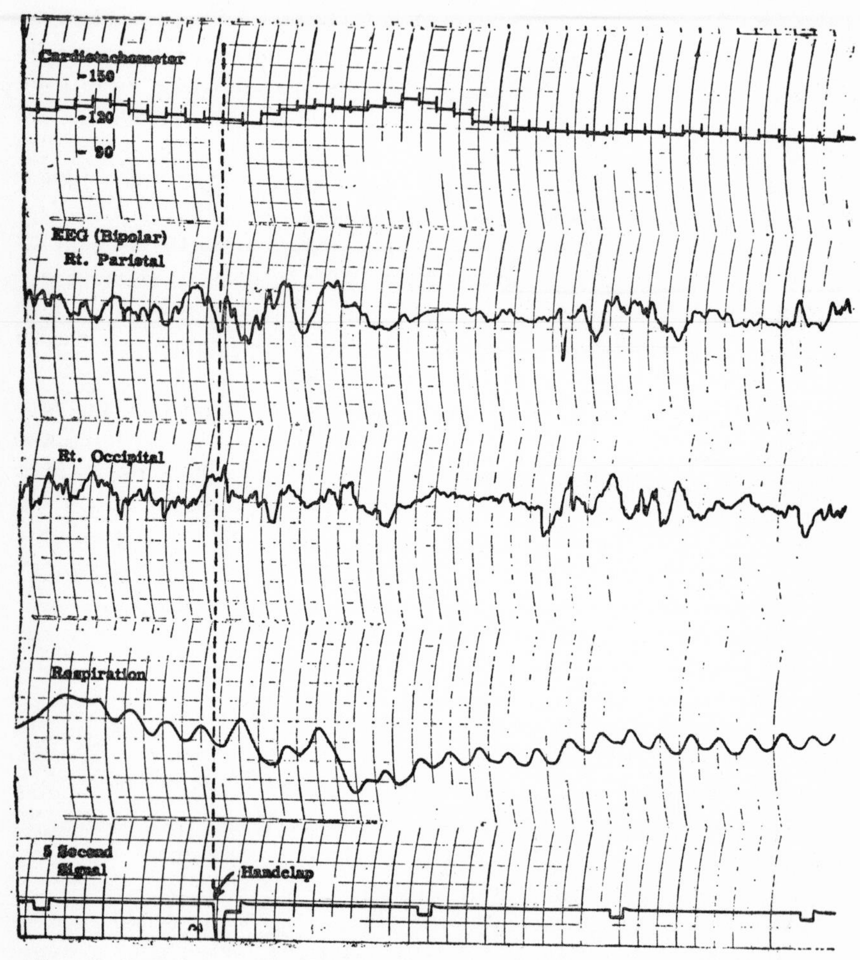

FIG. 10. Respiratory, heart rate and EEG responses to a sound stimulus (handclap) during sleep. Flattening of the EEG after 4 seconds is the typical "arousal" pattern. Autonomic changes precede this response.

may relate social and cultural backgrounds of parents, their psychological development and prenatal attitudes to infant and child development. These studies are difficult to design and to execute. Reports will of course be awaited with interest. The type of study reported by Sontag [44] which correlated maternal anxiety during the prenatal period with physiologic disturbances in the newborn infant have not been extended significantly.

Clinically, attempts have been made to create a "favorable" or more "natural" situation by the re-introduction of rooming-in programs for baby and mother during the lying-in period.[24] The many variables involved in such programs make it extremely difficult to obtain an objective evaluation of their effectiveness or their ultimate impact on parents and child. This should not discourage rooming-in as a clinical practice, however, since the history of medicine is replete with empirically derived practices which were validated long after the practice was introduced. It does indicate caution, however, in making inappropriate claims for the effectiveness of this practice as a mental health measure.

Future studies will necessitate a more quantitative approach to the study of parental attitudes and their patterns of care of the newborn infant as well as the relationship of these to later development of the child. Such research will necessarily be interdisciplinary; methodologic advances in the social sciences and in biology should facilitate these developments.

Measurement and description of parental feelings or infant response is not enough, however. The process of communication between the two begs further elucidation. The cues or signals emanating from the newborn and which engender a response from the parent, or vice versa, are subtle, elusive and very likely idiosyncratic for the particular parent-infant unit. Out of these cues emerge intricate patterns of interaction which determine the course of development of object relationships and ego structure.

It would seem in order to attempt to provide naturalistic descriptions of behavior during this period. For this purpose, with the collaboration of Dr. Helen Blauvelt, we have undertaken a study which includes high-speed film recording of parent-infant patterns of behavior in the "natural" setting of the obstetric ward. Laboratory studies of autonomic function and simultaneous motor behavior of the infant are also available. Clinical data concerning parental backgrounds and attitudes are being determined. Out of the study of these data, and the data of others, we hope a language which is more effective in describing the communication process will emerge. For the time being, it may very well be that the language is contained in film recordings which permit various observers to examine the same behavior on repeated occasions. Perhaps verbal descriptions must await such opportunities which provide not alone for repeated viewing but for the "dissection" of behavior by time and motion technique. From studies in process, we may learn more of how the spontaneous smiling movements of the newborn infant develop into the social smile at approximately three months of age and of the fate of early motor patterns such as startle movements and the rooting reflex in later development.

Other Experimental Approaches

The extension of our knowledge concerning neurophysiologic development and behavior of the human newborn will depend upon the accumulation of data from a variety of sources. Because, ethically, human subjects are not subjected to hazardous experimentation, studies of spontaneous behavior, congenital anomalies, central and autonomic nervous system injuries, and animal behavior and physiology will be necessary.

Infants born with anomalies can provide excellent investigative opportunities. Thus, by modern methods, including electroencephalography, the observation that neonatal behavior simulates that of a brain stem preparation such as is observed in the anencephalic monster would be open to serious challenge.[26] In addition to the study of the central nervous system anomalies, detailed studies of newborn infants having experienced possible central nervous system trauma, such as have been carried out by Graham and colleagues,[18] are in order. The occurrence of anomalies such as tracheoesophageal fistula provide natural experimental models, as has been demonstrated by the work of Engel et al.[14] The study of the significance of sucking for later development might be critically studied in infants with gastrostomies or who are tube-fed for some physical reason starting in the newborn period.

Studies of children with specific sensory defects have been very informative. Studies of sightless children might delineate factors other than visual which may be associated with the development of the social smiling response. The impact of a hearing defect on the development of object relationships and personality could be studied in infants and children with congenital deafness if recognized early.

Observation of conditioned responses in the newborn is important in understanding patterns of learning. Although the details are not available, Russian investigators have stated that the earliest conditioned reflex is "that expressed in sucking movements when the child is in the lactation position at the breast. This appears at three to four weeks of age. The conditioned reflex is a reflex to a complex stimulus with many components: visual (sight of breast and mother's face), aural (the mother's voice), kinesthetic (position of the body), etc."[11a] Within several weeks, conditioning was reported to occur with isolated visceral, tactile, or aural stimuli. Kasatkin noted a conditioned aural reflex in prematures during the first half of the second month of life, irrespective of the degree of prematurity. He states, "It is evident, therefore, that the functional maturity of the cerebral cortex depends upon its actual functioning: this alone can explain its earlier maturity in premature infants." For more detailed consideration of conditioning the reader is referred to the review by Carmichael.[8]

Animal studies relating to variations in maternal care of the newborn are helpful in establishing a better understanding of mother-newborn relationships and their implications for later development. Thus, Seitz[41] has studied the effect of litter size on later behavior in the rat. Scott[40] has observed the significance of early human contact for puppies as being critical for the development of their capacity to form relationships with human beings in later life. Dr. Helen Blauvelt[5] of our group, in her observations of goats at the Cornell Behavior Farm Laboratory, has demonstrated considerable biological deterioration following separation in the newborn period.

Also from our group and the Cornell Behavior Farm Laboratory, Hersher et al.[21] have observed the effects on later behavior of separation of newborn kids from their goat mothers for one-half to two hours immediately following birth. Observations were made on the relationship when the kids attained two and three months of age.

In these studies none of the separated mothers accepted their own kids in the normal manner. Half of this group nursed no young, neither their own nor others, during the observational periods (the "rejecting" pattern), and the other half nursed kids indiscriminately, suckling other kids as long or longer than their own (the "indiscriminate" pattern). The majority of the nonseparated group exhibited normal nursing behavior, nursing their own kids but not others. None of the nonseparated mothers nursed indiscriminately, although one third were "rejecting."

The effect of early separation on maternal care thus varies among individuals, some mothers reacting to separation by rejecting all kids and other mothers reacting by exhibiting highly maternal, though nonindividual-specific behavior. Thus, the immediate postpartum period is critical to the development of maternal behavior in goats, but the behavior which normally develops during that time consists of at least two factors, maternalism and individual care, and the former may develop in the absence of the latter.

Discussion

The data presented indicate the fragmentary nature of our knowledge concerning the neurophysiology of the newborn. Certainly, the knowledge available has relatively little clinical applicaton. Further studies of this period will be basic to our understanding of the development of behavior; without such studies we remain limited largely to retrospective speculations concerning this period of life.

From studies of the biochemistry and physiology of the central and autonomic nervous systems of the newborn, we can hope to learn more of the development of neural units and their emergence into more complex neural patterns which ultimately will have significance for the development of consciousness, memory, learning, and feelings. Although no series of dramatic experiments will tell us the precise moment when the infant develops an awareness that experiences from his environment mean "other than I" or "mother," we can direct efforts toward a better understanding of how this awareness emerges. As he begins to have a greater sense of separation of self from his environment, he also develops a relationship to his body as an object. Disorders in the development of this relationship may be observed in children with psychotic or psychosomatic disorders.

Though strikingly immature, the central nervous system of the human infant has within it infinite and unique potentialities for development. Whether these potentialities are fulfilled will be determined by its interaction with stimuli, in the form of life experiences. The direction and pattern of behavior will be determined not alone by the quality and quantity of these experiences but by their *timing* as well. As clinicians, called upon to influence the direction of the development of behavior more effectively, a deeper understanding of this brief, but developmentally significant, period is needed. In part, this understanding will depend upon research in neonatal neurophysiology and its implications for later child development.

Bibliography

1. Arey, L. B.: Developmental Anatomy. Philadelphia, W. B. Saunders Company, 1944.

2. Aserinsky, E., and Kleitman, N.: A motility cycle in sleeping infants as manifested by ocular and gross bodily activity. J. Appl. Physiol. *8:* 11–18, 1955.

3. Barron, D.: Genetic neurology and the behavior problem. *In* Weiss, P.: Genetic Neurology. Chicago, University of Chicago Press, 1950.

4. Benedek, T.: Toward the biology of the depressive constellation. J. Am. Psychoanalyt. A. *4:* 389–427, 1956.

5. Blauvelt, H.: Dynamics of the mother-newborn relationship in goats. *In* Group Processes, 1st Conference. New York, Josiah Macy, Jr., Foundation, 1955.

6. Bridger, W. H., and Reiser, M. F.: Psychophysiological studies of the neonate: An approach toward the methodological and theoretical problems involved. Paper presented at the annual meeting of the American Psychosomatic Society, Cincinnati, March 29, 1958.

7. Brownfield, E. D.: An investigation of the activity and sensory responses of healthy newborn infants. Ph.D. thesis, Cornell University, 1956.

8. Carmichael, L.: The onset and early development of behavior. *In* Carmichael, L.: Manual of Child Psychology. New York, John Wiley & Sons, Inc., 1954.

9. Clark, L.: Anatomical Pattern as the Essential Basis of Sensory Discrimination. Springfield, Charles C Thomas, Publisher, 1947.

10. Conel, J. L.: The brain structure of the newborn infant and consideration of the senile brain. *In* Association for Research in Nervous and Mental Disease. Research Publications, Vol. 19: The Inter-relationship of Mind and Body. Baltimore, The Williams & Wilkins Company, 1939.

11. Editorial: Dedication. Psychosom. Med. *15:* 372, 1953.

11a. Elkonin, D. B.: The physiology of higher nervous activity and child psychology. *In* Simon, B.: Psychology in the Soviet Union. London, Routledge & Kegan Paul, Ltd., 1957.

12. Ellingson, R. J.: Electroencephalograms of normal, full-term newborns immediately after birth with observations on arousal and visual evoked responses. Electroencephalog. & Clin. Neurophysiol. *10:* 31–50, 1958.

13. Engel, G.: Selection of clinical material in psychosomatic medicine. The need for a new physiology. Psychosom. Med. *16:* 368–373, 1954.

14. Engel, G., Reichsman, F., and Segal, H. L.: A study of an infant with a gastric fistula. Psychosom. Med. *18:* 374–398, 1956.

15. Fries, M. E., and Woolf, P. J.: Some hypotheses on the role of the congenital activity type in personality development. Psychoanalyt. Study of the Child *8:* 48–62, 1953.

16. Gerard, R.: Biological roots of psychiatry. Science *122:* 225–230, 1955.

17. Gesell, A.: Developmental Diagnosis: Normal and Abnormal Child Development. Clinical Methods and Pediatric Applications. Ed. 2. New York, Hoeber, 1947.

18. Graham, F. K., Matarazzo, R. G., and Caldwell, B. M.: Behavioral differences between normal and traumatized newborns: II. Standardization, reliability and validity. Psychol. Monogr. *70:* 17–33, 1956.

19. Hebb, D. O.: The Organization of Behavior. New York: John Wiley and Sons, Inc., 1949.

20. Hebb, D. O.: The mammal and his environment. Am. J. Psychiat. *111:* 824–831, 1955.

21. Hersher, L., Moore, U., and Richmond, J. B.: The effect of postpartum separation of mother and kid on maternal care in the domestic goat. Science *128:* 1342–1343, 1958.

22. Hooker, D.: Spinal cord regeneration. *In* Weiss, P.: Genetic Neurology. Chicago, University of Chicago Press, 1950.

23. Hooker, D.: Fetal behavior. *In* Association for Research in Nervous and Mental Disease. Research Publications, Vol. 19: The Inter-relationship of Mind and Body. Baltimore, The Williams and Wilkins Company, 1939.

24. Jackson, E. B., and Klatskin, E. H.: Rooming in research project. Development of

methodology of parent-child relationship study in a clinical setting. Psychoanalyt. Study of the Child *5:* 236–274, 1952.

25. Kennard, M. A.: Myelinization of the central nervous system in relation to function. *In* Problems of Early Infancy. New York, Josiah Macy, Jr., Foundation, 1948.

26. Kennedy, C.: Physiologic characteristics of human cerebral maturation. *In* Ross Pediatric Research Conference No. 23: Etiologic Factors in Mental Retardation. Columbus, Ohio, Ross Laboratories, 1957.

27. Kluver, H.: Porphyrins in relation to the development of the nervous system. *In* Waelsch, H.: Biochemistry of the Developing Nervous System. Proceedings of the First International Neurochemical Symposium, held at Magdalen College, Oxford, July 13–17, 1954. New York, Academic Press, Inc., 1955.

28. Lacey, J. I.: The evaluation of autonomic responses: Toward a general solution. Ann. New York Acad. Sc. *67:* 123–164, 1956.

29. ———, and Lacey, B. C.: The relationship of resting autonomic activity to impulsivity. *In:* The Brain and Human Behavior. Research Publication of the Association for Research in Nervous and Mental Disease. In press.

30. Langworthy, O. R.: Development of Behavior Patterns and Myelinization of the Nervous System in the Human Fetus and Infant. Publications 139–143, Carnegie Institution of Washington, 1933.

31. Lipton, E. L., Richmond, J. B., Weinberger, H., and Hersher, L.: An approach to the evaluation of neonate autonomic responses. Paper presented at the annual meeting of the American Psychosomatic Society, Cincinnati, March 31, 1958.

32. ———, ———, and Lustman, S. L.: Autonomic function in the neonate and psychosomatic disease (abstract). A.M.A. Am. J. Dis. Child. *90:* 491, 1955.

33. McGraw, M. B.: Maturation of behavior. *In* Carmichael, L.: Manual of Child Psychology. New York, John Wiley & Sons, Inc., 1954.

34. Mohr, G. J., Richmond, J. B., Garner, A. M., and Eddy, E. J.: A program for the study of children with psychosomatic disorders. *In* Caplan, G.: Emotional Problems of Early Childhood. New York, Basic Books, Inc., 1955.

35. Pratt, K. C.: The neonate. *In* Carmichael, L.: Manual of Child Psychology. New York, John Wiley & Sons, Inc., 1954.

36. Rao, L.: cited by Craigie, E. H.: Vascular patterns of the developing nervous system. *In* Waelsch, H.: Biochemistry of the Developing Nervous System. New York, Academic Press, Inc., 1955.

37. Riesen, A. H.: The development of visual perception in man and chimpanzee. Science *106:* 107–108, 1947.

38. Richmond, J. B., Grossman, H. J., and Lustman, S. L.: A hearing test for newborn infants. Pediatrics *11:* 634–638, 1953.

39. Richter, D.: The metabolism of the developing brain. *In* Waelsch, H.: Biochemistry of the Developing Nervous System. New York, Academic Press, Inc., 1955.

40. Scott, J. P., and Marston, M.: Critical periods affecting the development of normal and maladjustive social behavior of puppies. J. Genet. Psychol. *77:* 25–60, 1950.

41. Seitz, P. F. D.: The effects of infantile experience upon adult behavior in animal subjects: Effects of litter size during infancy upon adult behavior in the rat. Am. J. Psychiat. *110:* 916–927, 1954.

42. Shen, S. C.: Enzyme synthesis in the central nervous system during embryogenesis. *In* Ross Pediatric Research Conference No. 23: Etiologic Factors in Mental Retardation. Columbus, Ohio, Ross Laboratories, 1957.

43. Sherrington, C. S.: The Integrative Action of the Nervous System. New Haven, Yale University Press, 1947.

44. Sontag, L. W.: The significance of fetal environmental differences. Am. J. Obst. & Gynec. *42:* 996–1003, 1941.

45. Spitz, R.: No and Yes: On the Genesis of Human Communication. New York, International Universities Press, Inc., 1957.

46. Wolf, K. M.: Observations of individual tendencies in the first year of life. *In* Problems of Infancy and Childhood. New York, Josiah Macy, Jr., Foundation, 1953.

47. Yntema, C. L., and Hammond, W. S.: Experiments on the origin and development of the sacral autonomic nerves in the chick embryo. J. Exper. Zool. *129:* 375–414, 1955.

4

A Longitudinal Study of Personality Development*

By RICHARD MEILI

TYPOLOGIES (Kretschmer, Spranger, etc.) and characterology—that is, the study of character formation or, as it is now called, personality development—have never been and still largely are not genetically oriented. Individual characteristics are simply accepted as such, the aim being only to describe them as accurately as possible. When we consider the success of the genetic approach in the intellectual field (Claparède, Piaget) and take into account psychoanalytic concepts, however, we can no longer remain content with the more static descriptions of personality. Always, in those instances when it becomes necessary to understand a personality as fully as possible, the question arises: how did he come to be like he is? If we follow purely psychoanalytic lines of thought, this question leads to another, more precisely formulated; that is, we ask for the specific events and circumstances which formed the personality. Still other methods of approach, such as the relation between constitutional factors and personality or the study of genetics, lead us to ask: at what point in this man's development might we have discovered those traits which today seem an essential part of his personality?

These questions led to my desire to study a fully developed personality not through a hypothetical reconstruction of its development but rather through participation, as it were, in its formation. Thus, a longitudinal study was planned in which children were to be studied and observed at regular intervals from the time of birth on. At each examination the psychological characteristics of the subject, particularly as they were relevant to personality development, were to be carefully investigated. The study was then to determine how far these successive vignettes of a personality were in accord and how frequently new personality traits were encountered which could not definitely be said to have derived from those previously existing.

* For a more detailed exposition, see: *Anfänge der Charakterentwicklung*. Bern, Hans Huber, 1957.

Such a task obviously poses many problems concerning the nature of personality development, the nature of personality traits, the influence of experience, etc. It is not our intention to deal with these theoretical problems here, however; they will be discussed in those sections of the paper in which they can be shown to influence the selection of methods, or wherever the results of our observations appear to have some bearing on them.

The author's views are perhaps closest to those of G. W. Allport.[1] The empirical study of M. Shirley [12] was designed at least in part with the same aim as the present study, but differed somewhat in its methods.

Methods of Research

The writer feels that our present knowledge of the individual differences in the early years of life which determine the formation of the future personality is not sufficiently complete and accurate to permit formulation of definite hypotheses. No attempt has been made, therefore, to determine in advance which behavioral characteristics were to be assessed and compared with assessments made at later stages. Such a method entails the risk of overlooking material which could be of major importance. It was thus decided not to aim for carefully controlled experiments. Instead, we would attempt to observe each child as accurately as possible in his normal, everyday environment and to derive from these observations the traits characteristic of each child at each stage of development. We had to forego a certain amount of accuracy, which in the present state of our knowledge would have been illusory in any case, in the hope of gathering more inclusive, objective data which in turn would lead to a more exact formulation of hypotheses.

Our methods also precluded the use of certain, somewhat oversimplified, behaviorist modes of approach. As we know, many behavioral characteristics may be abandoned to be replaced by new forms of behavior, particularly in the early years of development. In many cases, therefore, it would hardly be possible to compare behavioral characteristics as such at different age levels. There then remain two choices: First, to compare arbitrarily various observations at one age level with various observations at another, in order to find possible correlations, a procedure which is hardly practicable; or, second, to interpret certain forms of behavior, trace them to their possible origins, and to determine, on the basis of behavior in the later stages, whether the same causes are still operative.

Our chief aim in the collection of the data was to gain the most complete insight possible into the normal behavior of children in their habitual environment, in a manner which would allow for comparison insofar as possible. At the same time we wished to determine more specific internal or external factors which might influence personality formation. This over-all program called for the use of three sources of information: interviews with the parents, observation, experiments.

Interviews with the parents, particularly, of course, with the mothers, did not follow a rigidly structured questionnaire. There was nevertheless an attempt to cover all aspects of the child's life and to proceed in the same manner each time, although some of the questions changed as the child grew older. The course of an interview is best illustrated by the following protocol:

Protocol 0:4 (20), March 26, 1953, 4 P.M.

Awake since 3:30 P.M., fed at 5:30 P.M.

Smiles at me. Later very alert.

After the movie:

Bell: no definite reaction. Smiles when I hold up the bell, looks in the direction of the bell after it is moved out of sight.

Grasping: I hold up two ribbons. About 5 seconds later the child quiets down. Moving both ribbons simultaneously I bring them close together, wait a moment, and she grasps at them.

Her reaction to mother is generally more marked before and after the movie.

When the ring is shown, her movements at times are also quite lively. Later, mother holds the ring. The latent period is unusually long. Then she holds the ring in one hand and a little horse in the other. She seems to be teething and drools a good deal.

She cries toward the end of the afternoon. She is sometimes given a pacifier during the day but never at night, and sometimes sucks her thumb at night. She sleeps with her hands up.

Her appetite is good. She eats two chopped vegetables, Paidol,* fruit juice, and vegetable juices. She does not like to use a spoon. She is always hungry, and half an hour before mealtime begins to fuss, demanding food from mother. She eats more than her brother did at the same age. The time required for eating is about average.

At this time she is with mother. She makes thrashing movements, breathing heavily.

She is alone a good deal (?). When someone has been with her and then leaves, she begins to fuss and cries steadily; a pacifier is of no avail. She weeps bitterly but without anger.

Minor noises frighten her. She is startled but does not cry. Her brother shows less response to such noises.

* A cereal preparation for infants.

Mother stresses that she is a lively child, although her activity appears to be no more than average.

Arm-raising test: When I raise her arms she remains quiet. When mother does this in the movie, she cries.

Grasping (see above): Perception is not always followed by grasping and the response, when it does follow, is never quick.

My presence does not inhibit her.

It is evident that, in the main, the parents' reports point in three directions:

1. Bodily factors (sickness, sleeping habits, and eating) which may possibly be correlated with personality development.
2. Psychic factors arising from the environment. We do not ask direct questions about methods of upbringing. These can be determined indirectly in part by asking about eating habits, cleanliness, and discipline. Sometimes we may ask a casual question about the mother's response when she tells us about some naughtiness of her child. In general, we refrain from interfering in any way with the parents' methods of upbringing, and we do not give advice unless it is specifically sought by the parents.
3. Behavorial factors.

It is evident that the mothers' accounts are neither complete nor entirely reliable. Some mothers give excellent, detailed observations, while others give only the most conventional, generalized accounts from which individual characteristics never emerge. The greatest difficulty, however, lies in the fact that no means for comparison are available. For instance, is this a good child, is he quick, is he clean? The presence of even one sibling may help in answering these questions, for instance, if the mother can say, "Of course, the baby eats much better than Johnny did."

To some extent, inadequate or inexact answers may be corrected by answers to the same questions at a later date. If both answers are the same, they may be deemed fairly reliable. If the answers are different, it is sometimes possible to decide what was lacking or inaccurate in one of the responses. Sometimes, mothers spontaneously offer comparisons between the present and the past, or the interviewer may ask them to make such a comparison.

The author's own observations served both as a supplement and as a control to the parents' responses. As with the interviews and "experiments," * these observations were made in the child's own home. Since our primary aim was to observe the child's development in terms of his normal behavior, it seemed to us essential to become acquainted with

* Ed. note: The term experiment is used in a broader sense in European literature, cf. Piaget. Here it is used principally in the sense of qualitative test or problem setting.

his usual environment and to observe the child in this milieu. Each home visit lasted about one hour, the first half of which was spent in interviewing the mother. Such an interview cannot, of course, aim only at the acquisition of facts, since it is essential to the progress of the investigation to establish a good relationship with the mother. The child remains in the room during the interview and usually other siblings are present as well, so that there is an opportunity for observation. According to the individual circumstances the interviewer may join in the play occasionally or remain a passive spectator. No attempt was made to write out a systematic protocol of the data thus observed unless a typical response was noted which gave more precision to some general information from the mother. A systematic protocol of certain everyday situations—mealtime, bedtime, an hour in a typical day, etc.—would, of course, have been invaluable. Such a study would have had to be repeated for several days at each age level, however, if accurate conclusions were to be drawn. Because of the amount of time required and the demands this would impose on the mothers, such a procedure did not appear feasible.

The "experiments" consisted of creating certain typical situations in which the children might be expected to show characteristic differences which could be compared on an objective basis. All of these systematically elicited responses were filmed. In the first four months we used one 15-meter reel for each child at each age level, approximately two minutes of action being filmed. Later, we used two reels each time for each child.

After a trial period the following experiments were worked out:

During the first few weeks, the infant's behavior immediately before and after feeding is observed, while the child lies quietly on a pillow without further stimuli. The same situation may also be filmed while the mother bends over the child and talks to him affectionately.

During the following period, up to six months, the following scene is filmed:

1. The child lies alone in his carriage, with mother out of his range of vision.

2. Mother approaches the carriage without smiling or speaking.

3. Mother turns directly to the child, smiling and talking to him as she is accustomed to do. At the same time, she places one hand on the edge of the carriage; this will be visible in the motion picture and will indicate the exact moment of her turning toward him.

4. Mother holds a small toy (ring, ball, or small animal), which is attached to a string, about 20 to 30 centimeters above the upper half of the child's body. (If there is no response, this experiment is repeated with another toy.) After several such observations, I would now suggest a new

experiment in which the toy is moved slowly from a considerable distance to a point close to the child's eyes. In some children it appears to be possible to rouse anxiety by this maneuver in the early months. All of these experiments are designed to test the response to an inanimate object. The object used should therefore be attached to a string, as described above, so that this stimulus may be clearly distinguished from the hand holding it.

5. The toy is moved slowly out of the child's range of vision.

6. Two objects are moved from a central point in opposite directions and are then brought back together. These procedures should be repeated several times to determine whether the response is always the same. No. 6 yields an interesting response only after the third month.

7. As soon as the infant is able to grasp objects, he is shown a ring (again attached to a string) which is easy to grasp. The child is allowed to keep the ring and is then shown a second object. (A rattle may be used in place of the ring, but this is less suitable.)

8. With a number of children the preceding experiment was modified to include the ringing of a bell after the child had grasped the ring. The bell was held to one side of the child, out of his range of vision. In view of the over-all design of our study, however, it was not possible to reproduce the same constellation of stimuli in the same way each time, and this experiment was therefore abandoned.

9. After the child has grasped the toy and has played with it for a minute, the toy is slowly raised until the child either relinquishes it or lets himself be pulled up with the toy. If his grasp is too weak, the same procedure is repeated with a different object.

10. Mother raises the child's arms and then holds them down on the pillow for about six seconds. Preferably, she stands behind the child where he cannot see her, but unfortunately it is difficult to get all mothers to perform this test in the same way.

Whenever possible, that is, when a part of the film was left over, we photographed the child while his mother held him and played with him in a manner as natural and spontaneous as she was able to achieve. Our chief aim here was to capture the essence of the contact between mother and child.

In the second half year the tasks for each age level were selected to correspond as closely as possible to the expected level of response. This, however, raised the problem that these experiments would begin to resemble intelligence tests; they were of necessity, in part at least, dependent on motor development. Comparison became increasingly difficult as the sequence of experiments was changed at each level. Therefore, while several of the experiments were found to be very revealing—a tennis ball which was rolled back and forth in the tenth month, a balloon which was inflated while the child was watching, and a strip of paper suspended before the child so that he could tear off pieces at will—we decided to restrict ourselves to a standard procedure which would remain constant at all age levels. We therefore evolved the following series of experimental procedures, which can be carried out with only minor changes up to two and a half years:

1. The child sits in his chair without toys or other objects.
2. A large wooden block decorated with pictures is handed to him.
3. The table in front of the child contains a small opening within his reach; a small wooden block is inserted here. The large decorated block is removed so that the small cube attached to the table is now directly in his line of vision.
4. The block is removed from the opening and while the child plays with it he is shown another block, which is then placed on the table.
5. Several additional blocks of different sizes, with the smaller blocks fitting into the larger, are placed on the table.
6. All toys are removed and a small top is made to spin out of the child's reach. (This approximates Siegfried's experiment with a tennis ball.)
7. A jack-in-the-box is demonstrated.
8. Mother holds a cracker, preferably hard and not easily broken, in such a way that her hand is just above the table and the cracker is within the child's reach but cannot be taken. It is best for mother to display a calm, rather than playful, attitude. After a few moments the cracker is handed to the child. Mother then asks him to return the cracker before he has quite finished eating it, first asking for it and holding out her hand, and then attempting to grasp and remove it; this should be done very gradually, however, until the cracker is finally removed.

If any unused film remains the series is concluded by placing a small hand mirror on the table in front of the child. Finally, a movie is made of the child sitting on his mother's knees, turned toward her, while she plays with him.

Unfortunately, it was only in the last few cases in our group that we used No. 8 in the above series as early as the eighth month. As this procedure has been found to be particularly revealing of personality traits, it is recommended that it be introduced as early as possible in the child's development.

Two changes were made in the second year. The situation involving a block attached to the table was replaced by the cracker which could not be pried loose. In retrospect, this change does not seem justified. A comparison of the two situations is very revealing and both should therefore be used. The second change consisted in substituting various toys for the wooden blocks, such as small cups, ducks, a mouse, or bells.

At two and at two and a half years the initial steps in the series are simplified. After the child has played with the picture block for a while, he is given a box of toys, containing everything but the top and the jack-in-the-box, so that he can take out the toys himself. Later, the mother puts the toys back and removes the box, and the series continues with the spinning top as described above.

The differences between the definitive series just described, which was evolved gradually, and that used in the beginning of the study are of theoretical importance and will therefore be discussed briefly.

1. We began with experiments which tended to resemble tests. Although our concern was not primarily with the child's capacity for certain responses, achievement was nevertheless a factor in these experimental procedures. Our orientation underwent a gradual change, under the impact of a modification in our concepts which will be discussed below. It became more and more apparent that children must be observed in the most simple and natural situations possible, to allow us to determine behavioral differences in these situations.

2. Despite our awareness from the start that no experimental situations should be used which placed too great a demand on children whose development was somewhat slower than average, it was nevertheless difficult, in some of the experimental procedures used early in the study, to determine whether the responses were influenced by the fact that the child's developmental level was not up to the procedure, that is, whether we were encountering technical difficulties. We therefore made it a rule to use those procedures which required a certain developmental level of behavior, for example, grasping, at a point of time at least two months later than the time when such behavior may normally be expected to appear. If, however, no tasks are set, as has been described, and the child is simply given the opportunity to behave in his customary manner in certain specific situations, the risk of making demands which are beyond his capacity is very limited.

3. As has been pointed out, the study of fewer experimental procedures with a longer period of observation is preferable to creating many different situations with a shorter period of observation. At first, we posed the question: How will the child respond to this stimulus? The answer to this usually was soon evident. However, sometimes the child showed no response; that is, from the investigator's point of view his response appeared totally inadequate. An attempt was then made to assist the child, or, if we were not willing to accept failure, the experiment was repeated. However, it would seem that the investigator's response, rather than the

child's, was at fault, since he attempted to distinguish between "right" and "wrong" behavioral reactions instead of accepting them as they presented themselves and investigating their meaning. In most cases, one had only to wait a few moments for one of several anticipated responses to take place. However, what precedes the response and what follows it is perhaps as interesting as the response itself. We therefore had to learn not only to watch for a particular response but to observe, if possible, a sequence of events. Thus, a series of experimental procedures came to form a sequence of closely linked play activities, each step in the sequence leading as spontaneously as possible into the next.

General Conditions of Research

As has been pointed out, the experimental procedures were carried out in the child's home, that is, in a familiar environment. This was done without exception in the first year, and with but few exceptions thereafter. Usually, the mother was the only other person present; siblings were sometimes present but were sent out of the room whenever possible. At one time, a female assistant was asked to perform the requisite procedures with the child; this was unsuccessful, however, since many of the children were upset by the presence of a stranger. Observation of several such situations demonstrated that test results in very young children must be interpreted with great caution if they are administered by someone who is a stranger to the child and if, in addition, they are given in an unfamiliar environment.

Although the mothers' presence created ideal conditions in some respects, it also created some disadvantages. Their presence inevitably introduces a variable into the experimental conditions. Many mothers find it difficult to play a completely passive role. They too believe (as did the investigator early in the study) that the child should react in definite ways and they may intervene in the experimental situation in an attempt to help him. Others cannot refrain from encouraging the child, laughing, or from expressing their approval verbally. On the other hand, the investigator cannot interfere with this to any great extent, as this would create a negative attitude in the mother. A further difficulty may arise from the presence of siblings, whom it is often difficult to keep at a sufficient distance.

The time of day selected for observation is of course of considerable consequence, especially in very young infants. During the first few months, I visited the home shortly before the feeding and made the observations either before or after the feeding, depending on the circumstances. Some children are very impatient before their meal, or they may cry so that nothing can be done with them. Others are so sleepy after their feeding that it is impossible to elicit any response. A suitable time therefore had to be selected on an individual basis. For older children the time immediately after a meal proved to be favorable. For greater accuracy of observation it would be desirable to select in advance the exact times considered to be most suitable.

With infants particularly it was not always possible to maintain constancy of experimental conditions. For example, it may happen that a child simply refuses to give up a toy. In such cases it is preferable to let him keep it rather than provoke screams of protest which would hamper subsequent proceedings even more; sooner or later he will abandon the toy in any case. If there is sufficient time, it is of course best to interrupt the experimental procedure altogether and to let the child play until he has had enough of the toy and is ready to enter the next procedure without resistance.

Motion Picture Technique

It was clear to us from the first that characteristic differences in the early months are related to behavioral variations or nuances which our eyes are not trained enough to observe. Moreover, we lack terms suitable for concise and accurate descriptions of such observations. However, since the individual characteristics of a behavioral response can be determined only by comparison of responses from different children, some method must be found whereby those responses can be compared repeatedly and at frequent intervals. Finally, it was essential to the aim of our study that we be able to compare each stage in the development of a child with any other stage in the most direct manner possible. This was considered preferable to comparing an earlier evaluation with a later one, since our evaluation might be at fault or might have failed to include an essential component.

For all of these reasons the use of motion pictures seemed indispensable. Our experience showed, in fact, that the advantages of this method were even greater than we had anticipated, as difficulties in observation and interpretation were likewise greater than we had expected. This of course is true primarily for the first few years of development. By the fourth year, goal-directed actions, which are more easily understood and described, begin to play a significant role so that motion pictures are no longer the sole means of gathering data, at least for a relatively crude research project.

The motion pictures were made by the investigator himself. A small camera without a tripod was used, again with the aim of creating as normal a situation as possible, not to introduce more strangers than necessary, and to avoid the use of unfamiliar apparatus. Moreover, by this method the investigator himself may decide at what point the movie is to begin and end.

Use of artificial light was avoided whenever possible in keeping with our desire not to change the normal environment. This is usually possible between 10 and 3 o'clock. It is best to operate near a window, using an f:1.9 lens opening. When this was not possible, a single lamp, small enough to be easily transportable, was used together with a small cardboard reflector.

All movies were made at a distance of two meters (6 feet, seven inches). If a 25 mm. lens is used, a full view of the child is obtained while none of the details of expression are lost. Attempts to reduce or increase the distance have not been successful, since with small children the impression one obtains is strongly influenced by the size of the picture. In addition, as the study progressed, we found it best to hold the camera at a constant angle to the child. With infants lying in the bassinette the camera, which is placed at the foot end, must be raised high enough to avoid foreshortening. The child's head should be raised slightly. Some of our observations were made in very overcrowded homes, and in these it was not always possible to meet all of the requirements described.

Just as in our selection of experimental procedures we learned not to set tasks but to create a field for the demonstration of behavior, we had to learn not to interrupt or end a movie because the child's actions did not appear interesting. From the psychological point of view, everything a child does is interesting. Since our camera runs for about 17 seconds at a time, we usually broke off at the end of that time. For infants up to four months, only a little over two minutes of camera time was allotted, so that the time for some sequences had to be reduced; later, more time is available. The following is an example of the series filmed in the second year:

1. Child alone	17 Sec.
2. With block	17 "
3. Block attached to table	17 "
4. Additional toy	17 "
5. Free play	30 "
6. Spinning top	Remainder of first reel.
7. Jack-in-the-box	30 Sec.
8. Cracker held	30 "
9. Cracker removed	17 "

The remainder of the film is used for the mirror and play with mother.

This plan remained quite flexible, since it may happen that at the end of the allotted time span a particularly interesting behavior pattern is demonstrated which it would be desirable to record. In such cases, one of the remaining sequences is allotted less time, unless the observer has an unlimited number of films at his disposal. In addition, it is desirable that the film end with the end of the sequence, since changing and winding a film requires at least 15 seconds, even with a magazine camera. In sequences lasting longer than one film, the change is a disturbing factor. I therefore prefer to change the film at a point when the child demonstrates a minimum of variation in his activity. When the supply of film is limited, some sequences cannot be photographed in their entirety; for instance, the sequence with the spinning top may last too long, or mother's clearing away of toys, or the child's free play. Thus, one of the spinning-top sequences was filmed for a brief period at the beginning and for a longer time at the end. When the toys were cleared away, I photographed the beginning of the sequence and interrupted the film, starting again at a point when the child showed a more marked reaction. The free-play period is filmed once at the beginning and for one or two time spans later. It should be noted that the total duration of all experimental procedures is of course many times greater than the filming time, partly because of interruptions which are technically necessary and partly because a child cannot be interrupted in his activity at all times. The series of experimental procedures is designed to represent a normal play situation, of which certain, preferably fixed, time spans are recorded. The beginning of each procedure should be recorded, as well as the introduction of any new factors.

The evaluation of results later in the study showed that the material obtained from movies yielded by far the most promising results. The written protocol of the remaining observations proved inadequate. They are useful primarily in supplementing and confirming the data recorded in the movie. Since the movies at our disposal represent an average of either two or four minutes for each age level in each child, the question arises whether this forms a broad enough basis for study, or whether our material represents nothing more than minute and quite accidental sectors of the total behavior.

These questions can only be answered by further research. Whenever possible, we adopted the following measures to guard against misleading results: In the early developmental stages, almost all of the experimental procedures which were recorded on films were repeated either before or afterwards, to determine whether the reaction was the same. In addition, after each experiment and sometimes after a very striking reaction we asked the mothers whether the behavior observed was typical of their child. The answer was almost always in the affirmative, even when we purposely asked the question in such a way as to imply doubt on our part. There were only a few children who were found to be more quiet and inhibited than usual.

Research Population and Duration of Study

The design of the study was based on a plan to include 30 children and to begin with a group of 12. It proved to be impossible to study a larger number of children of approximately the same age, since all observations were to be made by one person. Gradually, more children were added to the study, but because of limitations of time it was not possible to include more than a total of 26 children in the project.

Since our purpose was to study children who were growing up in a relatively normal environment, we could not use children from institutions. Thus, all the children in the study were living with their own families. Seventeen were referred to us from prenatal clinics; others came from various friends and relatives. There were no special criteria for the selection of children, except that those with obvious physical anomalies were not considered. First-born children insofar as possible were excluded from the study, since young, inexperienced mothers are often anxious and insecure and the presence of an unfamiliar observer may be disturbing. On the other hand, we found that when there were many children in the family the mothers were overworked and the observations were frequently interrupted. Mothers referred by the clinic were seen there and the purpose of the study was explained to them. If they were willing to participate for a period of several years the observations were begun.

During the first few months the children in the initial group were visited as often as possible. It was only during the second half that more definite time intervals were set. A fixed timetable was set for children added to the study thereafter, as follows:

First month:	2 visits if possible
2–4 months:	once a month
6–12 months:	every other month
Second year:	every fourth month
Third year:	every sixth month

In the fourth year the children were again studied and observed at more frequent intervals so that as complete and accurate a picture of their personality characteristics as possible could be obtained.

When they entered kindergarten at five to six years of age the children were observed in this new social environment with the help of the teacher. During the next several years (the oldest children in the study are now eight years old) more and more of the various standard, more familiar methods of personality investigation are combined with the method of observation described here.

Analysis of Data

It became apparent early in the study that our purpose of finding one category which would capture individual differences for each of the age levels observed was to meet with many obstacles. The application of concepts used in the study of the adult personality to the personality of children proved unsatisfactory. Basically, these studies of early development pose the same problems which are encountered in the study of adult personality. The data obtained from our movies must be evaluated like the protocols of projective tests. They cannot be used as a direct indication of what the child is like; instead, the observed patterns of behavior must be interpreted. Knowledge of adult psychology is of limited use, particularly since the observed behavior of adults is markedly different. It therefore becomes necessary first to study the fundamental nature of the experiences and behavior of very young children, and then to determine individual differences on that basis.

This is a painstaking task, and we have obtained results in only two areas. Even these results must be considered to be tentative and in need of further verification.

1. *Primary Actions.* An action is an event which is determined by internal or external changes in the subject's condition, and which is designed to relieve tension created thereby. This very broad definition would include reflex actions and feeding, although these cannot be regarded as purely psychological phenomena. Although we did attempt to determine from the way the child feeds and from the child's manner before, during, and after the feeding, differences which would bear upon the study of personality, these attempts have not been successful. It may be that our data are not sufficiently complete; it is also possible that these events have predominantly organic determinants.

However, repeated observation over several years of movies of three and four month old infants confirmed our conviction that the act of perception at this level carries with it a certain rudimentary process which may be regarded as a kind of activity. Our study was not begun with this hypothesis; on the contrary, it forced itself upon us despite a very differently oriented viewpoint.

When a small object is held at a distance of about 30 to 50 cm. from a child, or when through some sound he becomes aware of the camera and looks at it, his movements are usually arrested. (This has been observed by a number of authors.) A few moments later the child's face lights up, he may smile, and may resume his movements, sometimes, in the case of a four or five month old infant, directed toward the object.

I would like to offer the hypothesis that this process takes place between the polarities of tension and release, that the stimulus produces an excitation which must be resolved, through internal processes, so that release of tension is achieved, as evidenced by relaxation of movement and facial expression. I am aware that this hypothesis is based on concepts derived from gestalt psychology and will not be accepted without some question. Nor is this hypothesis a determining factor in the following discussion; it did, however, guide us in the further interpretation of our data.

For it proved to be relatively easy to evaluate a child in terms of the intensity and duration of excitation provoked by the stimulus. Some children demonstrate an increase in such disturbing tension when perception is experimentally stimulated; such stress reactions have also been described by Leitch and Escalona.[5] Other children demonstrate increasing manifestations of pleasure and relaxation.* In the preliminary discussion of these phenomena the two polarities will be discussed in terms of ease or difficulty in resolving excitation.

This initial finding led to three further problems of research. The first of these is to test the reliability of our observations and to determine whether the manner in which tension is released at this age remains constant and can therefore be considered an individual characteristic. The task of verification was undertaken by U. Pulver, who, in a group of 25 children, made four separate observations at two-week intervals under carefully controlled experimental conditions, with positive results. Although Sherman's well-known studies [11] are still referred to today, the study of facial expressions in children has fallen into disrepute. This is hardly justified, for Sherman's studies were based on particularly difficult, almost impossible tasks, so that the negative results obtained do not rule out the possibility of determining some individual emotional differences on the basis of facial expressions in infants. U. Pulver has demonstrated, on the basis of various observations, that an evaluation of behavior and of expression may be made with sufficient reliability for the problems at issue in this study.

* This has been analyzed in a doctoral dissertation shortly to be published.

A second task is to determine the significance of our findings for the study of personality. We are not in a position to generalize or to draw conclusions regarding the child's capacity to deal with any situation. This would lead to the conclusion that children who had more difficulty in resolving tension had poorer intellectual endowment. Consequently, our findings must be formulated in terms of attitudes or behavior rather than ability. We therefore offer the hypothesis that some children react to new environmental phenomena positively on the whole, without inhibition or constraint, while others have a tendency to withdraw and to react with some anxiety. This hypothesis remains to be tested through observations of the same children at later stages of development. So far, a few positive results have been obtained. U. Pulver found a positive correlation between observations made during the first half year, with reactions to the camera characterized by constraint or disturbance during the second half year, as well as with the degree of anxiety in the reaction to a jack-in-the-box.

A positive correlation has also been made between shyness toward strangers or in an unfamiliar environment observed during the fourth year and again observed in kindergarten in the seventh. Only half of those children who were rated on the middle point of the scale during the first year demonstrated no notable shyness in the seventh. All the other children behaved as expected.[6]

In this connection, we may point to the study of Gertrud Meili-Dworetzki [9] who demonstrated the operation of these primary differences in two brothers on the basis of a diary as well as extensive observations. Her study, which was carried to the tenth year, illustrates particularly well the extent to which different modes of behavior are related to the specific form of the primary reaction to environmental stimuli.

The third problem consists in determining the sources of the various degrees of difficulty in resolving excitation. We have recently begun to study these. According to certain psychoanalytic theories the causes must be sought in the mother-child relationship. Additional studies of our own material and of the more recently studied group of children point in this direction, but definite conclusions cannot yet be drawn. It is also extremely important to investigate constitutional factors.

2. *More Complex Emotional Reactions.* The first difference which is important from the point of view of individual personality characteristics is related to feelings of anxiety and feelings of pleasure, as has been demonstrated. This led us to investigate more exactly the origins of anxiety and of smiling (as an expression of pleasure), representing the earliest psychic reactions. During the second half year, additional, more highly differenti-

ated reactions appear, as has been shown by Bridges.[3] We offer the hypothesis that this differentiation of emotional reactions is at least partly the result of a differentiation in the psychic organization which lies at the root of behavior.[8] In the main, this hypothesis closely parallels Piaget's concept of the development of intelligence. According to Piaget, this consists in the formulation of structures of increasing complexity and in the gradually expanding coordination of ever-simplified systems. The relation between the development of affect and that of cognition as seen by Piaget has been discussed by B. Inhelder [4] and E. J. Anthony.[2] In our study, it is manifested by the fact that fear of new objects, such as the jack-in-the-box, appears at exactly that point in development (10 months) at which, according to Piaget, object perception begins.

On the basis of this concept, we were faced with the task of searching in our material for the time of appearance of new, more complex emotional reactions. An initial review of our data demonstrated that the various emotional reactions in these children follow each other according to a strikingly similar pattern. If our hypothesis is correct, we may derive from this time sequence an indication for the development and differentiation in the psychic organization. This would at the same time offer a basis for interpreting individual differences in emotional reactions.

A systematic study of our material based on this approach has not yet been made. Our present knowledge would indicate that a study of reactions to frustration should be undertaken in which there appears to be differentiation between active and passive reactions at quite an early age. The age at which certain reactions first appear may also be a significant factor in individual differences; however, we do not have sufficient knowledge of the normal time of their appearance.

Shuttleworth,[13] in his analysis of problems and methods of longitudinal studies, pointed out that new problems frequently arise in the course of such studies which the investigator is tempted to pursue. This applies particularly to the study of the earliest stages of development, as our knowledge in this field is as yet too inexact and diffuse. Our studies have shown, however, that the careful collection of data, which proceeds unencumbered by too rigid hypotheses may lead to certain insights which, in turn, give rise to more exact investigations. The collection of data by means of motion pictures is particularly valuable for research projects which are not based on specific hypotheses (as Gesell and Spitz have already shown) since it permits a re-evaluation of data in the light of later hypotheses.

Bibliography

1. Allport, G. W.: Becoming. New Haven, Yale University Press, 1955.

2. Anthony, E. J.: Six applications de la théorie génétique de Piaget à la théorie et à la pratique psychodynamique. Schweiz. Ztschr. Psychol. Anwend. *15:* 269–277, 1956.

3. Bridges, K. B.: Social and Emotional Development of the Pre-School Child. J. de Psychol. norm. et path. 1931.

4. Inhelder, B.: Die affektive und kognitive Entwicklung des Kindes. Schweiz. Ztschr. Psychol. Anwend. *15:* 251–268, 1956.

5. Leitch, M., and Escalona, S.: The Reaction of Infants to Stress. A Report of Clinical Observations. *In* Greenacre, P., and others: The Psychoanalytic Study of the Child. Vol. 3. New York, International Universities Press, 1949.

6. Meili, R.: Die Anfänge der Charakterentwicklung. Bern, Hans Huber, 1957.

7. ———, and Wild-Missong, A.: Konstanz von Verhaltensweisen bei Kleinkindern. (In press).

8. Meili, R.: Gestaltprozess und psychische Organisation. Schweiz. Ztschr. Psychol. Anwend. *13:* 54–71, 1954.

9. Meili-Dworetzki, G.: Zwei Menschen, zwei Welten. (In press).

10. Piaget, J.: La Construction du réel chez l'enfant. Neuchâtel, Delachaux et Niestlé, 1937.

11. Sherman, M.: The differentiation of emotional responses in infants: I. Judgments of emotional responses from motion picture views and from actual observation. J. Comp. Psychol. *7:* 265–284, 1927; II. The ability of observers to judge the emotional characteristics of the crying of infants, and of the voice of an adult. Ibid, *7:* 335–351, 1927; III. A proposed theory of the development of emotional responses in infants. Ibid *8:* 385–394, 1928.

12. Shirley, M. M.: The First Two Years: A Study of Twenty-Five Babies. Minneapolis, University of Minnesota Press, 1931.

13. Shuttleworth, F. K.: Sexual maturation and the physical growth of girls age six to nineteen. Monogr. Soc. Res. Child Development *2:* No. 5, 1937.

5

A Method of Studying Emotional Factors in Children with Rheumatoid Arthritis*

By GASTON E. BLOM and BABETTE WHIPPLE

INTRODUCTION

THIS REPORT concerns the development of a method of studying the emotional factors in psychosomatic diseases in children. It is based upon the experiences of a group at the Child Psychiatry Unit of the Massachusetts General Hospital that is conducting research on juvenile rheumatoid arthritis. Results or findings of the research are not the focus of interest in this report.

Our first contact with a child with rheumatoid arthritis was in 1948. During the course of the following decade, we developed a methodology for studying the emotional factors in children with this disease. A chronologic account of the stages through which our thinking went, with reference to our case material and our findings, is perhaps the best way to clarify the method we have now evolved. Although from the beginning, the research group has always included a psychiatrist, psychologist, and social worker, only one psychiatrist † and one social worker ‡ from the original group are still active participants in the research. Consequently, the referent of the editorial "we" is a group of research workers whose membership has varied.§

FIRST CASES OF RHEUMATOID ARTHRITIS

The first stage of our research is perhaps best described as our introduction to clinical cases of rheumatoid arthritis in children. Jackie, a nine

* This investigation was supported in part by a research grant from the National Institute of Mental Health of the U. S. Public Health Service, and in part by the Arthritis and Rheumatism Foundation, New England chapter.

† G. E. Blom.

‡ G. Nicholls.

§ The authors wish to express their gratitude to one of the group members, Robert T. Long, M.D., whose detailed criticism of this paper has been very constructive.

year old boy at the time of his referral to us, was our first case. He had had recurring episodes of the disease from the age of 18 months. At nine years of age, Jackie presented the typical features of juvenile rheumatoid arthritis: arthritis in multiple joints—neck, shoulder, elbow, wrist, finger, hip and knee; lymphadenopathy; splenomegaly; fever; anorexia; and weight loss.

The medical management of his disease was conservative, without the use of ACTH or cortisone. It consisted of bed rest, hot packs, exercise, adequate diet, blood transfusions, salicylates, iron and vitamins, and chemotherapy to prevent infections. The activity of the disease governed his regimen.

Jackie's pediatrician requested a psychiatric consultation because of difficulties in his management on the ward. He ate very little, withdrew from all friendly overtures on the part of the hospital personnel, was passively resistant to medication and physiotherapy, and was depressed.

We were able to help Jackie in his psychological adjustment to the hospital and to his illness, and the Pediatric and Arthritis Services began to refer other cases of juvenile arthritis to us in connection with similar problems in hospital management. We wondered whether this psychological picture was characteristic of children with rheumatoid arthritis. Over the next six years (1948–1954) our clinic saw 28 children with rheumatoid arthritis, ranging in age from 2 to 16 years. Four of them were in treatment for four years. The original team was augmented by other psychiatrists, social workers and psychologists, to a maximum total of nine. With all cases, we tried to follow the child-guidance approach standard in our clinic: daily visits of the therapist with the patient on the ward and weekly contact of the social worker with the mother in casework. This was not always possible because sometimes the patient was hospitalized for a short time only, and often the family lived at too great a distance for regular visits to the hospital.

Clinical Impressions from Twenty-Eight Cases

The period from 1948 to 1954 represents the second stage of our research, the formulation of our clinical impressions of juvenile rheumatoid arthritis. At the beginning of our contact with Jackie, our theoretical focus was on the obvious emotional disturbances resulting from the illness and hospitalization. When we examined our clinical data from other cases for psychological similarities, we also became interested in emotional factors causally related to the disease. With Jackie we observed numerous exacerbations of his arthritis in relation to current emotional stresses: an unexpected absence of his psychiatrist at a critical time in his psychotherapy, "anniversary episodes" during the month of July,* and the night following his tenth birthday party when he was overwhelmed by feelings concerning his age. From the psychiatric study of other children and their families, we became aware of emotional constellations which appeared to antecede the development of the disease. We then began to focus more on features in the case histories which antedated the illness and which seemed relevant to the development of arthritis. We regarded psychological factors as one of a complex set of factors that bring on disease and its recurrence.[2, 4]

In 1952, two workers, Blom and Nicholls, formulated these clinical impressions. We reviewed the 28 cases seen in the clinic to that date in an attempt to abstract the features common to them. Being familiar with clinical research studies of adult patients that pointed both to a relationship between emotionally stressful events and the onset of rheumatoid arthritis and to correlations between further stresses and exacerbations of the disease, we looked for similar patterns in children.[7, 9, 13, 15, 18, 19] We found, by tabulating information recorded in the patients' development charts, that in a third of the 28 cases an emotionally stressful situation was correlated with the onset of arthritis. In a quarter of the cases, a stressful event occurred at the time of an exacerbation of the arthritis.

Clinical impressions of juvenile rheumatoid arthritis covering these and other psychological findings subsequently were published.[5] A number of personality features observed in the children were striking in their similarities. Furthermore, they reflected those psychological patterns commonly reported in adult arthritics: obsessional patterns, personality traits of marked emotional constriction, and depression.[12, 13, 15, 16, 19] The children felt abandoned and deserted. As found in adult arthritics,[17] we noted frequently that the children reacted to emotional crises through intense autonomic activity. Typically, they were also unable to express their emotions, had primitive aggressive fantasies, and difficulty in forming relationships with other people and in achieving separateness from their mothers. During hospitalization, most of the children, even the older ones, had a strong depressive reaction to separation from home.

In examining antecedent factors in their life histories, we felt that research on children had many special advantages. We obtained well-documented data on the occurrence of early tragic events. Casework with the mothers led to a number of generalizations about some of the personality characteristics of the mothers and revealed striking similarities in

* At this time of the year, a highly charged emotional event had occurred when the mother was six months pregnant with Jackie (see Figure 2: Social Data).

their past histories, i.e., early deprivation. We had the opportunity to observe the parents directly, and the parent-child relationship, which is often not possible in the psychiatric study of adult arthritics. The unusual closeness and intensity of the mother-child relationship that had impressed us in the first few cases appeared to be common to the whole group. The mothers experienced separation to be as acutely disturbing as did their children. Their explanations about the disease were based upon a substratum of guilt and primitive fantasies more often than we had observed to be the case with other mothers seen in our clinic. Many of the mothers stated that the unhappiness or illness they had experienced during their pregnancy with the patient had affected the child and somehow had resulted in rheumatoid arthritis.

After 1954, we continued to see new cases and to follow the old ones. All children hospitalized for arthritis were referred to us for study and/or psychiatric treatment. We also began to see children with mild arthritis in the Arthritis Clinic. This meant that our cases were less selected in that we were seeing all the children on the wards who had arthritis and not just those judged by the pediatricians to have psychological difficulties. The socio-economic bias in our population from the lower class remained the same. From the study of new cases we hoped to clarify further our clinical impressions.[6] However, our major focus of interest was the formulation of an objective research method which could be used to confirm our clinical impressions of the psychological factors causally associated with juvenile rheumatoid arthritis.[4] It took us four years to develop our measuring instruments. In 1958, we are well along on our final stage, i.e., the collection of new cases and controls with which we will test the validity of our clinical impressions.

Research Team

The research group consists, at present, of four psychiatrists, one psychologist and two psychiatric social workers.* Periodically, new members have been brought into the group to replace those who have left.† Continuity was maintained by the two members, Blom and Nicholls, who have been permanent throughout. Stability of the group also became less of a problem as we formulated the research method more clearly. We decided, for example, to limit the collection of interview data on all new cases to the research team members, all of whom are psychoana-

* G. E. Blom, M.D., Robert Long, M.D., Norman Bernstein, M.D., John Lamont, M.D., Babette Whipple, Ph.D., Emily Sanders, M.S.S., and Grace Nicholls, M.S.S.

† Past members include Lovick Miller, Ph.D., Nancy Rollins, M.D., and Eleanor Clark, M.S.S.

lytically oriented and experienced. Otherwise, the variability in the collection of interview data would be too great. We encountered this problem with some of the early cases who were seen by people peripheral to the research group.

Initially, the problem the group members had was to find a common frame of reference within which they could function. All members of the research group were clinically oriented. They all had misgivings about rigorous methodologic procedures. They feared it would be too difficult to steer between statistics which prove only what one already knows and the meaningful, complex dynamic concepts which are difficult to translate into countable entities. Furthermore, most of the group lacked training in designing research and the application of statistical methods.

Consultations with well-qualified professional people who had such experience and training, e.g., a well-known social psychologist, helped overcome the initial resistance to the use of statistics. This psychologist explained the function of statistics. He also helped us to distinguish between "clean" and "dirty" research and pointed out the propriety as well as the necessity of lowering one's aspiration when working in the area of clinical psychiatric research.[14] However, the consultations did not only have positive results. No one within the group could apply what was learned about objective methodologic procedures to our research in a clinical setting. We also had communication problems between the research team and the consultant. The latter was familiar with different methods of study and problems with a much narrower focus. The research team found it difficult to formulate its problems clearly enough to the consultant to get useful answers. We found that our methodologic problems could be handled more easily when, in 1957, a psychologist with training in both research methods and clinical work became a member of the group.* She has been able to guide the methodologic discussions within the group, and make better use of outside consultation. The need for such consultation has decreased and, when it is necessary, it is focused on specific problems.

SETTING UP HYPOTHESES FROM CLINICAL IMPRESSIONS

In the development of a research method which could confirm our clinical impressions, the first step we took was to state clearly the specific nature of our clinical impressions. After achieving this we could then devise a means of determining their incidence of occurrence in the

* Babette Whipple, Ph.D.

original group of 28 cases of juvenile arthritis we had studied. Later, in going to a new research population we would expect similar findings if our original impressions were valid and our method of assessing them adequate.[1, 3]

Working from dictated interview data of both mother and child, we looked for the evidence that supported certain clinical impressions. The object was to relate behavior and content of interview to the impressions which we called hypotheses. The attempt was to partially exhaust the many impressions the group had about the cases. The hypotheses were then grouped into eight areas. What we mean by "hypothesis derived from clinical material" is explained most easily in terms of an individual case.

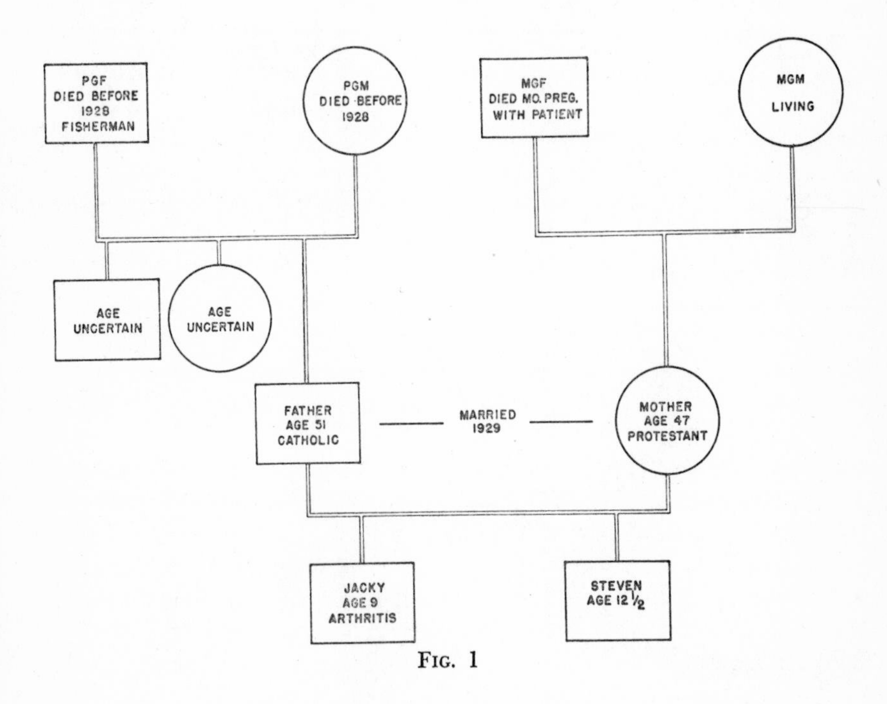

FIG. 1

We shall use the interview data from Jackie's case. Figure 1 shows his family constellation. The patient was the second of two children from an urban Catholic family. His brother, four years older, had no known psychological difficulties. Figure 2 illustrates Jackie's developmental history. Figure 3 gives his height and weight chart, which presents a picture of the progress of his illness. It shows that the growth pattern becomes more normal after the last severe episode of arthritis.

FIG. 2. Jackie's Developmental History

DATE	AGE	MEDICAL DATA	HOSP.	SOCIAL DATA
1/39–9/39	Prenatal			Family moves. Mother lonely. Marital discord.
6/39	"			Maternal grandfather dies. Mother depressed.
9/8/39	0	Long labor, no anesthesia.		
10/39	1 mo.	Breast feeding discontinued. Feeding difficulties.		
2/40	5 mos.	Pneumonia. Many colds.		
3/41	1^{6}	Scarlet fever.		Maternal grandmother joins family.
4/41–6/41	1^{6}–1^{9}	Polyarthritis, splenomegaly, lymphadenopathy.	3 mos.	
9/41–2/42	2–2^{5}		5 mos.	Psychological exam. in hosp.: like deaf child, apathetic. At home, more active, alert.
11/42				Breaks leg, cast.
12/42–2/43	3^{3}–3^{5}	Severe whooping cough with otitis.		
*7/43–11/43		Arthritis.	4 mos.	Baby talk, anorexia, inactivity.
12/43				Nightmares at home.
1/44–2/44	4^{4}–4^{5}	Arthritis.	1 mo.	IQ 96.
9/44–5/45				Attends kindergarten.
5/45	5^{8}	Otitis.		
7/45	5^{10}	T. & A.	sev. da.	
*8/45–2/46	5^{11}–6^{5}	Severe arthritis.	6 mos.	Anorexia, depression.
3/46–11/46	6^{6}–7^{2}			Home teacher. Thumbsucking, nailbiting, anorexia, depression.
4/47–7/47	7^{7}–7^{10}	Improvement in arthritis, uses crutches.		Mood improved. Attends school 5 weeks.

3/48	8^{6}			Father's heart attack.
7/48	8^{10}	Sore throat.		
*8/48–12/48	8^{11}–9^{3}	Severe arthritis.	3 mos.	Anorexia, withdrawal.
9/48	9^{0}	Psychotherapy begun.		In infants' ward, by himself.
1/49–4/49				Home teacher. Maternal grandmother leaves home.
4/49	9^{7}	Arthritis.	5½ mos.	IQ 99.
*7/49–12/49	9^{11}–10^{3}	Severe arthritis.		
10/51	11^{1}	Arthritis improved.		Starts school again, 6th grade.
10/52	12^{1}	Psychotherapy at long intervals.		
8/52	12^{11}			Mother has cholecystectomy.
8/53	13^{11}			Summer holiday with Mother.
10/53	14^{1}			In school, 8th grade.
10/54	15^{1}			In school, 9th grade.
				Good student, IQ 108.
5/55	15^{8}	Flare-up R. A.		Behavior problem: in court.
*7/55	15^{10}	Transitory activity.		Summer trip without Mother.
10/55	16^{0}	Arthritis worse.		New school, 10th grade.
				Leaves school after 2 mos.
5/56		Arthritis improves.		Part-time employment.
10/57–5/58	18^{1}–18^{8}	Psychotherapy.		Seeks full-time employment.
58		Persistent deformities.		

* Episodes of arthritis associated with anniversary event.

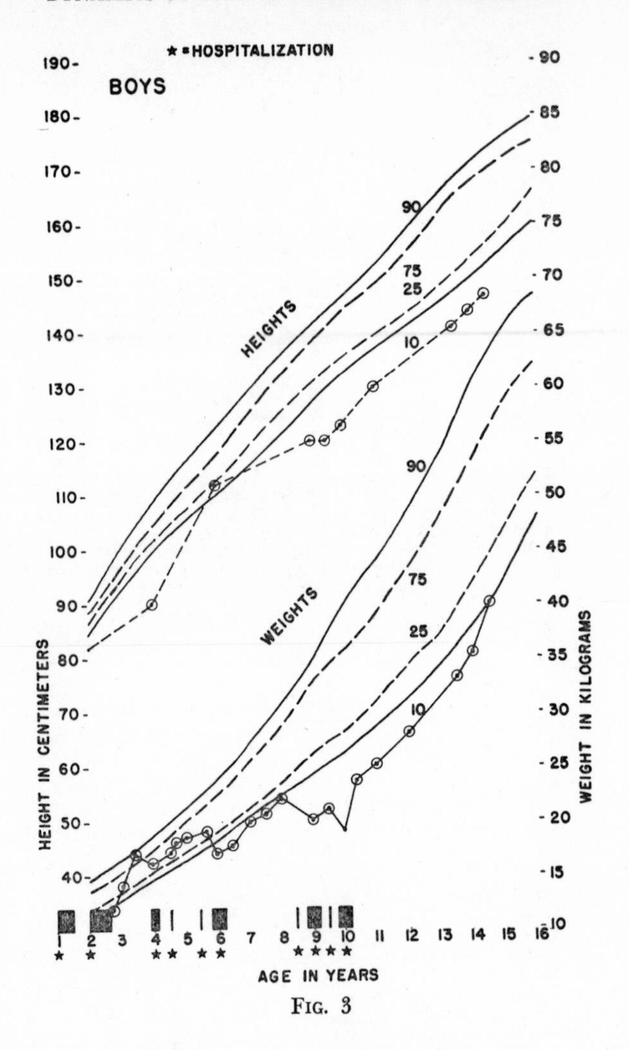

FIG. 3

Area	*Hypothesis*	*Interview Data*
I. Personality features of mothers of arthritic children.	(a) Depressive character traits are characteristic.	Mrs. G., age 47, was a short, attractive woman with sad eyes, who was very plainly dressed. A comment in the social worker's notes reads, "She appeared as always sad and serious." Mrs. G. was a person with very few friends and interests or activities outside her home. But she seemed unconcerned about this. She worried about the future and was

Area	*Hypothesis*	*Interview Data*
		pessimistic about the outcome of Jackie's arthritis and of her husband's heart trouble. Nevertheless, there was a stoical and fatalistic attitude toward life shown in her resignation to her husband's drinking and Jackie's illness.
	(b) They have difficulty in showing feelings.	Mrs. G. was cooperative but not very talkative in the beginning. She never expressed or admitted annoyance about such things as clinic delays and inconveniences or lateness of the social worker. She expressed her own feelings about hospitalization through talking about how Jackie and her husband felt. She became very anxious after several months of treatment when Jackie showed his despair about being sick and feelings of anger against her. Only after six months could she speak of anger at a doctor and after one and one-half years mentioned having an argument with her husband.
	(c) They are particularly masochistic.	Mrs. G. knew about her husband's drinking before they were married but had hoped to reform him. She made periodic threats of separation during the marriage. A particularly critical period occurred at the time of Jackie's conception. After she realized she was pregnant, Mrs. G. commented, "If I stuck eighteen years with him, I can put up with some more." Mr. G., though steadily employed, spent his money on weekend drinking and on the ponies. He would never take her out and was drunk on such occasions as their wedding anniversary and Jackie's baptism. Mrs. G. was slavishly devoted to the care of Jackie. Even when he was nine, she carried him up and down three flights of stairs, visited him almost daily in the hospital, and gave in to most of his excessive demands.

Area	*Hypothesis*	*Interview Data*
	(d) Mothers feel extreme guilt about the illness.	She expressed the idea that she was responsible for his arthritis because of her own unhappiness and her inability to be more affectionate. She said Jackie was born with a line across his face which represented a mark she had made. Because of her guilt and need to suffer, Mrs. G. could not get medical help for her own illness. One of the most important developments in her casework was that she was able to do so. After many years of gastrointestinal distress, she eventually had a cholecystectomy.
II. Past life of the mother.	(a) Mothers have experienced early deprivation.	Although Mrs. G. did not speak spontaneously or extensively about her own childhood, she said her parents were divorced when she was seven years old. For the next two years, she lived with her mother who worked. Then she moved to live with a maternal aunt, and later lived with her father. She was very unhappy during this period. She showed her deprivation in her transference to the social worker by excessive demands to arrange transportation, make clinic appointments, obtain a bicycle, crutches, and casts, speak to the doctors for information and act as a mediator.
III. Mother-patient bond.	(a) The relationship is overly close.	Mrs. G.'s closeness to Jackie, which was fostered by the illness, was revealed in many ways. It was a mutual need; she was the only one who took care of him, and he insisted she be the only one. She would never leave the apartment, even to go to the store across the street, since he might want something and no one would be there to get it for him. She told the social worker a dream she had in which she was carrying Jackie as a grown man and she was exhausted. Later, she spoke of feeling miles apart

Area	*Hypothesis*	*Interview Data*
		from him when he was in the hospital and she was at home, despite the fact she visited him daily. She brought food, even steak, to the hospital and wanted to take him home so she could do all the treatment herself. She questioned the social worker minutely about his illness, treatment and care, such as, did he drink his orange juice and did he get a haircut.
IV. Patient's infancy.	(a) The mother experiences a loss during the pregnancy or first two years of patient's life.	The pregnancy with Jackie was unwanted, occurring at a time of marital discord. During the pregnancy, Mrs. G.'s father died. She said that she was sick and unhappy through the entire pregnancy. Jackie was a poor eater from the age of three months up to the time of referral at nine years.
V. Personality features of the child.	(a) The child is in a depressed mood.	When first seen, Jackie was a small, thin boy sitting in a curled-up position in his bed. He was by himself in a room on the infants' ward from which he steadfastly refused to be moved. At first, he was unresponsive, with head bowed and sullen expression. There was little reaction to anything that went on. He refused to care for himself at all and insisted that only certain nurses wash him and brush his teeth. He just picked at his food. Whenever anyone approached him warmly, he bowed his head. His depressed mood was reflected in a fantasy in which he stated, "Today is cleaning day, let's jump out of the window, get swept up in the garbage and taken to the dump, and get eaten up by the rats." He also mentioned that the only way the babies on the ward can talk is by crying. He would have the psychiatrist draw pictures of freaks such as "goofy ears, fathead, and skinny" which were self-images.

Area	*Hypothesis*	*Interview Data*
VI. Child's relationship with psychiatrist.	(a) He forms a close relationship slowly. (b) He relates through concrete giving.	It took a great deal of time to develop verbal contact. The psychiatrist saw him daily and brought him candy and later small toys. He took them without saying much at first but then began to demand them constantly. Later attempts to switch from food to toys and decrease the quantity of giving met with anger expressed in stony silence and bowed head. It was two months before Jackie would leave his room voluntarily, and three months before he would leave the floor to go to a playroom. After discharge from the hospital, in the out-patient department he would scarcely say a word until he was in the playroom. Months later, he showed his closer relationship to the therapist through games in which he was Tonto and the psychiatrist was the Lone Ranger, or he was one of Edgar Bergen's puppets. He developed great difficulty in ending his treatment hours and insisted on every one of his sixty minutes, extracting time for lateness.
VII. Child's fantasies.	(a) Significant fantasies are of an oral aggressive type.	His aggressive fantasies were revealed very slowly. At the time they were first being expressed in play, the psychiatrist was absent for three days because of illness, and on the second day Jackie developed an acute flare-up of his arthritis. Subsequently, he played games in which he would shoot the doctor with honey bullets so he would die sweetly. He spoke of a pirate called Bloody Rogue who tore out people's tongues and inflicted other types of torture on them. He had a recurring dream in which a wolf breaks into a house where his mother is, and he, his brother, and father try to save her. As they get in the wolf is chewing up his mother.

Area	*Hypothesis*	*Interview Data*
VIII. Occurrence and recurrence of arthritis.	(a) Emotionally significant situational events coincide with occurrences and recurrence of the disease.	One of the observations on Jackie which intrigued us was the frequency with which recurrences of his arthritis coincided with emotionally charged situations. The onset at age eighteen months occurred following scarlet fever and shortly after Mrs. G.'s mother came to live with the family. This was a critical situation for Mrs. G. as she had not lived with her mother since adolescence. She felt her mother as an unwanted, additional burden. Later recurrences of arthritis followed a tonsillectomy and Mr. G.'s heart attack. He also had a flare-up during an unexpected absence of his psychiatrist at a critical time in his psychotherapy, and the night following his tenth birthday party when he was overwhelmed by his feelings. He would not admit that he was ten, saying he was five and five. Five of the eight episodes of arthritis occurred during the month of June or July, which was the anniversary of his maternal grandfather's death.*

The interview data from the case of Jackie as well as other cases led to a psychodynamic formulation of the emotional conflicts of children with juvenile arthritis based on the following clinical features:

1. A depressive mood disturbance in the arthritic child.
2. An overly close mother-child relationship.
3. The occurrence of a loss in the family prior to the onset of the disease.
4. Personality features of the mother such as depressive character traits and masochism.
5. The loss, early in the life of the child, of a key person to his mother.
6. Severe deprivation early in the mother's life.

* See Figure 2. In the course of psychiatric treatment, both Mrs. G. and Jackie anticipated the month of July with anxiety and verbalized their fears of an exacerbation of arthritis. No mood change other than anxiety was observed. In June of Jackie's tenth year of contact with Dr. B., in his termination interview, he stated, "You know, June is a difficult month for me." Then he mentioned that for the previous four years his hay fever had started at this time.

Repeatedly, we have revised the psychodynamic formulation based upon these clinical impressions, though its essential core involving the problem of unresolved grief and loss has remained unchanged.

Briefly, the formulation is as follows: the mother experiences deprivation and losses in her own childhood. Because of the pattern of handling feelings characteristic in her family, she learned to cope with these losses by excessive control of feelings and masochistic and depressive patterns.* During her pregnancy with the arthritic child or in the early years of his life, a tragic event occurs such as loss of a key person to the mother. Her feelings of deprivation and previous loss are reactivated and intensified, and along with them the defensive patterns she utilized in her childhood. A new factor enters, however: the child becomes the object through which she handles her feelings. As a consequence, a pathologic element is introduced into the mother-child relationship which is necessary but not sufficient for the emergence later of rheumatoid arthritis.

As to the role in which the mother places the child for the handling of her grief, the mother identifies him with the object and objects who deprived and left her. Her attitude toward the child is ambivalent, as it was to the other objects. In the negative aspects of her ambivalence, the mother holds the child responsible for her own past and current unhappiness. She handles her resentment and disappointment through her masochism and depression. Her positive feelings are reflected in the sacrificial way she gives to the child what she wishes she herself had received. In this way the overly close mother-child bond develops which is characteristic of juvenile rheumatoid arthritis cases. This closeness becomes an obstacle for the mother and child in achieving separateness from each other. In the process of development, the child's normal attempts to move away from the mother are experienced as a threat of loss by both. The mother exerts control over her own feelings and those of the child. This struggle for separateness becomes more critical at the time of onset of the disease when an emotionally significant event occurs which threatens the close interrelationship or reactivates the problem of loss. The illness in turn fosters the overly close mother-child bond. Our impression is that the mother makes continuous but unsuccessful restitutional efforts to resolve the grief from her past life, and that the rheumatoid arthritis of the child is associated in a complex causal fashion with her failure to resolve that grief.

We recognized at the outset that our theoretical formulation involved

* The personality structure of the mothers is strikingly similar to that of adult arthritic cases.[8, 13, 17] A psychological study of children with psychosomatic disease reported the mother of an arthritic child as compulsive, unemotional, and perfectionistic.[10]

interpretations concerning the meaning of our clinical impressions. We knew other workers might evolve a different psychodynamic formulation, and, at this stage of our research, we had not even any basis for believing that they would arrive at the same clinical impressions from the case material. We did feel reasonably sure from communications with other observers that some of our clinical observations would be confirmed. For example, the child's feelings of unworthiness, his slowness of movement and retardation of thought processes were high on our hierarchal list of confirmable data. We were much less certain of our observations regarding the mother's guilt. Therefore, we felt it was important to develop a method of deriving clinical impressions from case material which, in the hands of clinically experienced people, would lead to uniform appraisals of the data. Therefore, we wanted to obtain a measuring instrument which had high reliability and which was capable of yielding valid results (that actually measured what it was designed to measure). With this, we would be in a position to ascertain whether our clinical impressions represented accurate generalizations not only for the cases of juvenile rheumatoid arthritis which we had seen but also for new cases at the clinic or elsewhere, although we realized that the interpretation of our findings would still be open to different opinions.

We then proceeded to the construction of scales.

The Construction of Scales

We first reviewed the clinical impressions as stated by Blom and Nicholls for a preliminary evaluation of their testability. The research team, as a group, went over one case which had been in treatment four years. In this process the group became familiar with the clinical impressions from the study of the first 28 cases and with the kind of interview material from which these impressions had been derived.

Our review of a single case revealed that we could not always agree with each other on interpretation of the case material. Occasionally, the original impressions stated by Blom and Nicholls were too generally phrased to be sure whether the clinical data supported them. In this event, we tried to state the ideas more exactly and in a form that would point to the kind of clinical data that would corroborate them.

Some of the impressions seemed testable. For example, the occurrence of a loss to the mother early in the arthritic child's life could be checked, once we agreed as to what constituted a loss and specified the time period called "early." Too narrow a definition of loss, limited to death or separation from an immediate member of the family, might exclude cases in which a lesser event had had the same emotional impact. Some definition was obviously necessary to make confirmation possible. Other original impressions seemed not immediately open to this approach. The close, or symbiotic, mother-child relationship, for instance, could present itself in such various or subtle manifestations as to escape definition that was testable. Such concepts in the psychodynamic formulation we had to set aside, and pursue those that could be more directly verified. We then made a reliability study of eleven protoscales based on testable concepts.

Mother

a. Loss of object in relation to pregnancy or infancy of child.
b. Threat of loss at this time.
c. Depression following separation from the child—verbal.
d. Depression following separation from the child—nonverbal.
e. Tendency to depression.
f. Stoical, depressive characteristics.

Child

g. Feeding problem in infancy.
h. Separation concerns—verbal.
i. Separation themes—nonverbal but in play.
j. Affect withdrawal demonstrated.
k. Difficulty with object relations.

We divided the research team into two groups, each one reading the same two cases and making a clinical judgment of yes or no on the 11 items. The two groups were in complete agreement (i.e., identical rating on dichotomies) on both cases on four out of the 11 items (a, e, g, and i), while they disagreed on both cases on only one item (c). We assumed that further improvement of our definitions on several of the remaining items and a better measuring instrument than yes or no categories would have increased the possibility of agreement.

Up to this point, we limited ourselves to the construction of scales in the area of feeding, separation, and depression. As an illustration, Table I presents some clinical material from Jackie's case and the scales relating to these interview data. We are concerned here with the construction of scales which measure the mother's mood. Column I, "Clinical Observations," shows the depressive characteristics of Jackie's mother: the sad and serious facial expression, fatalistic acceptance of an unhappy marital relationship, and a restriction of interests and activities outside of the home. Symptoms usually associated with grief and melancholia were lacking.

We then made a scale to describe these observational data, cf., the second column of Table I under "General Depressive Rating": A) represents characterologic depression, B) depressive symptoms, C) mood swings and defenses against depression, and D) absence of depression or mild mood disturbance. These items were selected on the hypothesis that the arthritic mothers would generally be classified in group A.

In the third column of Table I are three additional scales that relate to depression. These were designed to give an objective measure of the frequency of some of the specific characteristics of depression in the mothers, i.e., rare crying, pessimistic attitude toward disease, infrequent expression of feelings.

In a similar manner, starting from clinical observations on both mother and patient, we constructed a total of 67 scales: 20 which related to feeding, 24 to separation, and 23 to depression.

Separation and depression were selected because they impressed us from our clinical experience as being of importance. We included feeding because of a theoretical interest: some of us were impressed by the problems of oral masochism in the mother-child relationship and oral-aggressive fantasies in the child. If they were important, they might be reflected in the feeding histories of the children.

Initial Results on Scales

We assessed the discriminating capacity of our scales by applying them to a research group of rheumatoid arthritis cases and a control group of asthmatic patients, which comprised a large and homogeneous group of patients similarly studied. Analysis of the asthma patients' records was also being carried on by another research team in our clinic concurrently.

Our research and control groups—20 patients in each—were selected from the total clinic population of 40 cases of rheumatoid arthritis and 57 cases of asthma. The cases were selected according to the best individual match we could obtain for sex, age of onset of disease, and age of first psychiatric contact. We excluded inadequately studied cases. One of the difficulties was the difference in the sex ratio in the two populations, two to one in favor of girls in our arthritic group and a reverse ratio of two to one in favor of boys among the asthmatic children. Table II shows the results of the matching. Though the mean age at contact is the same, we did not always have chronologically identical children to compare, as the data on range in age indicate. A few arthritic patients were younger than any of the asthmatic children when we first saw them in treatment. The mean age at onset is considerably higher for the rheumatoid arthritic than for the asthmatic group. This reflects different times of onset of these diseases. On this variable, a poor match was obtained.

TABLE I. Illustration of Scale Construction

Clinical Observations	General Depressive Rating	Ratings on Specific Depressive Manifestations
(1) Social worker's description of mother:	A. Comments to the effect that the mother is depressed, unhappy, "unsmiling," etc., as a characteristic trait without reference to B. (Score here depressive character traits.)	Crying
(a) Short attractive woman with sad eyes, plainly dressed, cooperative but not very talkative.		A. Comments in the record that mother frequently cries or shows tears in interviews.
		B. Comments in the record that mother occasionally cries at appropriate moments such as when talking of a recent death or illness in the family, etc.
(b) "Appeared as always, sad and serious."		C. Comments that mother typically never cries or eyes tear up in interviews except under extreme conditions.
(c) Was constantly worrying about the future, who would take care of patient if something happened to her, where they were going to get enough money to live on, etc.	B. Comments to the effect that mother is morbid, or has fantasies of unworthiness, thoughts of suicide, etc. (Score here depressive symptoms.)	D. No comments on mother's crying.
		Attitude toward disease
		A. Mother comments to the effect that the course of the disease in her child will be long, or crippling, or severe. In general, she is quite pessimistic about its outcome.
(d) Very few interests and activities.	C. Comments to the effect that the mother is hypomanic, there is a "push" of words, behavior, etc., and/or major swings in mood from one extreme to another.	B. Mother's attitude toward the disease fluctuates with its course and with the current medical opinion. Comments to the effect or attitude are appropriate to the situation.
(e) Unable to be affectionate with family.		

(2) Mother's comments: When thinking of divorcing husband after pregnancy with patient: "If I put up with him 18 years, I guess I can put up with him some more."	D. No information, or comment to the effect that the mother varies only slightly in her moods or is more often of even temperament.	C. Mother's attitude is typically more cheerful than the disease warrants, and in general her comments lack the morbid, pessimistic overtones described in A. D. No information about mother's expectation of the course of the disease. Mother's expression of feeling A. Social worker makes comment that mother shows little or no feelings of any kind. B. Description of variety of feelings. C. Description of considerable feelings or comment on lability, emotionality. D. No comment or no information.

In scoring the interview data we did not make blind ratings of the cases for the following reasons: by this time all of us were very familiar with the cases; we wanted to improve the scales by comparing the objective results with our clinical assessment of the data through an awareness of the patient's identity; and, finally, to make the records blind, so much of the case material would have to be deleted as to destroy the coherence of the data. We accepted the inevitability of bias, but hoped later to minimize its effect on our results by assigning cases for ratings to the members of the group who had not been the ones involved in the treatment of the cases and to people who were not associated with the research project.

TABLE II. Matching Obtained for Twenty Rheumatoid Arthritis and Asthma Patients.

		Rheumatoid Arthritis	Asthma
Sex			
Male		8	8
Female		12	12
		—	—
	TOTAL:	20	20
Age at Contact			
Mean age		9.0	9.0
Range		2–15	5–16
Age at Onset			
Mean age		6.9	3.9
Range		1.5–15	.2–9

In the analysis of each of the scales, we used the chi-square technique.[11] For each of the 67 scales we calculated the chi-square and determined the level of confidence with which we could reject the possibility that our control and research groups were drawn from the same population. We found that ten of the scales differentiated the two groups at the .05 level of confidence or better. Two others showed considerable promise of being able to differentiate this well, if improved. Many others which did not differentiate between our asthmatic and rheumatoid arthritis cases at this level of confidence still impressed us at a clinical level as being valuable to retain.*

* From 67 scales, some would be found statistically significant by chance alone. This possibility would indicate the need for cross-validation.

Tables III, IV, and V illustrate the procedure. Table III shows the scale on mother's depression and the results obtained from applying it to our two groups of 20 cases each. The results are contaminated since the scales were derived from many of the cases we also used in the ratings. Of the

TABLE III. Comparison between Research and Control Groups Using an Early Version of a Scale to Measure Depression.

Depressive Rating—Mother	Rheumatoid Arthritis	Asthma
A. Comments that the mother is morbid, or is preoccupied with feelings of unworthiness, or suicide, etc.	2	1
B. Comments that the mother is characteristically "depressed," "withdrawn," "uncommunicative," "unhappy," "unsmiling," etc. (If alternating between depression and elation, score here.)	14	5
C. Comments that mother is occasionally depressed, but recovers quickly, or there are equal comments between depression and even temperament. (Depressive reaction to current life situation scored here.)	0	5
D. Comments that mother varies only slightly in her moods or is more often of even temperament or no information.	4	9
TOTAL:	20	20

$x^2 = 7.40$
Level of Confidence=.01

rheumatoid arthritic mothers, 14 were described as having depressed character traits (scored in B) in comparison with 5 of the asthma mothers. To test whether the difference in distribution among rheumatoid arthritis mothers and asthmatic mothers is greater than a chance phenomenon, we calculated the chi-square for the two by two table based on values obtained for B vs. A + C + D for the two groups.[11] The chi-square of 7.40, which can be accepted at the .01 level of confidence, indicates other than chance differences between the two groups on this variable.

Our evaluation of these early scales indicated that the following dif-

TABLE IV. Comparison between Research and Control Groups Using an Early Version of a Scale to Measure Mother's Mood.

Mother's Expression of Feeling	Rheumatoid Arthritis	Asthma
A. Comments that mother characteristically expresses little feeling.	9	1
B. Description of variety of feelings.	6	13
C. Comments of excessive expression of feelings or comment on lability, emotionality.	4	4
D. No comment or no information.	1	2
TOTAL:	20	20

$x^2=6.21$
Level of Confidence=.05

ferences probably were not fortuitous: that mothers of children with rheumatoid arthritis as compared with the mothers of asthmatic children more often showed depressive character traits, expressed fewer feelings and more rarely spoke of their own past; they were more pessimistic about the child's disease and were masochistic in the care of the child; more of them had sustained a loss of a key person during their pregnancy with or

TABLE V. Early Scale on Mother's Loss of a Key Person.

During the Pregnancy and/or the First Two Years of the Arthritic Child, Mother Experiences:	Rheumatoid Arthritis	Asthma
A. An actual loss by death or separation of a significant person or an acute or chronic threat of loss of such a person.	13	3
B. Mother comments that there was no loss or threat of loss, or no information concerning loss.	7	17
TOTAL:	20	20

$x^2=6.83$
Level of Confidence=.01

infancy of the arthritic child; the children with rheumatoid arthritis also were more depressed than the asthmatic children, had greater motor inhibition, fewer interests outside themselves, slower response to the therapist, and more control of feelings.

Of those scales with smaller chi-squares, only one of the 20 scales on feeding showed promise of differentiating the two groups. Our case records often did not have enough specific and detailed information to make ratings on these variables. However, the frequency distributions strongly suggested that the feeding history of the rheumatoid child is not characterized by outstanding disturbances.

Of the 24 scales on separation, one differentiated the two groups. The separation scales were based primarily on the reaction of the child and mother to the hospitalization. The asthmatic children were hospitalized infrequently and for short periods of time, and did not serve as adequate controls. However, the frequency distribution obtained on the scales on separation in the arthritis group alone tended to corroborate the impression that separation was important. A number of scales were constructed on separation experiences that occurred during treatment through changes of social worker or psychotherapist. These did not show any distinguishing features or differences in the two groups.

At this point, we felt most of the scales seemed to describe the clinical data fairly adequately. Strictly speaking, we had evolved category sets which could measure the presence or absence of various characteristics of the mothers and children but which did not provide us with a way of determining a quantitative measure of the characteristics in question. The use of category sets seemed to decrease our chances of finding differences. Therefore, in a revision of these scales they included a measurement of intensity.

Revision of the Scales to Increase Reliability and Validity

From this set of 67 scales covering the areas of feeding, separation, and depression, the research team constructed an improved and expanded set of scales (101) which included other areas that impressed us as having clinical importance. Some of the previous scales were left out because they offered no promise of differentiating, and because there was a consistent insufficiency of interview data on which to make judgments. The previous scales were changed from category sets to linear scales. With new scales we limited ourselves to those which could measure descriptive and factual phenomena. We also selected items for which there was a good chance of finding relevant evidence in the interview data. We also omitted the "no information" category on scales.

These 101 scales were again applied to our previously matched groups of 20 rheumatoid arthritis and asthma cases. Several research workers scored the same cases so that we could obtain measures of observer reliability. When consensus was low, attempts were made in group discussion to determine the basis for this. Often, the discrepancies were due to lack of clarity in the wording of the scale. We sometimes decided the scale actually did not measure what it was supposed to measure. Revisions were then made so that the scale would be more appropriate to the clinical phenomena.

When, in 1957, two new members joined the research team who had no acquaintance with the method, they were asked to score a case with which the research group was thoroughly familiar, and their ratings were compared with those of a long-standing group member. The reliability obtained on this run was discouragingly poor. We then reworded the scales so that people clinically skilled, but unacquainted with the hypotheses, might achieve better agreement in their ratings. After many revisions, three psychologists, unfamiliar with the research, applied the pre-final set of scales to a different case and made ratings that were very close to those which had been made by six members of the research team on the same case.

Final Application of Revised Scales to Arthritic and Asthma Cases

Before deciding on the final version of the scales, we rescored our matched asthma and arthritis groups so that we could learn more about the characteristics of our scales and make one more revision. To improve the matching with respect to age of patient at initial contact and age at onset of illness, we reduced the number of cases in each group to 15.

This time, four psychiatrists, two social workers, and one psychologist made the ratings. Each case was assigned to two members for independent scoring. The pre-final set consisted of 76 scales, the majority being five point linear scales. The experience of the group was that, on the average, it took from four to six hours to score one case.

The analysis of the ratings was undertaken primarily to help us evaluate the discriminatory power of the various scales. We knew that some of the scales differentiated rheumatoid arthritis from asthma cases, but we were not sure about a large number of the scales. With a new research group of our own or of other workers, it would be helpful to label each scale with respect to its differentiating capacity and its ability to yield clustering in the ratings of the rheumatoid arthritis group alone. Finally, we hoped to make final changes so that the scales would measure what we intended them to measure.

Using the same cases previously rated, we noted all differences in scoring of more than one on any given scale; then the two raters in question discussed the differences until combined agreement was reached. Their initial ratings were discarded in favor of the revised ones for results on measurement. The original ratings were retained, however, for a reliability study.

A rough measure of the reliability of the scales can be obtained from the percentage of agreements we had. The total number of judgments made per case was 110, since a few of the 76 scales involved more than one rating. On the average, agreement was obtained for approximately 90 per cent of the ratings (i.e., 10 disagreements out of 110 judgments). A precise statement of the reliability of our scales will be reported when the statistical analysis is complete.

We also studied the reliability of individual scorers. Social workers were more familiar with the mother's material and agreed with psychiatrists in their rating of it better than on ratings of the child's interviews. There was better agreement generally when the two observers were of the same sex. In this connection, it is important to note that the psychiatrists were all males and the social workers females. Furthermore, the best agreement was obtained by the two original members of the research team (Blom, a psychiatrist, and Nicholls, a social worker).

Examples of the five-point rating scales * we pre-tested are shown in Table VI, with the results obtained for the 15 matched arthritis and asthma cases. The numbers give the distribution of judgments; 15 cases scored by two observers total 30. Illustrated here are scales which (a) clearly differentiate the matched arthritis and asthma group and (b) show clustering in the ratings of the arthritis group. At this time, we cannot report the results obtained on the total number of scales since the data on the 15 cases are in the process of being analyzed.

The research group considered all scales which had given rise to rating differences of more than one. A large source of variability in the scores came from the raters' failure to read the scale or the interview data carefully enough. Discussions between the two scorers in many instances re-

* These scales contain positions for rating between descriptions given for positions 1, 3, and 5.

vealed no real differences of considered opinion. However, variance in the scoring could also be attributed sometimes to the case material itself. The interview data were very clear on certain cases, with a considerable amount of supportive evidence for a judgment. On other cases, relevant information had not been obtained. In some instances, the wording of the scales was still ambiguous or inaccurate.

The process of constructing scales, scoring them, revising and rescoring obviously could become an endless one. After the third rescoring of the matched research and control groups, no more scales were constructed and we stopped revising them.

TABLE VI. Illustration of Scales with Results of Pre-Testing.

Scale #3.24 *Degree of Overt Depression* *	Rheumatoid Arthritis	Asthma
Interviewer describes mother as:		
1. Having *depressive symptoms* Mother has prolonged crying spells, thoughts of suicide, feelings of unworthiness.	2	0
2. (Between 1 and 3)	4	0
3. Depressed Worker says mother is withdrawn, uncommunicative, stoical, fatalistic, unhappy, unsmiling—indicates these are personality traits of depression.	18	4
4. Having *temporary depressive reactions* to current life situations, but no personality traits of depression.	6	16
5. Not depressed Mother shows *no signs* of persistent depression or temporary depression.	0	10
TOTAL:	30	30

* *Qualitative remarks:* Note manic episodes or mood swings; describe situations involved in temporary depressive reactions.

TABLE VI. (cont'd.) Illustration of Scales with Results of Pre-Testing.

Scale #7.1 *Conception of Etiology of Patient's Illness*	Rheumatoid Arthritis	Asthma
In discussing the cause of patient's illness, mother reveals her conception of it as:		
1. Subjective Mother ascribes the illness to an unrealistic, personal conception of the etiology, giving a cause that has no medically recognized basis.	14	0
2. (Between 1 and 3)	6	2
3. Popular but inaccurate Mother ascribes the child's illness to a commonly held, but not medically accurate cause, e.g., rheumatoid arthritis is due to weather changes, poor diet, etc.	4	6
4. (Between 3 and 5)	4	12
5. Accepted scientifically Mother accepts the medical explanation of the cause of the child's illness, e.g., the disease is bacterial, or allergic, or psychosomatic in origin, or doctors do not know the cause, etc.	2	10
TOTAL:	30	30

TABLE VI. (cont'd.) Illustration of Scales with Results of Pre-Testing.

Scale #3.41 *Response to Patient's Illness*	Rheumatoid Arthritis	Asthma
Mother's behavior indicates her response to patient's illness is:		

1. Extremely masochistic Mother subjugates her life to her sick child's by renouncing her own pleasure to care for the child. (E.g., she takes sole responsibility for the child's care, meets excessive demands of child, neglects responsibility to other members of her family, prolongs excessive care of child during convalescence.)	24	2
2. (Between 1 and 3)	4	8
3. Moderately masochistic Mother cares for the child as necessitated by the illness, sharing the responsibility with others and finding time for activities not associated with the patient.	2	12
4. (Between 3 and 5)	0	8
5. Minimally masochistic Mother completely rejects the responsibility of her ill child by giving the entire care to institutions or other people.	0	0
TOTAL:	30	30

TABLE VI. (cont'd.) Illustration of Scales with Results of Pre-Testing.

Scale #9.11 *Mood in Manifest Behavior*	Rheumatoid Arthritis	Asthma
Therapist describes patient (child) as:		
1. *Depressed,* unhappy, etc., and/or having *major swings in mood* from one extreme to the other.	22	0
2. (Between 1 and 3)	4	4
3. Usually of normal temperament or varying only slightly in mood.	0	14

4. (Between 3 and 5)	0	8
5. Hypomanic, with a push of words or behavior	4	4
TOTAL:	30	30

TABLE VI. (cont'd.) Illustration of Scales with Results of Pre-Testing.

Scale #9.14 *Manifestations of Emotion*	Rheumatoid Arthritis	Asthma
Therapist comments that the patient (child) characteristically expresses feelings:		
1. Excessively or inappropriately The patient has a constant exaggeration of emotional expression, or the feelings he expresses are not appropriate to the situation.	4	2
2. (Between 1 and 3)	0	12
3. Appropriately and with variety The patient expresses a variety of feelings which appear appropriate to the situation involved.	0	8
4. (Between 3 and 5)	8	6
5. Infrequently The patient does not express his feelings very often.	18	2
TOTAL:	30	30

Our final set consists of a total of 76 scales in ten areas. They are in large measure identical with those which we pre-tested on the 15 matched arthritis and asthma groups. The scales form a part of an 88 page mimeographed form which also includes instructions for rating and a number of statistical tables to be filled out from the psychiatric and hospital records. An explanation of the scale groups and the index to the 76 scales is given in Table VII.

TABLE VII. Explanation of Scale Groups.

Decimal notation is used to facilitate organization of the scales. Groups 1.0 through 7.0 are scored from mother's material. The remainder, groups 8.0 through 10.0 are scored from patient's material. Within these groups the decimal notation is used to refer to sub-areas of special research interests within the mother's and child's material.

1.0 *Mother's mood during early life of patient:* This group pertains to mother's mood and health during pregnancy and early life of the child.

2.0 *Mother's childhood:* This group pertains only to those factors which are pertinent to our research, e.g., loss and deprivation.

3.0 *Mother's personality:* The areas covered here again are those essential to our research and do not attempt to be a total assessment of the mother's personality.

3.1 *Dependence:* This group of scales pertains to the degree of dependence established by mother in her personal relationships.

3.2 *Feelings:* In this group of scales we explore the various emotions expressed and the degree of control maintained over allowing their expression. We do not attempt to measure the depth or extent of any feeling.

3.3 *Guilt:* Here we are concerned with the salience of guilt as manifest in interview material and in real-life situations. We measure also the degree to which the guilt or blame tendency is kept under control.

3.4 *Masochism:* Here we attempt to measure the degree to which the mother makes her claims for self-pleasure subservient to those about her, in particular her family.

3.5 *Object relations:* This group of scales aims at description of the dominant attitudes which characterize mother's adult relationships.

4.0 *Mother's reaction to patient's current hospitalization:* This group of scales involves a descriptive account of mother's moods and actions incident to separation from patient through hospitalization. These scales apply ONLY to mothers whose children were hospitalized during this explicit study.

5.0 *Mother's image of patient pre-illness:* Here we are concerned with mother's retrospective views of patient's early health and development.

6.0 *Mother's handling of socialization of patient:* We are concerned here with only two aspects of socialization, i.e., the manner in which mother handled separation from patient and how she handled the social maturation of the child.

6.1 *Separation:* These scales deal with the frequency of the separations between mother and patient prior to onset of patient's illness.

6.2 *Frustration/gratification:* This group of scales refers to mother's ability intelligently to frustrate the child in line with normal social maturational

TABLE VII. (cont'd.) Explanation of Scale Groups.

process, e.g., feeding, toilet training, as well as handling the frustrations incident to the disease itself.

7.0 *Mother's fantasies:* This scale refers only to fantasies concerning the etiology of the child's illness.

8.0 *Significant events in patient's history:* Again, this group of scales refers only to those circumstances relevant to the main ideas in the research, e.g., significant loss to the mother during patient's infancy, and environmental stress around onset and recurrences of RA.

9.0 *Patient's personality:* The areas covered here are those central to our research and do not attempt to be a total assessment of the patient's personality.

9.1 *Characteristic feelings:* In this group of scales we explore the various emotions expressed and the degree of control maintained over their expression. Again we do not try to measure the depth or the extent of the emotion.

9.2 *Negative feelings:* This group of scales is treated separately because of the clinical importance of the manner in which RA patients handle negative feelings.

9.3 *Passivity:* This group of scales is included because of the obvious limitations of activity imposed by the disease of RA and concerns the amount of physical activity.

9.4 *Dependence:* This group of scales pertains to the degree of dependence established by patient in his personal relations.

9.5 *Fantasies:* These scales include only those which were striking clinically, e.g., self-destruction and abandonment.

10.0 *Patient's object relations:* This scale aims at a description of the dominant attitudes which characterize patient's relationships to adults.

TABLE VII. Index to Scales.

TABLE VII. (cont'd.) Index to Scales.

TABLE VII. (cont'd.) Index to Scales.

#	Title	Page
4.20	*Actions mother takes*	
4.21	Relinquishing of responsibility for patient	49
4.22	Handling medical recommendation of hospitalization	50
4.23	Balancing demands of patient and family	51
4.24	Handling interruption of visits	52
4.25	Visiting pattern	53
4.26	Maintenance of oral tie	54
5.0	MOTHER'S IMAGE OF PATIENT PRE-ILLNESS	
5.1	Patient's general health	55
5.2	Demands of patient during infancy	56
5.3	Early feeding history	57
6.0	MOTHER'S HANDLING OF SOCIALIZATION OF PATIENT	
6.10	*Separation*	
6.11	Frequency of separations before illness	58
6.12	Delegation of patient's care before illness	59
6.13	School attendance after illness	65
6.20	*Frustration/gratification*	
6.21	Ability to frustrate	60
6.22	Oral socialization	
6.221	Timing	61
6.222	Manner	61
6.23	Bowel training	
6.231	Timing	62
6.232	Manner	62
6.24	Mother's description of patient's behavior	63
6.25	Handling frustrations related to illness	64
6.26	School attendance after illness	65
7.0	MOTHER'S FANTASIES	
7.1	Conception of etiology of patient's illness	66
8.0	SIGNIFICANT EVENTS IN PATIENT'S HISTORY	
8.1	Age at time of mother's reactive depression	67
8.2	Stressful events prior to onset of illness	68
8.3	Stressful events prior to recurrence or continuation of illness	69
9.0	PATIENT'S PERSONALITY	
9.10	*Characteristic feelings*	
9.11	Mood in manifest behavior	70
9.12	Degree of overt depression	71
9.13	Interest in environment	72

TABLE VII. (cont'd.) Index to Scales.

Collection of New Research and Control Populations

We now come to the cross-validation part of the research. The process of developing objective measuring devices had been undertaken to apply the scales to a group of rheumatoid arthritis cases and a group of control cases which had not been involved in the construction of the scales. Members of the research team collected the data on the new cases. We also made the arbitrary decision to limit ourselves to ten interviews each with the child and the mother. This was necessitated by practical considerations of time. Since the data obtained from our original research cases came in large measure from forty or more interviews, it is quite possible that this limitation on the number of interviews might not give us sufficient data so that ratings could be made. In one of our cases we learned only in the tenth year of contact with the family that mother had had an abortion for an illegitimate child with father a year prior to the birth of the patient. However, our experience also indicated that sufficient descriptive and historical data often occurred in the first ten interviews.

When we set up our research design, we felt that one of the most interesting areas to investigate was the effect on the arthritic child of the separation from his mother brought about by hospitalization. We believed that many of the clinical observations, in particular the depressive features in the child, would not be as evident without separation. Our research design, therefore, involved four groups of cases to be compared: (1) hospitalized arthritis cases, (2) nonhospitalized arthritis cases, (3) hospitalized control cases, and (4) nonhospitalized control cases. We lowered the number to ten cases in each group because of practical considerations of time and limitation in the number of cases.

The selection of the control cases has also been determined by our wish to match them with the research cases according to sex, age of patient at initial contact, age of patient at onset of illness, severity of illness, and length of hospitalization. We have included the variable "severity of illness" because most of the nonhospitalized arthritis cases have a milder form of the disease, and most of the hospitalized arthritis cases have a severe form of the disease. It will be important to differentiate the effect of severity of illness on our psychological findings from the effects produced by hospitalization. We do not know the extent to which the psychological findings on our old cases, for the most part hospitalized at the time of initial contact, characterize just severe arthritis, or are associated with severe illness in general, or are a function of hospitalization. Our research design permits us to factor out the effect due to nature of the disease keeping the severity and hospitalization constant. We will also be in a position to say whether hospitalization and severity of illness taken in conjunction exert an influence on the psychological features of the arthritis patients. But, unless we obtain a sufficient number of mild hospitalized cases of arthritis and severe nonhospitalized arthritis cases to permit statistical analysis, we will not be able to distinguish in our findings between the effects of each of these two factors.

We were limited by the above considerations in the choice of our control groups. A mixed control group would have certain advantages. Severity of illness rather than effects associated with a particular type of illness would be the focus of attention. Our control cases will, therefore, include asthma, poliomyelitis, orthopedic problems, nephritis, and behavior problems. We will select half of the control group in the hospitalized and nonhospitalized categories from cases of asthma, yielding a total of 20 cases, to enable us to investigate a number of further questions, such as: (1) differences between psychosomatic and nonpsychosomatic diseases, (2) similarities among patients with different psychosomatic diseases, and (3) differences between patients with different psychosomatic diseases. Our choice of control cases also may make it possible to make statements concerning the effect of immobilization.

Potential Applications of the Methodology

A possible extension of this research project is the application of the scales we have developed to other psychosomatic groups. Statistical analyses of these data would yield information concerning psychological features common to the various psychosomatic diseases as well as points of difference between them. It is our hope that other research workers may want to undertake a study of this type, using our mimeographed scoring manual, or perhaps study another group of juvenile rheumatoid arthritis cases to test the generality of our findings.

It is appropriate to ask what has been learned from the project that might be helpful in formulating a research study. Our experience indicates it is of importance to consider the interests and the qualifications of the people who are available to participate in the research project. The distinction between clinical studies and experimental ones is relevant. If the group is composed of clinicians only, they should be aware of the difficulties they will encounter in undertaking an experimental research project no matter how simple the methodology appears to be. They cannot expect to get sufficient help from outside consultants to guide them because they will find it extremely difficult to communicate their methodologic problems. Also, the consultant is put in the position of trying to answer questions he has not understood. Our experience indicates the group probably would regret their departure from the richness and familiarity of clinical study.

If one of the research team members can bridge the gap between clinical interests and methodologic considerations, a statistical research project can be contemplated. The responsibility will be placed upon this member to work out a research design which does not compromise the value of the clinical material but which does retain the essential features of a rigorous methodology. The services of a consultant under these conditions is both needed and effective. We feel confident of the value of trying to confirm clinical observations experimentally through a rigorous methodology. On the next occasion, however, we would be less ambitious in terms of the number of clinical observations to subject to experimental confirmation.

There are various factors relative to the morale of the members of the research team which affect the selection of the research project. Ideally, the clinicians in the group should already be working with the kind of cases that will supply the data for the project. It is trite to mention that interest in what they are doing will increase their effectiveness as participants in the research study. When deciding on a research design, it is easy to overlook that clinicians will be called upon to devote a great deal of their time and effort to activities they find uninteresting. Discussion in advance of the amount of nonclinical work that people are willing to commit to the research project might help establish a more realistic basis for deciding on the merits of one type of study versus another. A corollary of this point is the administrative matter of clearly protecting the research time of clinical people from other responsiblities in the clinic. There is more of a tendency to let this happen when the type of work the research project calls for is uninteresting.

It also becomes profitable to take stock of the type of cases which routinely come to the clinic. The rate of supply of various types of psychiatric problems will affect the choice of research area and research design. It is important to go over the factors which account for large numbers of cases in order to find out whether such a good supply is apt to continue.

Another important consideration relates to the motivation patients have for participating in a research project. It is difficult to enlist the cooperation of people in a psychiatric research project unless something therapeutic is done for them. Even if they come, the type of psychological material one obtains is not the same as when a person feels he is in a therapeutic relationship with the interviewer.

A great deal of wasted time can be avoided by consideration in advance of the hypotheses one is going to investigate. First comes a sorting of the hypotheses into those which are special to the group of patients under consideration and those which apply not only to them but to other groups of patients also. The research design can be simplified by limiting the investigation to the hypotheses which are specially relevant to the research cases. For example, we unnecessarily complicated our study of emotional factors in juvenile rheumatoid arthritis by retaining, because of their clinical importance in the understanding of this psychosomatic disease, scales that did not differentiate between the rheumatoid arthritis and the asthma cases. If we had explicitly related the kind of hypotheses we wanted to investigate to the composition of the control group required by such an investigation, we might have decided in favor of retaining only those scales which differentiated our two psychosomatic groups in the pre-testing. We allowed our clinical interest in the nondifferentiating scales to persuade us to keep them. Later, we realized we had forced ourselves to change the composition of our control group in the cross validation part of the study.

Another kind of useful discussion about hypotheses concerns what kinds of hypotheses are to be verified. It is important, particularly when one is dealing with hypotheses derived from psychoanalytic theory, to distinguish between the assumed premises of the research and the hypotheses based upon these premises. For example, in our project we have taken for granted that mothers can deal with their own feelings of deprivation through their children. While we gather further empirical evidence for this in our study of mothers of children with juvenile arthritis, we do not attempt to prove or disprove the general statement. Our hypotheses concern specific verifiable statements such as the prevalence early in the life of the arthritic child of events which represent the loss of a key person to the mother.

There is another reason for considering the kinds of hypotheses to be verified. The earlier in the research project one is able to differentiate between verifiable and less easily verifiable hypotheses, the better the chance of avoiding the pursuit of unprofitable research leads. Clinically, we were impressed in our first cases with a "symbiotic relationship between the arthritic patient and his mother." We constructed scales to assess the prevalence of this phenomenon without seriously asking ourselves whether we expected to be able to construct scales and rate instances of symbiotic relations from ten interviews with the mother and the child. In our experience we found that our research techniques were most applicable to the investigation of descriptive and factual phenomena. Phenomena that involve intrapsychic variables and more complex constructs present greater difficulties in measurement which we arbitrarily chose to avoid.

To verify a hypothesis a definition of all basic terms is desirable. However, the definition of an abstract term is not always necessary (e.g., depression). Measurement of the phenomenon referred to by the term can be made without defining the term if agreement is obtained on the type of concrete instances that are relevant.

Sometimes the hypotheses of greatest clinical interest are considered verifiable, yet the conditions of observation are such that they cannot easily be verified. Our first rheumatoid arthritis cases were all hospitalized. We were impressed with the prevalence of depressive symptoms in both the mother and the child. Later, when we had seen these same patients and others in the outpatient clinic, we suspected that the separation between the mother and the child during hospitalization had also played a role in their depressive behavior. We, therefore, proposed investigating differences between hospitalized and nonhospitalized cases. We were aware that new cases seen on the wards for the first ten times were usually more severely ill and that those seen in the Arthritis Clinic had milder arthritis. Hence, we would be unable to isolate the effect due to severity of disease from that due to separation between mother and child. We could not test directly the hypothesis that separation leads to depressive reactions in children with arthritis and in their mothers. We knew we would have to content ourselves with a prediction, i.e., that we would find depressive behavior more prevalent in hospitalized than in nonhospitalized cases. But we could test the hypothesis indirectly by comparing the hospitalized cases with severe arthritis to severely ill, nonarthritic hospitalized cases. This comparison would enable us to make certain statements about the relationship between severity of disease and depressive behavior. But we could not assess the relative importance of the two variables in arthritis with our research design.

SUMMARY

This research in progress had its origins in clinical observations of children with arthritis and their mothers who were seen in psychotherapy and casework. The object was to see if these observations could be tested by an objective method. The first step consisted of the development of objective scoring devices. We used the original population to construct and refine rating scales. After a number of successive evaluations of the scales on our original rheumatoid arthritis cases and a control group of asthma patients, we decided on a final set of 76 scales.

The next step is the application of the scales to new research and control groups, each consisting of twenty cases, of which half are hospitalized and half nonhospitalized. We have not completed the collection of those cases, nor have we rated them. The final stage of the research will be the statistical analysis of the data from cross validation. The results of this analysis will test the confirmation of our hypotheses.

We are encouraged about the potentialities of the rating scales in terms of their discriminatory power and reliability. In our research we encountered a number of problems. A handicap at the beginning was the lack of training and experience of the group in research methodology. A recurrent problem was the difficulty of reconciling methodologic procedures with clinical case material. Other difficulties involved scale construction. We limited ourselves to those scales based on historical and descriptive data for which we could find relevant data in the case records.

In both the original research and control groups and in the new population groups, the problem of matching presented itself. We controlled only a few of the variables when we were developing the scales. In the new population groups, we are trying to determine the effect of illness itself, severity of illness, hospitalization, and immobilization on our psychological findings. Controlling a large number of variables results in reducing the number of possible cases. Our total pool of arthritic cases did not and does not allow us to be as rigorous as theoretical considerations would require.

The problem of observer bias, both in the scoring of scales and collection of data, was recognized. We also tried to obtain some measure of its effect. Two psychologists, unacquainted with the research, scored one case and we found their ratings sufficiently similar to those of the research team members.

Finally, there were problems due to differences in professional background of the research group. The members came from three disciplines, and although accustomed to working together as the clinic treatment team, had numerous problems in a research focus. Social workers found it difficult to make the compromises with casework method which the others felt were necessary. Psychologists wanted to make the method more rigorous and limit the examination to a few variables. Psychiatrists tended to stress the many dynamic factors operating in the clinical observations which were difficult to measure. Not only were there discipline biases and differences but individual ones as well. However, the group learned to work as a research team and eventually handled these difficulties.

We believe that the method reported in this paper represents a combination of intuitive and systematic approaches. We have tried to isolate significant emotional factors in a psychosomatic problem which could be statistically treated. The attempt has been a scientific validation of results obtained by a dynamic clinical method.

Bibliography

1. Beck, S. J.: The Six Schizophrenias. New York, American Orthopsychiatric Association, 1954.

2. Benjamin, J. D., Coleman, J. V., and Hornbein, R.: A study of personality in pulmonary tuberculosis. Am. J. Orthopsychiat. *18:* 704–707, 1948.

3. ———: Methodological considerations in the validation and elaboration of psychoanalytical personality theory. Am. J. Orthopsychiat. *20:* 139–156, 1950.

4. ———: Directions and problems in psychiatric research. Psychosom. Med. *14:* 1–9, 1952.

5. Blom, G. E., and Nicholls, G.: Emotional factors in children with rheumatoid arthritis. Am. J. Orthopsychiat. *24:* 588–601, 1954.

6. ———, Long, R. T., and Whipple, B. S.: A psychosomatic study of juvenile rheumatoid arthritis. Unpublished paper.

7. Cecil, R. L.: Environmental factors in the etiology of rheumatic conditions. M. Clin. North America *29:* 566–570, 1945.

8. Cleveland, S. E., and Fisher, S.: Behavior and unconscious fantasies of patients with rheumatoid arthritis. Psychosom. Med. *16:* 327–333, 1954.

9. Cobb, S., Bauer, W., and Whiting, I.: Environmental factors in rheumatoid arthritis. J.A.M.A. *113:* 668–670, 1939.

10. Gerard, M.: Genesis of Psychosomatic Symptoms in Infancy. *In* Deutsch, F. (ed.): The Psychosomatic Concept in Psychoanalysis, pp. 82–95. New York, International Universities Press, Inc., 1953.

11. Guilford, J. P.: Psychometric Methods. New York, McGraw-Hill Book Company, Inc., 1936.

12. Halliday, J. L.: Psychological aspects of rheumatoid arthritis. Proc. Roy. Soc. Med. *35:* 445–455, 1942.

13. Johnson, A., Shapiro, L. B., and Alexander, F.: Preliminary report on a psychosomatic study of rheumatoid arthritis. Psychosom. Med. *9:* 295–300, 1947.

14. Lindzey, G. (ed.): Handbook of Social Psychology, vol. 1. Cambridge, Mass., Addison-Wesley Publishing Company, 1942.

15. Ludwig, A. O.: Emotional factors in rheumatoid arthritis. Phys. Therapy Rev. *29:* 1–6, 1949.

16. ———: Psychogenic factors in rheumatoid arthritis. Bull. Rheumat. Dis. *2:* 15–16, 1952.

17. ———: Psychiatric Studies of Patients with Rheumatoid Arthritis. *In* Slocum, C. H. (ed.): Rheumatic Diseases, pp. 112–115. Philadelphia, W. B. Saunders Company, 1952.

18. Nissen, H. A., and Spencer, K. A.: The psychogenic problem (endocrinal and metabolic) in chronic arthritis. New England J. Med. *214:* 576–581, 1936.

19. Thomas, G. W.: Psychic factors in rheumatoid arthritis. Am. J. Psychiat. *93:* 693–710, 1936.

6

Rumination in Infancy

By RENATA DE BENEDETTI GADDINI and EUGENIO GADDINI

RUMINATION OR MERYCISM, the active bringing up into the mouth of swallowed food which has already reached the stomach and which may have started to undergo the process of digestion, is a rare syndrome in humans. The condition was first described in adults by Fabricio di Acquapendente in 1618. Since the nineteenth century it has been known to occur in children, being observed recently, however, less frequently than in the past.

The food may be partially reswallowed, partially lost, with serious consequences for the infant's nutrition. Unlike regurgitation, where the food runs out of the infant's mouth without any effort, in rumination there are complex and purposeful preparatory movements, particularly of the tongue and of the abdominal muscles. In some cases the hard palate is stimulated by fingers in the mouth. When the efforts become successful and the milk appears on the back of the pharynx, the child's face is pervaded by an ecstatic expression.

Rumination is commonly believed to occur in retarded children. The most recent observations,[10, 13] however, do not seem to confirm this view; neither can we, on the basis of our experience. The possible meaning of a phylogenetic regression (suggested by the analogy to rumination in herbivorous animals) or of an atavistic degeneration in abiotrophic subjects has been considered in the study of the pathogenesis.[9] No organic change has been demonstrated in the esophagus. It is of interest, however, to know that many erroneous diagnoses may be made before recognizing rumination as such; among others: pyloric stenosis, pylorospasm, adrenal insufficiency, celiac syndrome, food allergy, esophageal chalasia, duodenal ulcer.[13] In the past few years the approach has been directed mostly to the psychosomatic aspects of the syndrome.

In view of the growing interest which has been given in the last decade to environmental as well as to constitutional factors in the study of child development, since 1950 we have studied the cases of rumination occurring in our wards from this point of view, and we have followed them up after their discharge from the hospital. There have been six cases altogether (approximately 0.05% of all admissions in that period). The complete and repeated physical, radiologic, hematologic, and biochemical studies routinely made in the hospital have been integrated in each of these cases with the sociopsychological study of the child and of the family constellation. The patients' behavior (when alone in their beds before being fed, their approach to food, their reactions to the attempts to discontinue the feeding, the rumination itself—usually between feedings, their reactions to the various environmental stimuli brought to them in a selective way) has been studied with motion pictures.

While no relevant information was obtained from the physical, radiologic, hematologic, and biochemical studies, some sociopsychological data were found to be significant, as will be seen in the following description of cases.

Methods of Study

Observation of the babies was carried out in three main ways, apart from the physical and biochemical studies: (1) direct observation in the hospital, (2) study of films made of them, and (3) indirect study through repeated interviews with the mothers by social workers. For all the infants, three observation periods were established: (1) an hour or more before feedings, (2) five to ten minutes before feeding, (3) during and after feeding, in some cases for as long as two hours.

The observations were first recorded by means of notes, with, occasionally, more than one person observing the same child. A few weeks later the observer began to document the details of rumination with motion pictures. The filming was never undertaken until the observer had spent some time with the baby.

The babies did not seem to be disturbed by the filming. They were only photographed when the natural light was sufficient; no artificial light was ever used. Rarely, if ever, were their beds moved into the sun. The babies' attention was not distracted, nor was the rumination process interrupted. Occasionally, the sound of the camera, which is an old-fashioned and a quite silent one, caused a brief hesitation on the part of the infant. But a few seconds later rumination was always resumed.

We have chosen from our films a sequence (pp. 178–179) which shows the outstanding stages in the process of rumination. As can be seen, in the first stage the baby (CASE #3) carries his thumb to his mouth, introducing it at full length and pushing it against the posterior part of the hard palate. The stimulation of this area is accompanied by sucking movements and by rhythmic contraction of the pharyngeal and epigastric muscles; presumably, the muscles of the esophagus, of the cardia and of the stomach are also involved. Meanwhile, the tongue is rhythmically projected forward, with its central part depressed.

During this stage, which can last from 15 to 20 seconds to a couple of minutes, the baby maintains an absorbed, intense expression and shows no interest in his environment.

In the following stage, small quantities of milk begin to appear in the bottom of the oral cavity, and the movements are rhythmically increased so that the oral cavity is quickly filled. This usually requires a few seconds, during which the previous tense expression of the child rapidly changes into one of extreme relaxation and beatitude. His finger falls from his mouth, and while one part of the milk, usually the larger amount, is again swallowed, a lesser amount dribbles from the corners of his partly opened mouth. The expression of the baby at this point is quite similar to that of the sucking infant who, completely gratified, spontaneously gives up the breast.

The interviews with the mothers revealed significant social and psychological data. Therapeutic help was freely offered to all the mothers with a minimum of formality (i.e., they were not required to have a fixed appointment long in advance). Some to a greater, some to a lesser extent took advantage of this help, which they received sometimes from the observer, sometimes from the social worker who was following the case. The number of interviews they received varied from as many as daily visits (CASE #5) to widely separated interviews. One of them (CASE #3) hardly came at all.

Our data have been summarized in two tables. Table 1 concerns the mothers and table 2 the children.

Case Reports

(1) *Franco B., aged 7 months, 26 days.* His father was a miner in Sicily. Because of his job the father was away from his home for periods of six to seven months at a time. The mother was described as very prone to worry. Apparently, they wanted the baby as a replacement for an older child who had died of typhoid two years before and whose name he was given. The result, however, was a disappointment. Talking about the child, the mother regretted bitterly the many physical and financial sacrifices that his arrival had caused and recalled how difficult her pregnancy had been.

One night she was suddenly informed that there had been an accident in the mine where her husband was working and that thirteen miners had lost their lives. Although the husband's name was not among them, there was uncertainty about the safety of three other miners whose names were not given. It was on that

TABLE I. Mother

Patient	Characteristics	Pregnancy	Delivery	Marital Relationship
Franco B.	Age 35. Very prone to worry. Apparently she wanted the baby, but very rejecting toward baby.	Very difficult.	Normal.	Practically separated because of his job (miner). Fear that he had died in an accident in the mine.
Franca D.S.	Age 23. Resentful of female role. A previous illegitimate child was in an institution.	Very difficult in first months. Entered the hospital at seventh month because of "discharge".	Forceps.	Unmarried; she was not sure who the father was.
Ugo P.	Age 32. Extreme resentment toward husband and baby. Forced by husband to accept the baby.	Nausea and vomiting all through pregnancy.	Difficult.	Resented husband's sexual irresponsibility.
Angelo C.	Age 31. Aggressive. Resentful at having twins.	Nausea and vomiting first few months.	Forceps.	Dependent, aggressive.
Mario E.	Age 34. Authoritarian, nervous, impatient, identifies herself with her own domineering mother.	Many attempts at abortion until guilt feelings supervened. Extremely difficult; hypertension.	Normal.	Aggressive toward passive, dependent husband. Could not tolerate independence in others, including her children.
Adriano B.	Age 30. Strong feelings of inadequacy. Greatly dependent on her own mother. Ashamed of sexuality.	Difficult throughout.	Difficult.	Ambivalent; mutually dependent.

Table 2. Child

Patient	Birth Order	Sex	Breast Feeding	Weaning from Breast	Vomiting	Admission		Rumination			Neurotic Traits
						Weight	Age	Age Onset	Time Onset	Cessation	
F.B.	Last of four, of whom two living.	M	Until 2 months, 15 days.	Abrupt. Mother said milk spoiled.	Appeared with mother's fear of father's death. Followed by diarrhea and fever.	4.8 Kg. (birth 3.7 Kg.)	7 mo., 26 days	3rd mo.	Shortly after eating.	(Died)	
F.D.S.	Last of two.	F	Until 2 months.	Abrupt. Mother "did not have milk."	2 months, 15 days, with diarrhea.	4 Kg.	3 mo. 20 days	3rd mo.	Shortly after eating.	11 mo.	

U.P.	Last of three living children. Previous pregnancy deliberately aborted.	M	Until 2 months with only one breast.	Abrupt. Milk insufficient.	2 months, 15 days.	6 Kg. (birth 4.5 Kg.)	8 mo. 14 days	3rd mo.	Shortly after eating.	11½ months	Head-banging
A.C.	Second twin, last of three living.	M	One month with supplement.	At 1 mo.	3 months.	2.9 Kg. (birth 1.9 Kg.)	3 mo. 15 days	4th mo.	Shortly after eating.	18 mo.	
M.E.	Last of three living children.	M	Six months.	Abrupt. Mother "was tired."	7 months.	7.8 Kg. (birth 4.2 Kg.)	10 mo.	8th mo.	Soon after eating.	14 mo.	
A.B.	Only child.	M	A few days.	—	3 months.	4.7 Kg. (birth 4.7 Kg.)	4 mo.	4th mo.	1–2 hrs. after eating.	4 yr.	

night that the child started vomiting, and according to the mother, it was because her own fears and anxiety had "spoiled" her milk.

The vomiting lasted a few days, during which the child was weaned and put on a rigid diet, while the mother's milk disappeared completely. After a few days a moderate fever appeared, and he was put for the first time in a children's hospital (age two months, twenty days). He was left there for eighteeen days. Apparently, during that period some scattered manifestations of rumination were noticed. Nevertheless, when the fever and other acute symptoms disappeared, the child was given back to the mother by the crowded hospital because "the malnutrition could be cared for at home." At six months of age the child was put back in the hospital again because of the continuous "vomiting." After five days he was at home again. The mother reported that he was continuously hungry, but weight gain was extremely small. Shortly after eating he would start rumination, bringing up the ingested food and at the same time looking at the empty dish to see if he could get some more food. The only food that was kept down was apple sauce. Loss of weight soon started. The mother then brought the child to our Clinic.

On admission he was a pale, skinny baby weighing 4.8 Kg. at the age of seven months (birth weight 3.7 Kg.). He was in a condition of extreme malnutrition. During his stay in the hospital, rumination was observed between feedings, shortly after, or even during feedings. Part of the milk was again reswallowed, although most of it flowed out at the corners of the mouth.

In spite of all physical care he died of bronchopneumonia a couple of months after admission.

(2) *Franca D. S., aged 3 months, 20 days.* She was an illegitimate child. Her mother, of course, had not been pleased the moment that she noticed she was pregnant. Furthermore, up to the sixth month of pregnancy she complained that she could not perceive any smell without nausea and vomiting. In the seventh month of pregnancy, at her own request she entered the hospital. What she particularly wanted was a boy as "it is always easier to be male than female." In any case she had always been "very fond of little boys."

F. was breast-fed for two months, at which time she was suddenly put on the bottle because the mother "had no milk." After a few days the baby developed serious diarrhea and vomiting; she was therefore admitted to a children's hospital in Rome where she stayed for one month. Far from improving, the vomiting increased. For this reason the mother on her own responsibility took the baby away from the hospital and brought her to our Clinic for admission. Here, she was found to be very much underweight (4 Kg.; birth weight 3.9 Kg.). The medical history reported continuous loss of weight since weaning. From our observations in the hospital we decided that the vomiting was actually part of a complete pattern of rumination. Although the vomiting took place shortly after each feeding, most of the milk was reswallowed. This would explain the moderate and inconsistent loss of weight. Several days after admission one of the young nurses was observed to take a special interest in the child. Thereupon, the head of the mental hygiene clinic made an effort to give the nurse some guidance in her role of mother substitute. The behavior of the child slowly began to change to some social participation. She was discharged at the age of fourteen months and a half weighing 8.4 Kg., having shown no signs of rumination for nearly three months. At this time she did not walk or talk. After discharge, regular follow-up studies were made. She started to walk at eighteen months and to speak a few words at about twenty months. At the age of three years and six months her weight was 13 Kg., her height 90 cm. Developmentally she was within normal limits. No rumination was reported.

At age five years, a diagnosis of tracheobronchial adenopathy was made. Because the mother refused hospitalization, the child was treated at home and she improved and continued to gain weight.

(3) *Ugo P., aged 8 months, 14 days.* The father seemed to be pleased at the arrival of the baby and tried very hard to persuade the mother to accept him. He had given the mother a gold bracelet to discourage her from attempting abortion.

The mother displayed contempt for the father and made him responsible for all the evils in her life. She was particularly resentful at his not having used any means of birth control. She definitely had not wanted the baby. However, her own fears of physical damage in addition to the father's strong desire to have the child prevented deliberate abortion.

All through her pregnancy she had nausea and vomiting. In particular, she could not tolerate perfumes, and even gave up using talcum powder on the other children after their bath.

Apparently, she had never had much milk. Nevertheless, the baby was breast-fed for two months with only one breast, the other being withheld because of cracks. She weaned the baby in fifteen days, partly at the insistence of the father who thought that the milk was insufficient and that the baby was suffering from hunger. The child "after feeding was hungry, and because of his hunger, nervous." He was put on a formula of cow's milk; in the interval between feedings a pacifier was given. At two and a half months he started to have vomiting and diarrhea with fever. The mother said the cow's milk was spoiled, and that four other mothers had had their children sick with diarrhea at the same time.

It was at this time that the baby was first brought to the hospital. He weighed 6 Kg. Rumination was observed, always in connection, as the mother had maintained, with thumb sucking. He was discharged after a month and a half. Apparently the doctor felt he would do better at home. The mother thought that rumination was due to the baby's thirst "because the nurses did not provide water for him." She felt it had been a great mistake to have brought the child to that hospital. After that, "he always had difficulties in swallowing," "he always had a lump in his throat," "he never could swallow like the other children."

At home, his vomiting continued with no change. He kept losing weight, and his general physical condition deteriorated. In July, when he was three and a half months old, with great financial sacrifice, he was brought to the Roman Castles for the "fine air"; nevertheless "the baby did not make any progress." At four and a half months he was again brought to the hospital, where the mother "gave her own blood." She mentioned significantly that "father's blood was miraculously good for the child." After two months, again the doctors in the hospital recommended taking the baby home and feeding him anything he wanted. He was then kept at home for almost two months, but severe rumination continued with progressive loss of weight. Finally the mother brought him to the hospital for the third time, this time to our Clinic (age eight months, fourteen days). He stayed there until he was twelve and a half months old. While there he continued to ruminate in spite of many procedures adopted to prevent or reduce it (tying the jaw, arm restraints, thick feedings, sedatives, etc.). He seemed avid, yet he continued to lose weight. He began head-banging. His average D.Q. (Gesell) in that period was relatively low (88%).

After some time in the hospital he found in a ward nurse a mother substitute who established with him a very selective, positive relationship. Interestingly enough, the nurse was obviously embarrassed about her intimate rapport with this skinny rejected baby. At twelve and a half months the child, who had not ruminated for a month and was gaining weight, was sent home. There he started to eat his meals with his parents. The mother said that rumination had stopped "because of the grown-up food." Regular follow-up examination showed normal growth thereafter. At the age of six years and three months, he was a stubby, rather aggressive child, who had very happily attended kindergarten for one year. His I.Q. was 92 (Terman Merrill).

(4) *Angelo C., aged 3 months, 15 days.* The father was an unskilled worker, and the family was living in a suburb in extreme poverty. There was already one child in the family when Angelo and his twin were born. "We didn't want any more children. One was enough. It was terrible when we saw there was not one more, but two." The mother's milk was insufficient, and even during the first month the breast was supplemented by the bottle. After the first month he was put exclusively on the bottle. At three and a half months, because of diarrhea and vomiting, he was admitted to the hospital (the Pediatric Clinic) seriously ill with toxicosis.

Because of severe dehydration he was given intravenous infusions and no food by mouth. The vomiting disappeared. After five days the vomiting reappeared with the peculiar characteristics of rumination. After eight days the ruminant pattern was well established, occurring after every feeding. It was never observed, however, if the baby was held in someone's arms following feeding. This situation saw no change for months, and there was no real gain in weight. During that period the mother had repeated interviews with social workers in which attempts were made to clarify for her the main difficulties preventing a better acceptance of her child. After four months in the hospital the mother decided to take the baby home. No attempt was made to discourage this decision as it was felt that some progress had been made in her relationship with the child, as evidenced by her desire to take him home.

At home he was put in a crib in the kitchen where the mother worked. Every time she saw him put his finger in his mouth and attempt rumination, she would stop working, pick him up and "distract him." At times, when she could not stop working, she would just shout at him, and he would stop. On follow-up examination the parents eagerly said that he was their best loved child; however, he slept by himself while the other twin slept in the parents' bed. Furthermore, the parents were constantly extolling the precocity of the other twin.

At age one year the D.Q. (Gesell) of the healthy twin was 101% compared to 90% for the ruminator. The last time he was seen, at age eighteen months, rumination had stopped completely. The child continued, however, to be seriously underweight, a poor eater and prone to intestinal disorders.

(5) *Mario E., aged 10 months.* The father was a clerk at the city hall and was described as a rather passive and dependent person. The mother came from one of the Greek Islands (Rhodes) which had belonged to Italy until the last war. She was rather authoritarian, describing herself as "nervous and impatient." In her own family, she said, it was the mother who was head of the house. She did not want a new baby now that her youngest child (the second) was seven years old. Incapable of accepting his growing up and maturing, however, she was still spoon-feeding him. Bitter at the pregnancy, she had made various attempts at abortion without success. Finally her own guilt feelings made her give up the attempts. The baby was breast-fed for six months. After weaning, his contacts with his mother became scattered and rare since "there were six people at home to be cared for and there was no time." He spent long hours alone in his crib. When he was eight months old, the mother noticed for the first time that when the child was alone in his crib, he produced noises in his mouth as if he were "gargling." This was more likely to happen after a fluid meal. In addition to the noises, she noticed that he was bringing up the ingested food and losing part of it out of the corners of his mouth; this happened at almost every meal. The whole process would start with rotating movements of the tongue, which was pushed against the hard palate. The rumination would start soon after a meal and continue almost until the next meal. The food was often brought up only after a long period (two–three hours) of the preparatory movements, sometimes still liquid, sometimes coagulated. The baby neither gained nor lost weight, although he was continuously avid.

In our Clinic the mother was allowed to stay at the child's bedside and could hold him in her arms whenever she decided to. Rumination symptoms disappeared completely after six days. However, fifteen days after admission he got streptococcus tonsillitis with high fever. The mother was particularly tense and worried, and rumination started again. One month following admission, the baby having recovered both from the tonsillitis and rumination was sent home.

At home, rumination reappeared occasionally during the first few months, but vanished completely after the child reached fourteen months. After that the gain in weight, which had been spectacular in the Clinic, was constant. He started to walk and talk at fifteen months. He is lefthanded. At two and a half, he was overweight (15.7 Kg.) and oversized (height, 89 cm.). His D.Q. (Gesell) was 101%. His relationship with his mother appeared to be a close, tender and dependent one.

(6) *Adriano B., aged 4 months.* The father held a job as radio announcer, working only two hours a day. He just managed to support his family. Although a graduate of a university (Arts and Letters), he could not find a better job because of his collaboration with the fascists after the September 1943 armistice. At first, he welcomed the baby as evidence of his virility, but soon he was annoyed by the child.

The mother, who had been a bookkeeper, was later relegated to a job as typist. She suffered a great deal from this and from other signs of her inadequacy, but she would not discuss her sorrow with anyone. The sexual act also caused her shame, and when she learned she was pregnant, she felt the baby would purify her of this shame. Yet, she knew beforehand that she would not be able to nurse the baby. "The child used to cry and vomit my milk all the time." She said that her own mother knew much better than she how to raise the baby. "The baby would laugh more at grandmother and play games with her."

The baby was breast-fed for only a few days. He always cried between feedings. According to the mother, he started to swell "because of her bad milk," and his breath was sour. He began to vomit one or two hours after feeding: "It would make me all dirty." Because of the continuous vomiting the baby was brought to the hospital.

In the hospital, rotating movements of the tongue were noted, followed by the typical movements of rumination. Loss of weight was continuous. Finally, a wet nurse was brought in since the baby was seen to suck avidly at the breast although he had been weaned within the first week of his life. He improved somewhat with the new kind of feeding and started to gain weight; he left the hospital. Toilet training came late (four years); kindergarten, also at four years, was not a success. The mother said that he "had" to leave kindergarten for a tonsillectomy and that anyway he hadn't liked it. Rumination continued until he was four, particularly at night.

When he was three, a baby brother made his advent. With this brother, A. was always aggressive and competitive. The mother described him as "nervous and egocentric." On the last follow-up (age five and a half) he appeared to be a tall boy for his age, in good physical condition, rather unstable in his interests and his games. His I.Q. was normal (97). He did not play with other children, was tense and nervous, and produced hostile reactions in his parents. His mother said: "He does not enjoy my tenderness like the other one."

Observations

All the mothers in our cases had particularly immature and inadequate personalities. Faced with maternity they tried to deny their involvement, insisting that the baby had come by accident and against their will, and accusing their husbands of having forced them to it. Some showed their unwillingness by developing somatic symptoms (CASE #2) or by acting-out behavior.

All of them bore their pregnancies with great difficulty, three of them (#2, #3, #5) suffering extremely, #5 having hypertension during pregnancy. In almost every case the pregnancy was accompanied by profound anxiety and fear of death. Their evident rejection of their babies had obviously the same roots in anxiety and fear.

Delivery was with forceps in two cases (#2 and #5), difficult in two others. Only one mother succeeded in breast-feeding her baby for six months, although as a painful duty. This mother had breast-fed her first child for 18 months. Like the other mothers she had a definitely rejecting attitude. She picked the child up only for feeding, claiming she had no time for him in between since there were "six people at home to take care of." This baby, therefore, never had enough care, warmth and affection from the mother; he scarcely gained weight, was insufficiently fed and was continuously left alone in his crib between feedings. When at six months the mother suddenly stopped feeding him, the baby remained alone in his crib for entire days.

Five out of six of the ruminants were the last ones born in series of two or more children. One was a first boy (#6). His mother, however, was deeply disturbed by her own inability to fulfill an adult role in life. In the relationship to her child, whom she accepted theoretically as a purification of her own dirty sexuality, the inadequacy became even more apparent, with a return of her dependence on her own mother. She said that she knew in advance that she could not nurse her baby. Having tried for a few days, she saw immediately that her milk ". . . was making him swollen and sour smelling . . . his liver would get all swollen."

Of the other mothers, one breast-fed her baby for two and a half months, the others for two months or less and one for a few days. When these babies had nutritional disorders with diarrhea and vomiting, the mother's attitude was usually one of annoyance and irritation. The mothers reacted to their guilt feelings by aggressive behavior with the nurses and doctors who were taking care of their babies, accusing them of bad will, insincerity, and incompetence.

In conclusion, the most outstanding features of their personalities seemed to be their immaturity, their disturbed object relationships, their profound anxiety, their death fears, their ambivalence toward their babies and, in general, their marked inadequacy when faced with the demands of their feminine role.

Unfortunately, studies in rumination are very rare, and there are not many cases in the literature to compare these with. Our findings, however, seem on the whole to confirm what Richmond observed of the personalities of ruminators' mothers on the basis of his four cases.[13]

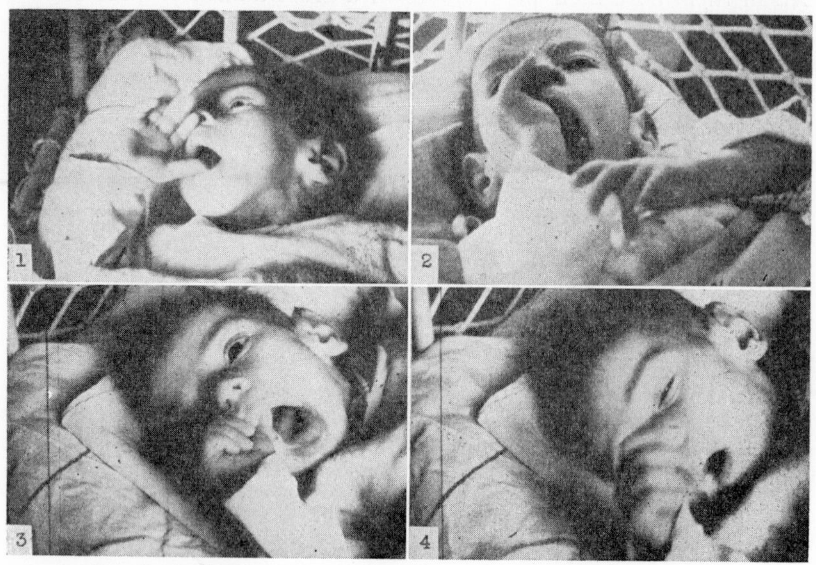

FIG. 1 (1–4). Stages in the process of Rumination. Case #3.

The onset of rumination was within, but not before, the third month of life in three of our cases which is somewhat earlier than in Richmond's series where the earliest onset was three and a half months, and earlier than the date given by Cameron[4] as the earliest possible time of onset, i.e., four months. This does not necessarily invalidate Richmond's opinion that visual recognition of the love object is prerequisite to the onset of rumination. Our fourth and sixth patients, for instance, who were suddenly withdrawn from the breast at one month and at a few days respectively, did not start rumination before the third month. This seems also to be in agreement with the following statement made by Prugh: "By the third month (or at times earlier) most infants have progressed in neuromuscular maturation to the point at which they are able to coordinate successfully tongue and hard palate movements in such a way as to carry a bolus of strained food to the pharynx and swallow it (retrusive reflex.)" [12] We will come back to this point in the discussion.

Rumination in our cases never started suddenly. It was always the result of a gradual process, at the end of which the infant had acquired his peculiar skill more or less efficiently. In our cases, it was almost always (except case #5) preceded by a prolonged period of vomiting. It has never been observed during sleep.

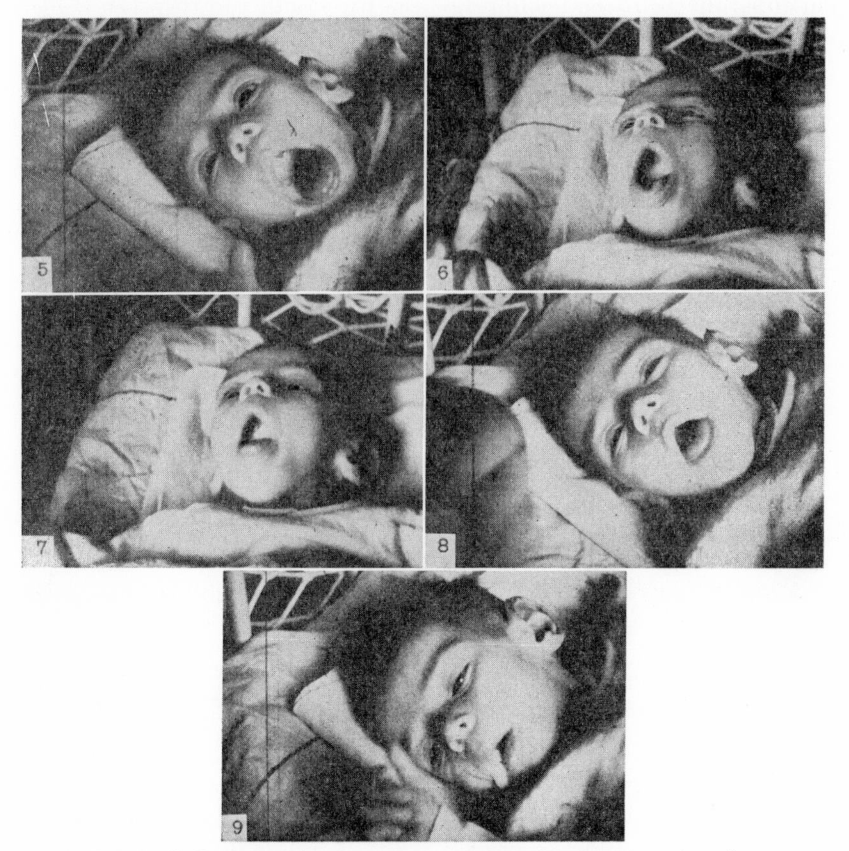

Fig. 1 (5–9). Stages in the process of Rumination (continued).

Of our six cases, five were males and one female. From the few published cases we have the impression that males are more often affected than females. Further observations would be needed to verify this point.

It would be interesting also to have more observations of these infants when actually engaged in rumination. We have been able to observe that the act of carrying the thumb to the mouth is not always followed by rumination. It seemed to us that, as the episodes of rumination became less frequent, the thumb was more and more simply sucked as it would be by any baby in his first year of life. In other words, rumination seemed to occur in relationship to a particular tension whose immediate motivation was not easily understandable. It might develop immediately after a meal or a few hours later. When it did begin, however, the baby's tension was evident. He might, for example, while sucking his thumb, stop all of a sudden, grasp the sheet, try to carry it to his mouth and then begin again to suck his thumb with feverish, anxious movements.

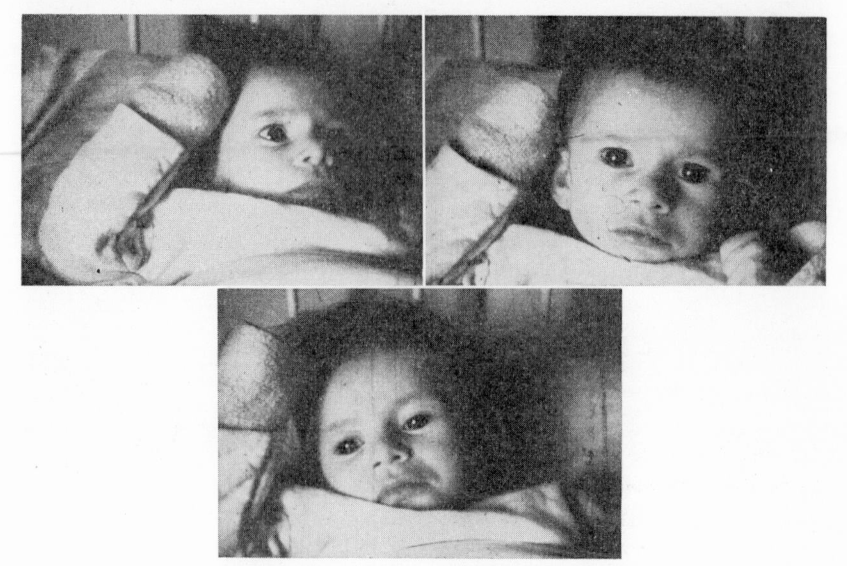

FIG. 2. See text, below.

Case #2, the little girl, did not suck her thumb in the first of the two phases described above. A few minutes after almost every meal, she began to make light sucking movements with her lips. These movements became gradually more intense, with her mouth partly opened; the tongue, in the previously described chanelled shape, was pushed rhythmically forward. At the same time, she would convulsively grab the bib or blanket. As soon as she reached the climax of the ruminating act and her mouth was full of milk, the grabbing movements ceased; there was a rapid diminution in tensions and her arms and hands relaxed.

Even apart from the ruminating activity, this little girl did not suck her thumb but often repeated the light lip-sucking movements, without, however, necessarily carrying this through to rumination. Interestingly enough, when the condition was progressively improving and the baby was participating more actively in the events around her, she began to carry objects to her mouth, including her own fingers. In her case, as in all the others, attempts to interrupt the first phase of rumination or to prevent it aroused angry reactions followed by restlessness full of anxiety (FIG. 2).

In general, the behavior of the babies did not lead us to think that they should be considered as completely deprived children.* Apart from the fact in all our cases the babies had been breast-fed for a certain period, even if it was only for a few days,† the impression we received was that ruminators are babies who have experienced serious frustrations, too severe to be tolerated in relation to their age, to their level of development and to their biological needs. In the very first period of life, every baby is inevitably subject to a certain amount of frustration, but normally there is a greater quantity of gratification which enables it to tolerate the frustration. In rumination, this ratio seems reversed. In our opinion, we are dealing with babies who had some gratifying experiences but not nearly enough to compensate for the frustration that they suffered as a result of a profound alteration in the symbiotic relationship with the mother figure. As a matter of fact, in eight years of constant search among children in foundling homes who have never had a consistent mother figure, it has been impossible for us to locate a single case of rumination.

We wonder whether it is because of the serious, although not permanent and complete, deprivation that these children appear somewhat retarded, a phenomenon which has struck the previous authors who have shown interest in the problem. The retardation, far from being a permanent impairment, tends to disappear when the child's relationship with the mother figure improves, as we were able to demonstrate with the follow-ups of our cases. We agree with what Richmond calls the "potential brightness" of these children, although we did not find in them the alertness, the prompt response to environmental stimulation, the "radar-like eyes" that he describes, except in those who were less seriously affected or who were in the procss of recovering.

Discussion

The meaning of rumination in children is still in the realm of speculation and we do not intend to minimize the difficulties involved in its elucidation. In general, it should be kept in mind that the reactions of an infant in his first year of life, apart from individual constitutional differences, cannot be considered independently of his mother's reactions.

* Compare, for example, some of the infants described by Spitz[14] in his study on hospitalism. Some of these foundlings had never had even a minimum of consistent mother-child relationship, whereas in our cases it was experienced, although not properly and not sufficiently.

† In the literature, cases are reported in children who had never been breast-fed (Cameron, Richmond, Lourie).

"This is most apparent," according to Greenacre, "in comparing the development of infants who have had very limited or inadequate maternal aid and protection . . . with those in whom there has been a more usual course of early mother-child relationship." [7] It follows from this that harmonious development implies a well-balanced ratio between indulgence and deprivation, in which indulgence should prevail greatly over deprivation.[8] According to our experience, in rumination this ratio is reversed.

We are aware, however, that this reversal is not sufficient in itself to account for the onset of such a syndrome and that constitutional factors must be admitted as important determinants of its peculiar conformation. Yet, other problems arise that we feel should be discussed.

It has to be remembered that, although it did not happen in case #5, in all the others the stage of rumination proper was preceded by two other stages, the first of which was characterized by a nutritional disorder with diarrhea and prolonged vomiting, the second by the fact that the vomiting was gradually being transformed into rumination.

The nutritional disorder started, in our cases, in a clear temporal connection with a sudden and early weaning. Among the four cases of Richmond's, the only one described in detail had apparently the same evolution: weaning was not from the breast, however, which the child never experienced, but from the bottle, at eight months. Richmond suspected that it was abrupt. Our case #5, who was the latest to be weaned (at six months) was also weaned abruptly, but from the breast. We suggest that our case, although weaned two months earlier than Richmond's case, experienced more indulgence. This child was certainly more indulged than the other children in our group. It is well known, however, that individual responses to weaning vary according to the mother-child relationship, which is the most important single factor determining them.[12]

We would have liked to have known more about Richmond's cases. From the data reported in one table, from the fact that the only case given in detail was described "as an illustration of the case material," and from the suggestion made in the paper that previous vomiting could play a role in symptom choice, we are led to believe that the other three cases also went through an initial period of organic disorder associated with vomiting and diarrhea. One further case, described by F. H. Clark, does not seem to differ from Richmond's cases (and from ours) except for the fact that the child was operated on for pyloric stenosis at an early age. At the age of five weeks, "mother reported baby vomiting breast milk"; then the baby was "placed on a cow's milk and dexin formula." A week later the baby was operated on. At nine months, vomiting started again, and one month later, while the baby was in the hospital, rumination was recognized. (Richmond also reported a case in which a prior diagnosis of pyloric stenosis was made, and another case in which a preliminary diagnosis of pylorospasm had been made). Unfortunately, Clark's case was never considered from the point of view of the child's development; no data were given about the mother-child relationship and none about the follow-up.

All this case material seems to indicate that rumination is a complex psychophysical defensive syndrome, the achievement of which implies a certain level of maturation although within a climate of marked deprivation. The fact that, in the great majority of cases, it is preceded in its development by vomiting, which in turn is a part of a physical disorder (gastroenteritis), suggests that the latter also should be considered as an expression of the same developmental troubles that later will bring the child to ruminate.

According to Greenacre, "Development of defensive measures of the human organism seems to proceed in an ontogenetic fashion from early direct or reflex reactions of a purely physical nature operating against the environment to the complex structure of psychophysical responses." [7] Ruminators seem to provide strong evidence to support Greenacre's views. In fact, if we consider the earliest time of onset of rumination (third month, according to our experience; third or fourth month in the average) and the latest time (ninth or tenth month, not usually later than the first year of life), then the evolution of the entire process, from the starting physical disorder (gastroenteritis) to the final establishment of ruminative activity, might well be located within the first and perhaps the beginning of the second period of the child's development as these periods are outlined by Greenacre; namely: "(i) *The period of predominantly physical responsiveness of the infant organism under the domination and protection of the mother*" and "(ii) *The period of dominance of the primary process.*" [7]

When established, however, ruminative activity appears at intervals which do not seem to have any regular relationship to the feeding schedule: it can take place immediately after feeding as well as two hours later, and variations are observed also in the same child. Our impression was that ruminative activity was always accompanied by visible mounting tension as evidenced by restlessness. The child would withdraw his interest from the environment and focus it upon the sensations deriving from his own body. More than the stimulus of hunger, the child seemed to suffer a tense "stimulus hunger" [6] that feeding not only could not satiate but seemed instead to promote or just exasperate. It was as if feeding, not corresponding to the satisfactory lost experience, brought about the same frustrating result that usually comes to the infant from hallucinatory experience.

That the greedy attitude shown by these children while fed is not only an expression of hunger seems to us demonstrated by the fact that the tension may last after feeding and then be relieved by ruminative activity. On the other hand, this demonstrates also that it is not a hunger stimulus which starts an episode of ruminative activity. In our opinion, these are continuously tense children whose only means of obtaining temporary relief from the tension is the bodily experience of rumination.

Far from being a syndrome connected with irreversible conditions, as it once was considered, rumination seems to be the result of an unsatisfactory developmental situation. Prognosis, consequently, should change considerably. Above all, the very serious mortality rate (from 25 to 50% according to different authors [11]) should be sharply reduced. Among our cases, one died. We feel that it should be pointed out here that it was the first of our cases of rumination (1950) and thus we had had little experience in handling this syndrome. The condition, in fact, should be considered a reversible one when properly handled. Therapy should include offering the child a temporary mother substitute capable of giving him all the indulgence he needs. If this is done, the condition will change in a short period, sometimes dramatically. The mother, obviously, should be treated at the same time, an attempt being made to reduce her own anxieties to the point where she can better accept her own child. Help should not end when the child is cured. We would recommend regular follow-ups because we found them very helpful for the mother in lessening for her the feeling of being too soon alone again with her baby.

Bibliography

1. Arensberg, B.: Loving care does the trick. Am. J. Nursing *56:* 622–623, 1956.

2. Benedek, T.: Toward the biology of the depressive constellation. J. Am. Psychoanalyt. A. *4:* 389–427, 1956.

3. Bradley, J. A., and Menon, G.: Regurgitation in infants. South. M. J., *49:* 1317–1320, 1956.

4. Cameron, H. C.: Some forms of habitual vomiting in infancy. Brit. M. J. *1:* 872, 1925.

5. Clark, F. H.: Rumination, a case report. Arch. Pediat. *73:* 12–19, 1956.

6. Fenichel, O.: The Psychoanalytic Theory of Neurosis. New York, Norton, 1945.

7. Greenacre, P. Toward an understanding of the physical nucleus of some defense reactions. Internat. J. Psycho-Analysis *39:* 69–76, 1958.

8. Hartmann, H., Kris, E., and Loewenstein, R. M.: Comments on the formation of psychic structure. Psychoanalyt. Study of the Child *2:* 11–38, 1946.

9. Kanner, L.: Child Psychiatry. Springfield, Charles C. Thomas, 1957.

10. Lourie, R. S.: Experience with Therapy of Psychosomatic Problems in Infants. *In* Hoch, P. H., and Zubin, J.: Psychopathology of Childhood. New York, Grune & Stratton, 1955.

11. Parmelee, A. H.: Diseases of the Esophagus and Stomach. *In* Brennemann's Practice of Pediatrics. Hagerstown, W. F. Prior Co., 1957.

12. Prugh, D. G.: Psychological and psychophysiological aspects of oral activities in childhood. Pediatric Clinics of North Am.: 1049–1072, 1956.

13. Richmond, J. B., and Eddy, E.: Rumination: A psychosomatic syndrome. Psychiatric Res. Rep. *8:* 1–11, 1957.

14. Spitz, R.: Hospitalism. An inquiry into the genesis of psychiatric conditions in early childhood. Psychoanalyt. Study of the Child *I:* 53–74, 1945.

7

Antisocial Young Children and Their Families

By EVEOLEEN N. REXFORD

Introduction

IT HAS BEEN observed for many years that a number of youthful offenders and adult criminals have a childhood history of antisocial behavior. In their ten-year survey of 500 delinquent adolescent boys, Sheldon and Eleanor Glueck [9] reported that over 50 per cent of these boys had demonstrated symptoms of severe behavior disorder by the age of eight and nearly 80 per cent by the age of eleven. John Bowlby writing of court cases of theft declared that exactly half of those found guilty have been under 21 years of age and over one-sixth of the total were under 14. "The evidence strongly suggests that in many, perhaps the majority of serious cases, the offenders developed delinquent habits well before puberty. It is in this period, therefore, that the origins of the trouble are to be sought." [5] Psychoanalysts such as Franz Alexander in their therapy of adult criminals have uncovered evidence of early severe emotional and conduct disturbances in these patients.[2]

Douglas A. Thom, interested for many years in juvenile delinquency and its relation to adult crime, came to the conclusion that the group of aggressive and destructive young boys in their early grade school years constitute an important pool from which many later serious delinquent individuals are recruited. He initiated, therefore, in 1947, a treatment research project * in early delinquency at the Thom Clinic (then the Habit Clinic for Child Guidance).

This report describes the various studies of antisocial young children and their families which have been carried on at the Thom Clinic during the past eleven years.

Psychiatrists by the nature of their training and professional experience are not comfortable with the global concepts of delinquency and

* Supported from Mental Health Act funds through Commonwealth of Massachusetts 1947–1952.

crime. They have been understandably reluctant to develop a typology of delinquency, preferring to study the antisocial individual as a human being whose acts must be understood in the context of his personality structure and life experiences. Although there have been brilliant exceptions, such August Aichhorn, Kate Friedlander and William Healy, psychoanalysts and psychiatrists have not concentrated the attention upon the field of antisocial behavior which they have accorded the areas of neurotic, psychotic and psychosomatic disorders. The emergence of systematic clinical studies by child psychiatrists since World War II is an important development in an area to which the earlier Healy-Bronner researches remain the most careful and significant contributions from child psychiatry.

Although the Thom Clinic studies concern a modest number of children, they represent a continuity of experience regarding an important group of children which it seems worthwhile to describe for the critical examination, stimulation, and assistance of other clinicians working with similar children and families.

Brief Survey of Pertinent Literature

William Healy's clinical studies of individual delinquents in the United States and August Aichhorn's application of psychoanalysis to the treatment of delinquent youth in Austria constitute for all students in this field the two principal sources of stimulation for the understanding and treatment of antisocial behavior in the child. They established the etiologic importance of severe disruptions in the early lives of these children such as: separation of children from the parents, loss of affection for or confidence in the parents, prolonged absence or death of parents, repeated changes in foster homes, and institutional life which provides no opportunity for the development of personal attachments.

Healy [11] emphasized the value of a careful diagnostic study of the child, his family, and his social milieu to achieve an understanding of the individual child's delinquent acts. Aichhorn [1] explained delinquency as "an interplay of psychic forces, which has created the distortion which we call dissocial behavior," and distinguished between the symptoms of delinquency and the fundamental problem underlying delinquency. Aichhorn concluded: "To find the causes of delinquency, we must not only seek the provocation which made the latent delinquency manifest but we must also determine what created the latent delinquency. It is the task of reeducation to weaken the latent tendency to delinquency. Later we shall learn that this is tantamount to altering the ego structuring of the child."

The publications of several other authors whose work has proved especially helpful to us are mentioned below without any attempt to present a complete survey of pertinent literature.

Kate Friedlander's long experience with antisocial children in child guidance and psychoanalytic work led her to a psychodynamic formulation of the antisocial character.[7] She describes the various crucial steps in the development of the child's social adaptation, highlighting the key roles of his early relationship to his mother, the nature of his oedipal conflicts, the formation of the superego and the group formation in his family. She defines the antisocial character formation as follows: (this formation) "shows the structure of the mind where instinctive urges remain unmodified and therefore appear in great strength, where the ego, still under the dominance of the pleasure-principle and not supported by an independent superego, is too weak to gain control over the onrush of demands arising in the id. This character formation is at the basis of the condition which Aichhorn calls the state of 'latent delinquency' and it will depend upon the various factors exerting their influence in the latency period and in the puberty whether delinquent behavior becomes 'manifest' or not."

John Bowlby[4] in his extensive work has stressed the role of physical separation from the mother during the first three years of life as a crucial factor in the causation of the antisocial character. His study of 44 juvenile thieves[5] published in 1944 represents an important attempt to classify the characters of the young children. Here, he first described the affectionless characters as "essentially delinquent characters who form the hard core of the problem of recidivism while the depressed, circular, hyperthymic and schizoid characters all had counterparts among the controls." With very few exceptions, the children classified as "affectionless characters" had suffered the complete emotional loss of their mother or foster mother during infancy and early childhood. In his researches, Bowlby looked also for more subtly damaging aspects of the mother-child relationship and he emphasized as well the frequent history of severe emotional traumata such as death and illness in the family during the first decade of the child's life.

Since 1942, Adelaide Johnson, S. Szurek and their colleagues[13] have published a series of papers in which they conclude: (1) the causes of the child's delinquent behavior can be deduced by a study of family inter-relationships as with any other type of emotional disturbances; (2) parental neurotic difficulties are expressed in the child's delinquent behavior; and (3) the child frequently "acts out" the parent or parents' unconscious antisocial wishes and is aided and abetted in his activities by them.

The Judge Baker Guidance Center in recent years has published various papers regarding delinquency and the pre-delinquent character. Irving

Kaufman [14] describes three factors found repeatedly in pre-delinquent children: (1) the specific trauma of losing a parent figure; (2) fixations at pregenital levels of psychosexual development; and (3) specific types of ego and superego disturbances. He points out that the loss of the parent may result from an actual physical separation or from a lack of or withdrawal of affection for the child, and postulates that this traumatic loss of the parent is responsible for an unresolved depression which he believes is the core of the delinquent's pathology and which the delinquent attempts to handle by his acting out. Kaufman's material shows graphically how the early and repeated deprivations in the child's life interfere with his developing adequate ego defenses to control his anxiety and to direct his aggressive and libidinal energies into socially acceptable behavior patterns. The Judge Baker studies emphasize also that the superego disturbances include a faulty ego ideal, often based on a delinquent model in the child's background which reinforces his difficulties in developing an adequate conscience.

Fritz Redl [16] in his work first in Detroit and presently at the National Institute of Mental Health, has concentrated upon understanding the ego functioning of the aggressive, destructive boys under his observation. In this work, Redl has courageously chosen children whose aggression seems to flow uninhibited in a more primitive, more total type of hatred and destruction than in children whose hatred and aggression are more neurosis-bound or more ego-controlled. His detailed descriptions of the personalities of these children with a careful dissection of their ego and superego functioning opened up possibilities for clinical understanding and realistic planning for this group and raised fascinating questions regarding the behavior of less primitive antisocial children. His *Children Who Hate* documented brilliantly the need for a new design, a strategy of different dimensions to deal with the children who present incredible problems of management to educators, therapists and penologists.

The literature on antisocial children describes in general prepubertal and adolescent individuals. Although a few children of early grade school age are included in the clinical material given and the generalizations regarding the antisocial character may well apply to the younger child, the clinical focus has centered upon the older child.

The Study of Fifty-Seven Antisocial Young Children

The initial research project which Douglas Thom set up in 1947 was a treatment study carried out by one experienced child psychiatrist, Kurt Rose,[19, 20] and four successive psychiatric social workers.* The project

* Beatrice Stone, Marjorie Hyde, Rose Bernstein, and Margaret Shriver.

involved 57 children, 55 boys and 2 girls, from the ages of six to ten years who were referred to a child psychiatric clinic for aggressive destructive antisocial behavior of at least two years' duration, behavior which had not proved amenable to the usual methods of control in the home, neighborhood, and schools. Because of their youth, none of these children had as yet been brought into court; the majority of the parents, yielding to considerable community pressure, referred their children because they were already serious antisocial problems at an early age. It is important to emphasize that their acts were not the occasional minor outbreaks common to the majority of children in their struggle for socialization and control. When Mrs. Sheldon Glueck and we applied the Glueck Social Prediction Scales to the group of 57, 47 of the 57 children rated within the "high probability of later delinquency" scores.

These children were not a group of feebleminded or dull individuals. All were of at least average endowment and twenty demonstrated superior intelligence on psychological testing. However, only 12 of the entire group were doing well in school and 22 were barely passing their grade. Eight children suffered from serious physical disability, one had a history of brain injury, and another had had progressively more abnormal electroencephalographic tracings.

The unstable home environment emphasized by so many workers in the field was conspicuous in this group of children. Twenty of the 57 did not live in the traditional family unit with both parents; 14 had a history of significant separations from the mother at an early age. It was striking that a study of these families showed that only nine could be considered a cohesive family group and only 31 showed some elements of integrated family living in the terms described by Sheldon and Eleanor Glueck.[9] The contrast with the families of our total clinic case load in 1953 was dramatic: there, 134 out of 221 families were described as cohesive family units, 70 with some elements of integration and only 16 as unintegrated.

The fathers' reported emotional difficulties included persistent delinquency since early childhood, severe alcoholism, and frank psychosis in one instance. The twenty least disturbed fathers were markedly passive, taking little responsibility of any kind for the home, while within this group, eleven had assumed in a conspicuous way the maternal role in the care of their sons. Although four of the mothers were psychotic and two severely alcoholic, it was our impression that, on the whole, the mothers were the more adequate and responsible parents. However, casework with them was difficult and frequently ineffective. Only 30 of the mothers came regularly for varying periods, another 14 came for brief periods, while the remainder maintained an episodic contact at times of family crisis. The contact with the fathers was even less satisfactory: 28 of the 57 were never seen in the clinic, 25 came for one or two visits, and only four were willing to visit for more frequent interviews.

The clinical diagnoses of the 57 children varied from that of psychoneurosis with antisocial trends to psychosis with aggressive and destructive behavior; the majority resembled most closely those children described by Friedlander as "antisocial character disorder."

Follow-Up Study of the Fifty-Seven Children

In 1954, we had an opportunity to investigate the status of this group of 57 children.* Rose was still seeing regularly two of the long-term treatment cases; the period of time since the termination of clinic contact with the rest of the group ranged from six to two years. All of the children were then in prepuberty or early adolescence. This study,[17] carried out by van Amerongen, Schleifer, the author and two caseworkers, Helen Friedman and Diana Waldfogel, is divided into two parts: namely, an evaluation of the status of the children at the time Rose terminated treatment with them and an appraisal of the follow-up data obtained by the two caseworkers during the period from April to July, 1954.

Of the group of 57, nine children had been seen for diagnostic study only and we could not obtain information about three of these. Forty-eight children comprised the treatment group: of these, three had been treated with weekly psychotherapy for five years or more, two from three to four years, three from two to three years, 16 from one to two years and 23 under one year. Only one mother of the treatment group refused an interview to the caseworker and she asked for a postponement rather than refusing outright. The records of the Social Service Exchange, other social agencies and schools were consulted to supplement the reports of the parents.

Reviewing Rose's and the social workers' records, we placed the treated children in one of three categories at the time of end of treatment: much improved, improved or unimproved. We took into account in these characterizations not only the occurrence or cessation of antisocial acts but also the quality of the child's object relations, the nature of his ego defenses and of his superego functioning as we could infer them from the recorded interviews. Four were placed in the much improved group, 29 in the improved category, and 15 in the unimproved category.

* Partially supported by funds made available by Department of Mental Health, Commonwealth of Massachusetts.

The data obtained by the caseworkers in 1954 were analyzed and charted in six categories: evidence of any recurrence of delinquent behavior, progress in school, relationship with peers, recreational and work interests, health, and present structure of the family.

A review of the data corroborated our initial hypothesis and clinical findings, namely, that the pattern of persistent aggressive destructive antisocial behavior in young children from 6 to 12 years is symptomatic of a severe character disturbance. Of the children treated psychiatrically, the pattern of delinquent acting-out had been curbed in at least 32 out of the 48 cases. However, the great majority of these children (at this time in prepuberty and early adolescence) were still deficient in their social relationships, performed below their intellectual capacity in school, and showed little interest in constructive work or recreational activities. Several boys suffered from somatic symptoms for which no organic cause could be found.

Of the group of 15 considered unimproved at the time of termination of clinic contact, six were not continuing delinquent behavior so far as could be determined at the time of the follow-up study. On the other hand, one girl belonging to the improved group, and one boy in the much improved group, relapsed into serious delinquency at the onset of puberty. The number of families of the children treated at the clinic who showed considerable improvement socially and economically at the time of the follow-up studies was larger than we would have expected from our evaluation at the time of termination of clinic contact.

Therapeutic Techniques

Our experiences at the Thom Clinic with the psychotherapy of antisocial young children (now numbering approximately 175, including Kurt Rose's original group) permit us to draw certain conclusions about therapeutic methods with these children. Our therapy with early delinquents is based upon the understanding that these children suffer from maturational defects of varying degrees of severity; the extent of modification of the techniques used with neurotic children depends upon our diagnostic appraisal of the level of the child's ego and superego functioning. It should be emphasized that the approach and techniques used are those of child psychotherapy and not of child analysis.

Those children who suffered a primary emotional and physical deprivation during infancy are the most traumatized and most difficult to treat because of their very limited capacity for object relations and their tenuous reality grasp. Their acting out expresses forbidden impulses which they cannot or will not control because of poorly developed ego defenses and a lack of inner discipline. They show a marked intolerance for anxiety and for frustration, and their aggressive outbursts often express their perception of anyone who denies or thwarts them as an enemy. They cannot tolerate delay of satisfactions for reality reasons and demand immediate gratification of their wishes. Their life experiences and intimate relationships have yielded them no confidence that their needs will be met and they expect and provoke deprivation and hostility at every turn. Denial, projection and withdrawal are their principal mechanisms of defense which are replaced only very slowly in treatment by more mature defenses. They are isolated individuals, rejecting and rejected repeatedly by everyone with whom they come in contact. While they come regularly to the clinic from the beginning, their distrust of the therapist is profound and their testing of him prolonged and ingenious. Their narcissism finds expression in many of their delinquent acts which have an obvious exhibitionistic and omnipotent coloring. These children suffer from very disturbed relationships with their parents. In some instances, the obvious vicarious satisfaction the parent gains from his child's delinquent acts encourages the lack of control and contributes to the feeble motivation for discipline. Conscious and/or unconscious severe rejection by the mother and a close tie to a sadistic father appear to foster strong sadomasochistic fantasies to which the child reacts in terms of kill or be killed. The child may be dominated by his fantasies with an intensity which seems almost delusional in character and his behavior may be viewed as an obvious attempt to protect himself from danger. Many of the homes from which these children come are characterized by a lack of ethical standards and a flagrant defiance of authority in any form. The developmental history of these children mirrors the depriving emotional and physical milieu; at each stage of psychosexual development, disturbances are reported: in feeding, in toilet training, in socializing, and in learning.

Another group of early delinquents represents a paler and less serious edition of the first because they suffered emotional and/or reality deprivation at a later stage in their development. The birth of a sibling with withdrawal of affection by an immature mother incapable of loving more than one child at a time, departure of father from the home because of imprisonment, a commitment, death or desertion, serious illness with a long hospitalization are events that for a number of children appear to interfere drastically with their previously relatively normal development. They have a greater capacity for a trusting relationship with an adult, their defenses are less infantile and their conflicts more on the neurotic level.

In a third group, the delinquent behavior appears to be the direct expression of a specific neurotic conflict, or of a strong identification with a particular emotional disturbance in a parent. A few of our children belong to a fourth group in that their aggressive and antisocial behavior represents a relatively transient stage of development readily worked out in psychotherapy.

The basis for therapy in each instance is the establishing of a trusting, confident relationship with an adult who is aware of the needs of the child. The task of therapy involves (1) the promotion of object relations, (2) the strengthening of useful ego defenses, (3) the encouragement of suitable identifications, and (4) the modification of superego functioning.

It is obviously the first group which presents the most difficult technical problems for psychotherapists. The task of building a working relationship with a child whose way of relating to others is predominantly hostile and whose image of the interchange between human beings is so colored both by his unrewarding life experiences and his sadomasochistic fantasies has frequently proved insoluble in the child guidance clinic or casework agency. For this reason, a brief description of crucial elements in the early stage of the therapy may be helpful to other clinicians.

In the initial phases of psychiatric treatment, which may last from one to two years, the therapist must be prepared to tolerate overt physical and verbal hostile outbursts which may be extreme and persistent and may recur again later at times of rising anxiety. He must be patient and permissive without being masochistic and indulgent; at the same time, he needs to be able to set definite limits, to avoid both injuries to others and undue property destruction, without being punitive to the child. The child needs to learn that the therapist can protect himself and the child from the latter's aggressive destructive outbursts, which are so very frightening to the patient. We believe that failures in therapy with delinquents often occur precisely because the permissiveness adequate for treatment of the neurotic child does not provide the stimulus to inner control vital for the delinquent. The therapist must make clear from the beginning that he does not approve of, or side with the child's unacceptable behavior, although he is not punitive nor moralistic in his attitude. The child will test him out in every conceivable manner, looking for weaknesses in the therapist's standards, trying to prove that he, too, steals, cheats, or lies when it is to his advantage. The child will impose on the therapist's patience and sympathy, certain that the affection and tolerance will fail if the adult is tried sufficiently. The therapist must be scrupulously honest with him, consistent in attitude, and mindful of reality as well as of the child's inner needs.

The combination of emotional acceptance and presentation of definite behavior standards enables the therapist to contribute to the child's inner control while making some restitution for the emotional deprivation the child has suffered. During this relation-building phase, which may last many months, the child is strengthened by learning about his problems and other people's difficulties. His misconceptions are clarified, his isolation relieved, and sublimations are encouraged. Therapy is a new emotional experience and an orientation toward reality and away from destructive fantasy life. As the acting out diminishes, more mature patterns of behavior develop and neurotic conflicts and fantasies emerge which become the focus of the therapy. The more mature the child is emotionally, the more predominant the neurotic elements in his delinquency; as the very infantile child matures in therapy, neurotic difficulties play a larger part in his problems.

There are other significant differences in the techniques required during the relation-building phase, for instance, the importance of gifts from the therapist of actual food, drink, and small articles. These children's instinctual cravings are very strong and it is extremely difficult for them to understand and appreciate the symbolic gifts of the therapeutic situation, to a far greater extent than is true of the neurotic child. In several instances, Kurt Rose gave a regular allowance to boys who stole persistently and to others he gave the guns, knives, or jewelry which the children had been stealing persistently from stores. In each instance, the gifts were indicated by the therapeutic situation and were used purposefully both to make restitution to the deprived child and to remove him from the reality dangers of actual thefts. It must be faced that the boys may regard such gifts as seductions or bribes, and precise clarification of the reasons for the gifts has been helpful in dealing with this complication.

Impulsive aggressive children are usually overactive and react to the suggestion of restraint with anxiety, restlessness and destructive outbursts. They may find it impossible during the relation-building phase to remain in the playroom so that regular trips are a necessary part of the therapy pattern. The therapist must obviously develop the technique of utilizing the locale and the experiences of the trip for clarification of the boy's problems and anxieties. As Rose [19] observed, "Where we followed them out on the street, we did not simply exchange the restrictive and threatening clinic setting for the freer atmosphere of the open air; we were not just buying ice cream at the drugstore; we were always on the track of the unconscious forces which were responsible for the selection of the locale or of the activities and even of the specific choice of food. We followed them into church, where Frank lit candles for his deceased criminal father; we accompanied Billy into the department store where he unconsciously repeated his first public theft, committed three years earlier, by taking a gun; we watched Walter's contorted facial expression when we walked toward a collection of pocket knives at Sears Roebuck. Inner forces had driven this boy to steal fifteen knives previously. We noticed John's greedy intent to steal candy from the corner drugstore."

John first told Rose of his frightening homosexual experiences after he had seen a reproduction of Blake's "Adam and Eve"—Eve with the snake's head in her mouth—at the Museum of Fine Arts. At the Museum also, Tony began to tell his therapist of his fears of death when he returned repeatedly to the exhibit of Egyptian mummies.

It is evident that "relationship therapy" alone is not adequate to deal with these suspicious, anxious and acting out children. Their way of relating to others is predominantly hostile, and their ego defenses against their wishes and fears are of such a primitive nature that clarification and interpretation of their feelings and anxieties must accompany each step in the therapeutic process. Such interpretations are more effective if couched in as direct and primitive a verbal form as these children experience their thoughts and fears.

The impressions gained from other Thom Clinic therapists working with similar children corroborates the findings in Rose's progress notes regarding his forty-eight children that weekly psychoanalytic psychotherapy carried over several years' duration can lead to significant changes in the child's behavior and psychopathology. The child develops a more trusting attitude toward adults through his confidence in his therapist and identifies in varying degrees with the latter's behavior and standards. His image of the outer world as a totally hostile and dangerous milieu gives way to a more realistic appraisal of the intent and behavior of others and his own need for hostile action is greatly diminished. Insatiable oral cravings and fears of total annihilation or abandonment become greatly modified and he gains some perception of the role his own destructive wishes and behavior play in what happens to him. His longings for warm affectionate relationships come to his awareness and he can reach out cautiously to adults other than his therapist for support and understanding.

In all of the boys who progressed markedly in treatment, a consistent finding has been the modification of the predominantly hostile image of the mother, with the appearance of a more oedipal type of attachment to her. Repeatedly, the boy's strong identification with a criminal, psychotic or highly inadequate father has proved a strong barrier to further working out of the boy's oedipal conflicts. When the father was dead or permanently absent from the home, the therapist was apt to be more successful in promoting the boy's identification with a different kind of father figure which made it possible for the child to progress further in resolving his oedipal conflicts.

The development of more mature ego defenses such as reaction formations, repression and sublimations leads to a curbing of the antisocial behavior, but the status of the treated children in the original treatment group on follow-up points to the defects in character structure which remained: the predominantly narcissistic orientation, the paucity of solid object relations, the few skills and achievements possible for most of the boys, and the generally restricted nature of their personalities.

The curbing of the antisocial pattern is an achievement in itself but if we are to aim for a more mature and self-reliant personality in the treated child, our Thom Clinic experiences raise important questions. Would it be possible to achieve further changes in character structure by the continuation of therapy for longer periods? Would therapeutic sessions two or three times weekly bring the desired results? Or do we have to conclude that the ambitious redistribution and transformation of instinctual forces we seek can take place only in psychoanalysis? The possibilities of a residential total treatment program are very attractive but the experiences of the Redl group [10, 16] both in Detroit and at Bethesda illustrate both the technical difficulties and the great expense of such a program. As our attention has turned more persistently to the emotional milieu in which these children are brought up, another question emerges, namely, if it is possible to find a way to work with the parents to modify the emotional climate of the home, would this support enable the child to move toward a more optimal level of adaptation?

Glueck Scales Study

The Glueck studies had so clearly defined the crucial role of the family relationships in the causation of delinquency that their Social Prediction Scales [9] were constructed from five factors in the social background of the boy: (1) discipline of boy by father, (2) supervision of boy by mother, (3) affection of father for boy, (4) affection of mother for boy, (5) cohesiveness of family. At the suggestion of Eleanor Glueck, we had applied these Scales with her assistance to the 57 antisocial young children to study the correlation between our clinical diagnoses and the Scale results.

From 1954 to 1956, Virginia Clower studied the application of the Glueck Social Prediction Tables to our general clinic caseload. The Scaling applied to the 57 of the original research group had correlated well with our clinical impressions, that is, those children whom we considered to be suffering from an antisocial character disorder received high scores while those whose personality disorder fell more into the category of neurotic difficulties received lower scores. We found that the children among the 57 whom we finally diagnosed as psychotic (four in number) also received a very high score, a finding analogous to that of the Hawthorne-Cedar Knoll School study.[3] In each instance, our psychotic children had been referred for long-continued aggressive destructive behavior rather than the psychotic symptomatology of withdrawal, preoccupation with fantasy and general inactivity.

The second step in our study of the Social Prediction Scales involved their application to consecutive application interviews regarding 100 boys, from 6 to 12 years of age, referred to the Thom Clinic in 1953 and 1954 for a wide variety of behavioral and emotional difficulties.

Chart I

Age	5–6	7	8–11	*Total Number*
Antisocial character	11	8	12	31
Neurosis	16	10	32	58
Other	8	2	1	11

The following is a chart which shows the Glueck scores, the number of cases in each group and the clinical diagnostic impressions.

Chart II

		Clinical Impression		
Glueck Score	*Number of Cases*	*Antisocial*	*Neurotic*	*Other*
Under 150 (2.9 chances)*	0	0	0	0
150–199 (15.7% ")†	6	0	5	1
200–249 (37.0% ")	25	0	22	3
250–299 (63.5% ")	28	8	18	2
300–349 (86.0% ")	18	7	10	1
350–399 (90.0% ")	16	11	2	3
400 and up (98.0% ")	7	5	1	1
Totals	100	31	58	11

As shown by Chart II, all of the boys diagnosed clinically as antisocial character disorder scored 250 or higher on the Glueck Scales whereas about half, 53 per cent, of those diagnosed neurotic fell into score groups of 250 or higher. The striking agreement between clinical impression and Glueck Scale rating in the lowest and highest groups is apparent at once.

* 2.9 chances in 100 of later delinquency.

† 15.7 chances in 100 of later delinquency, etc.

Clower observed in her report of this study, "The 250 to 299 group with a 63.5 per cent chance of becoming delinquent is a peculiarly complex problem in correlation. This may be called the mid-way group as far as clinical findings go. The 18 cases in the 63.5 per cent group called neurotic include the numbers which were the most difficult of any in the study to evaluate clinically. Many of these boys show some indication of over-activity, strong tendency toward aggressive and destructive behavior but also other symptoms more characteristically neurotic and not usually associated with antisocial character formation. The scoring sheets compiled for these children contained many questions, multiple notations and diagnostic comments which are a good indication of the difficulty in arriving at any clear-cut impression as to diagnosis."

The third stage of Clower's study during 1956 dealt with 40 of the above mentioned 100 children. These 40 had been accepted for further study and treatment in the clinic so that case material from treatment records of three months or longer was available. Clower read each one of the 40 treatment records and rescored and rediagnosed each one on the basis of the additional information from the treatment experience. She discovered that there were 11 cases in which some change was made, either in diagnosis or in scoring; nine of these changes concerned the "middle group" with scores of 63.5 per cent and mixed clinical pictures. Clower commented in her conclusions, "What emerges also from a further study of the middle group is that neither the scores nor the clinical studies place the child definitely in the category of antisocial character or neurotic character at the time we are seeing these families."

Glover [8] has commented upon the whole range of the Glueck Prediction tests: "Taken separately, none of these factors is a specific indicator of future delinquency: yet it is clear that, for example, the character set, when quantitatively scored, would tend to distinguish delinquents from all save psychotic reactions . . . so that fundamentally, the Glueck system, although apparently and essentially descriptive, can in the long run be correlated with etiological formulae. From the psychoanalytic point of view, however, its main deficiency is a negative one, i.e., that it indicates neither the main clinical group in which a prospective delinquent will ultimately fall, nor the specific etiological factor determining each end-product."

From our experience, we would agree with the Glover critique. However, precisely because the need for etiologic formulae and consequent management leads is so great in both clinical and corrective circles, we believe it important to follow up the Glueck Studies with clinical investigations. To define more precisely the role of each of the gross factors the Scales describe and, perhaps even more significant, the interrelationships among them may well increase their value as predictive devices. In our modest exploration of the use of the Social Prediction Scales, we have discovered another value, that is, their stimulation to further research in our field by encouraging us to study more systematically what goes on within the families of antisocial young children.

Psychotherapy with a Group of Four Mothers

Our growing interest in the emotional milieu within which the antisocial young child is brought up led us to undertake a psychotherapeutic study of four mothers who seemed representative of one group bringing their antisocial young children to a clinic.[18] Our experiences with subsequent families bear out the relevance of our formulations for one group of clinic families.

"The life histories as well as the behavior of this group of young children referred for persistent, impulsive acting out show striking similarities. Many of them have had serious feeding problems and all are characterized by the parents as hyperactive from the earliest age. The mothers describe them as lively in utero, hyperactive in early infancy, and particularly from the age of two, uncontrollable. At the time of referral to the clinic, they have reached the age of five or older and the presenting symptoms may be fire-setting, running away, stealing, or inability to get along with siblings and peers. The basic complaint of the parents, however, is repeatedly the same: the children are unmanageable and their mothers particularly feel completely at a loss with them.

"These women in referral interviews draw a picture of the child which suggests to the listener that they have a very dangerous individual living in the house, one whose demands are insatiable, whose strength is unlimited, and who transgresses all the boundaries of acceptable behavior so as to get what he wants, when he wants it.

"The children in the clinic do present a characteristic picture, but the therapists' interpretation of their behavior differs widely from that of their mothers. The children look much younger than their age, cling to their mothers' skirts, appear afraid to let the mother out of their sight and often cannot tolerate being separated from her. Once they can let the mother go, they relate to the therapist like a one and a half or two year old child, with extreme bids for attention alternating with markedly ambivalent provocation. They want to be chased and caught, to play hide-and-seek, to be tucked away into chests, closets and large dollhouses, eventually to be rescued by the therapist. They may suddenly withdraw into a corner, absorbed in compulsive play activities, completely ignoring the presence of their doctor, and as quickly return to an outburst of ruthless destruction. If the therapist attempts to limit their activity or fails to meet immediately their imperious demands, the children break out into a frenzy of defiant and dangerously aggressive behavior. They jump off tables and chairs, attempt to climb out of windows, break toys, and furniture, open faucets, brandish saws, totally oblivious of the dangers to themselves and others. If restrained bodily, they may abruptly cuddle up in the therapist's lap like a baby and quiet down as suddenly and totally as they had burst into action.

"At no time do they verbalize their feelings of disappointment, frustration, or anger. They do, take or leave. In the face of the slightest frustration, they seem helpless, as though with little ego strength upon which to draw. The anxiety aroused by interference with their gratification appears all-consuming and the resulting tension has to be relieved at once by aggressive activity.

"In their interviews, these women are constantly preoccupied with fears of what the children might do to them, if they did give, and equally concerned with what destructive effects limits and controls might have on the youngsters. In therapy, the discussion of the problems with her offspring rapidly leads to the mother's own anxiety about the loss of vital supplies, and her problems, past and present, with her mother. The giving or withholding of material things—food, money, clothing—becomes the focus of attention."

Processes of Interactions in Families with an Antisocial Child

When van Amerongen, Schleifer and the author in 1955 reviewed the Thom work up to that point along with the publications of other clinicians, we concluded that a more basic understanding of the specific factors leading to a persistent pattern of antisocial acting out in the young child was greatly needed. We were aware from many sources of the number of programs being organized throughout the country to combat the dismaying upward trend in juvenile delinquency. The author had attended two nationwide multidiscipline conferences in 1954 [6] and 1955,[22] one on the control of delinquency and the other on research in the field. The most striking conclusion to her of these conferences was the lack of basic knowledge about delinquency. There were obviously gross gaps in our understanding of its genesis and perpetuation and we knew little of the effectiveness [23] of the many projects, some operating for a number of years under highly respected auspices, in combatting delinquency. A number of the questions our clinical work had raised in our minds were obviously of central importance to the issues of prevention and management of youthful antisocial behavior.

When, therefore, the National Institute of Mental Health offered us the opportunity to continue our studies in a systematic manner, we decided to investigate the parental attitudes toward instinctual gratification and controls in the on-going relationship with the antisocial young child. To meet our own as well as the Institute's interests, we wished to use a methodology which would permit us to analyze clinical data in both a qualitative and quantitative manner.

There were many indications in our clinical material that the parents of antisocial children we had seen, brought up the child with particular attitudes toward instinctual gratification and control which seemed to interfere with the child's ability to develop necessary ego functions. As we saw the children in the treatment situation, their capacity to obtain satisfactions by means other than action, as, for example, fantasy formation or sublimation, was invariably limited. Their defenses against anxiety consisted principally of denial and projection which broke down rapidly under stress, leaving only highly eroticized play activity or aggressive-destructive action as their mode of response. Their attempts at control led invariably to their withdrawal.

What little we knew of the lives of the parents themselves suggested that their own attitudes toward authority, discipline, help for themselves and others had an important bearing upon the way they raised their child. We were impressed by the difficulties of working with them, from the point of their reluctance to consult a clinic until repeatedly prodded by others, to the ineffectiveness of our traditional methods in changing their attitudes or ways of dealing with their child when they did come for interviews. We speculated whether the specific demands of the psychotherapeutic approach, namely, that they assume responsibility, that they think and try to understand and to change themselves was for them an intolerable and devalued proceeding.

We were encouraged by colleagues who were deeply interested in our clinical material to develop a treatment project but the methodologic problems of analyzing satisfactorily such a mass of interview material led us to return to our original plan of carrying out a diagnostic study of each family to obtain the raw data for our research. We had developed for our regular clinic cases a diagnostic procedure which gave us a clinically relevant understanding of the functioning of a family. In our diagnostic appraisals, we assumed that the child's reactions to the psychiatrist would give us information about his expectations and use of the adult (parent figure) and his capacity to adapt his behavior to a therapeutic parent figure who allowed for a certain amount of gratification while insisting upon a degree of control. Similarly, we had postulated that the parents' attitudes toward the clinic personnel to whom they had come for help with their child's problems would tell us something about their expectations of a parent figure and reveal to us the use they could make of a consistent therapeutic figure willing to give help but putting certain demands upon them for this purpose. We planned to use senior staff, at least for the preliminary stages of our research, to take advantage of their skills and self-awareness in dealing with a group of families almost notoriously refractory to the usual psychotherapeutic and casework approach and well-known for their provocativeness in the interview situation.

Exploratory Study in On-Going Processes of Family Interactions

In May, 1956, van Amerongen and Schleifer undertook a pilot study to develop and test research instruments for the investigation of families with an antisocial young child.* This eighteen months' exploratory phase yielded a methodology which clearly differentiated the families with an antisocial young child from families with a child suffering from a different type of disorder in relation to parental attitudes toward the particular child for whom they sought help. The methodology included the use of scaling methods which produced quantifiable scores consistent with the clinical impressions and scoring patterns which supplemented and complemented the clinical understanding of the families.†

We investigated these families by the use of two hypotheses: the first, that parents of children who display persistently aggressive destructive antisocial behavior differ in their attitudes and responses toward gratification and frustration of instinctual drives from parents of children suffering from inhibition and overcontrol of activities; and, secondly, that the children who display persistently aggressive destructive antisocial behavior differ in their attitudes and responses toward gratification and frustration of instinctual drives from inhibited children.

For the purpose of testing our research instruments, we chose two groups of families whose children manifested antithetical ways of handling instinctual impulses, that is, one with an aggressive destructive antisocial young child, the other with a child suffering from inhibition and overcon-

* Supported by funds made available by Special Grants Division of National Institute for Mental Health (Grant No. 3M-9094).

† Psychiatrists interviewing children were Virginia Clower and Donald Ottenstein; Consultants included Morris Adler, Philip Dodge, William Hire, Katherine Spencer, and the author.

trol. The two groups of families were drawn from the regular clinic referrals and had had no previous psychiatric or casework treatment. The research group was made up of families with a child from five to twelve years of age whose antisocial behavior had persisted over a period of at least two years' duration and had proved intractable to ordinary disciplinary methods. The comparison group was one in which two parents had come for help with a child between the ages of five and twelve years who did not and who never had displayed the antisocial behavior pattern and whose siblings had not presented such a pattern. The children's difficulties were characterized by inhibition and overcontrolled behavior, such as compulsive states, marked passivity or hysterical learning blocks. In each group of families, both parents were the own parents of the child, married and living in the home, with no other adult members in the family unit; white, native born, and at least of average intelligence. The children possessed at least average intelligence and were free of serious physical abnormalities.

We matched the two groups insofar as possible in regard to age and sex of the child and to the socioeconomic background of the families. All of them came from lower- or mid-middle class groups and were, in each instance, self-supporting.

It is clear from these criteria for the research cases that we were dealing with families who differed in important respects from most of the initial research group of fifty-seven. When families with delinquent children present such gross social and emotional factors as broken homes, psychotic and/or criminal parents, illegitimacy and repeated placement of the child, the role of more subtle factors in the genesis and perpetuation of the antisocial pattern (such as the effect of persistent parental attitudes upon the upbringing of the child) become obscured by the overwhelming effects of grossly traumatic external and internal events in the child's early life. We, therefore, deliberately chose families with a relatively intact family life, demonstrating elements of cohesiveness which Sheldon and Eleanor Glueck [9] had found so significant in discriminating between families with a delinquent child and those with non-delinquent children. As we might have expected, we found it difficult to obtain research cases which met all of our criteria, although a number of antisocial children from the familiar disorganized background were referred during the period in which we were setting up our pilot study. By studying the ongoing processes of interaction among family members and of family members with the clinic staff, we hoped to learn as much as possible about the parents' attitudes in the present toward instinctual gratification and frustration of their child, while their reports of their child's development and their ways of handling his various maturational problems would give us information about his upbringing in the past in these regards.

We chose a group of families with a neurotic non-delinquent child to assist us in testing the validity of our research tools and to provide insights into comparatively unique or similar attitudes and modes of behavior the two family groups might display. Impulsive, aggressive, destructive, and egocentric behavior is after all normal and expectable to some degree in all young children. The processes and the tempo of the development of controls through maturing ego and superego structures in each child is a highly individual and complex matter. The parents provide the basic controlling and socializing forces impinging upon the child's primitive instinctual life. Their conscious and unconscious attitudes toward instinctual gratification and control must be of great importance in encouraging the processes of socialization in their offspring or in militating against the development of sound controls. We expect all parents to show some difficulties in the area, but we postulated that the parents with a child who habitually resorts to acting out as a mode of relating to the world would show discernible reactions in this area qualitatively and quantitatively different from those of parents with a neurotic child.

A brief description of one research case and one of the neurotic group follows:

Mr. and Mrs. A. and their son, K., aged 7:

Mrs. A. called the clinic because her son K. had set fire to their apartment while playing with matches. The home was almost totally burned out, with a loss of $5,000, and the family had moved to new quarters. K. had persistently played with matches since he was two or three years old, and had repeatedly stolen small objects from department stores since an early age. Neither Mr. nor Mrs. A. had ever considered seeking help for K. despite the persistence and severity of his antisocial behavior. Mrs. A. indicated that it was her husband's threat that he would chastise K. severely which motivated her to consult a clinic.

Mr. and Mrs. P. and their son, A., aged 10:

Mrs. P. called the clinic for help for her son A. He had always done poorly in school despite at least average intelligence. He had been kept back in the second grade, and was now getting very low marks in the fourth grade. In addition, he was shy, day-dreamed a great deal, and had few friends and seemed to his mother depressed and apathetic.

The main sources of raw data consisted of joint psychiatric interviews with both parents, individual psychiatric interviews with each parent, psychological tests of each parent, psychiatric interviews and psychological tests with the child, waiting room observations and home visits. The interviews with the parents were fully tape-recorded. The psychiatrist who saw the child wrote up a running account immediately after the session, with particular attention paid to the child's interaction with the therapist, the latter's emotional response to the child, and the child's communications about himself and others. The play space was divided into a number of areas to facilitate observations of the child's activities and his manner of proceeding from one activity to another; the same play materials were available for all interviews and were arranged similarly in the room at the beginning of each interview. A psychologist observer behind a one-way vision screen recorded his observations of the activities of therapist and child and noted the time spent by the child in any one area of the play space. The statements and behavior of parents and children during the testing sessions were noted by the psychologist and his description was written up following the session. The social worker recorded his home visit experiences the morning after the early evening visit and later in the day recounted to a colleague the events of the visit to facilitate recall of interactions among family members or with him which he had not recorded.

The adaptation of our usual clinic procedures to the research aims was an important part of the development of an adequate research methodology to study the phenomena in which we were interested. Items in this process of standardization included: (1) alerting of the intake workers to the aims and criteria of the research project, (2) their referral of possible suitable cases to the principal investigators, (3) the telephone call by the Chief Social Worker to the parents with the presentation of the opportunity for a more thorough and prompt study as part of our "special study interest," (4) a meeting with the Chief Social Worker to plan a home visit with the parents and to introduce them to the psychiatrist for the (5) joint application interview, (6) in which plans were made for future steps, such as for the psychological testing of parents and child, (7) the planning of specific areas of investigation for the psychiatric sessions with the child, (8) the observation of the interview with the child by a psychologist observer, (9) the division of playroom activity into specific areas for observation and recording, (10) the subsequent diagnostic conference of all the professional persons who participated in the diagnostic study, (11) the family conference at the end of the study, (12) and the later detailed conferences regarding the data collected with the chief investigators and other participants. These successive steps in the process of diagnostic study achieved a necessary degree of standardization without interfering with the collection of valid psychiatric, psychological, and social data.

When we examined the data collected by different persons using varying professional techniques, we found in the material from the different sources unifying and complementary elements which enabled us to obtain a picture of the family functioning as a unit in relation to the clinic experience. The observations from one area often led to fruitful conjectures about material collected in another area. The consistency of the patterns of behavior observed in relation to any one family by the different workers, each using his own techniques, was reassuring evidence of the usefulness of the research methods, while the specific contributions of each technique for collecting data to the total study enriched our understanding of the whole family and its interactions with the clinic staff. Most important in view of the purpose of this exploratory study was our demonstration that the research instruments discriminated clearly between the two groups of families.

The differences between the two groups of families have been striking and clinically relevant. The findings have corroborated and extended clinical impressions from previous clinical work with such families. We have noted that the data from the individual families are located upon a continuum in which certain families present the most extreme characteristics of the antisocial or neurotic group, while others present predominant modes of interaction which lie closer to the dominant patterns of behavior of the other group.

The interviews with the parents of the antisocial children have centered upon a description of the child's actions. In the joint interviews, the parents have been predominantly preoccupied with whether and how to control his actions. The mothers indicated their preference for drastic bodily reprisals, about which they showed minimal guilt and anxiety. The fathers have almost unanimously belittled the severity of the child's acts and interpreted the antisocial behavior as proof of a desirable masculine self-assertion not to be curbed.

The attitudes of the parents toward each other during the interviews reflect a strong nonverbal alliance; they have been more uncomfortable when seen separately than when seen in the joint interview. The attitude of both parents toward the interviewer suggests a strong wish to control the psychiatrist as they demand that she offer magic devices that will stop the child's actions. When the interviewer indicates her interest in the causes for the child's behavior, the parents skillfully evade or actively oppose her efforts. When pressure is put upon them, they resort predominantly to defenses of projection, denial, and withdrawal. The parents in this group have given minimal information about their feelings toward each other, the child, their own parents or others. They give the impression that they have a paucity of emotionally meaningful relationships. The feelings they do express are either neutral, guarded, or of a hostile nature.

We have observed certain characteristics of the antisocial children in their individual sessions with the child psychiatrist. They have shown no spontaneous interest in the psychiatrist while initially conforming to his wishes in a passive, subdued way. They have waited for his cue to initiate any activity in the playroom and have neither shown nor verbalized their interest in any of the play materials. When given permission and encouragement to use the play materials, they have turned away from the doctor and excluded him from their activities. They have used the play materials in a very unproductive fashion, showing most frequently random and destructive play activity. They display a good deal of motor activity, wandering or flitting from one toy to another.

They do not volunteer verbal information and give it meagerly when questioned. They do not actively enlist the psychiatrist's help, at best will passively accept when it is spontaneously offered, but most of the time shift their interest to a different toy, thus rebuffing his attempts to be helpful. They show few signs of disappointment or anger but will become hyperactive, increasingly anxious and excited when their superficial control gives way. They show little or no evidence of constructive activity and show no interest in using their energies for accomplishment.

Review of the joint interviews with parents of the neurotic children shows these parents have readily expressed their concern about the child's symptoms. They have been keenly interested in finding out why the child is inhibited and they put less emphasis on active techniques to change his behavior. The mothers have expressed a great concern about their occasional loss of control. They disapprove of their yelling and screaming and often cry when confessing corporal punishment of the child.

The fathers have blamed themselves for the lack of support given to their wives as well as their sons and indicated that they have a good deal of concern about the child's inability to assert himself successfully. In these joint interviews, the parents have interacted spontaneously with each other and the interviewer in verbal and nonverbal ways. In the individual interviews, they have been able to give considerable pertinent additional information about themselves and their child. Both parents try to enlist the interviewer's active participation; they ask for explanations and advice, try to get her to side with one partner or the other. They readily pour forth additional information when encouraged. Most of the time they are eager to volunteer, and one remark or question by the psychiatrist easily leads to release of more significant data. These parents give a great deal of information about their feelings toward each other, the child, their own parents and others. They have many meaningful relationships and are not reluctant to divulge positive as well as negative feelings.

The neurotic children even in the waiting room show a definite interest in the psychiatrist. While they may accept his suggestion to come with him eagerly or reluctantly, on the way to the playroom they speak of their feelings, ask questions about where they are going and what will happen. Upon arrival in the playroom, they will usually show an interest in a particular play area, comment on their likes and dislikes, often spontaneously and eagerly choose a specific toy. When given permission to play with whatever they like, several of these children have wanted to play a game with the doctor. Others have keenly observed his reactions to their choice of activity and continue to do so during the session.

They use the toys in a purposeful way, like to shoot at targets, draw and paint pictures, build with bricks or make creative use of clay. Verbal activity clearly outweighs motor activity. Their concentration span varies, but in general is much longer than that of the antisocial children. They usually start to talk spontaneously. When asked, they will indicate that they have an idea why they come to the clinic and will often be willing to discuss their side of the story. Help is frequently requested and if spontaneously offered, either accepted or frankly and verbally refused. They give evidence of easily recognizable emotional reactions in their facial expression and often verbalize their feelings of frustration and disappointment.

The psychological testing of the child and both parents elicited data which correlated well with those derived from the interviews. There was a striking difference between the two groups of families in the kind and pattern of communication within the family about the common testing experience. The parents of the antisocial children never indicated that each knew that the partner would or had been tested nor displayed any interest in what the marital partner had experienced. The parents of the neurotic children, on the other hand, made clear in many ways that they had discussed the sessions with each other, sharing responsibility and attempting to help one another deal with this new experience.

The style of storytelling with the Murray Thematic Apperception Test cards provided promising leads in differentiating between the two groups. Both groups had difficulty in accepting the material realistically. The parents of the antisocial group manifested this problem by a persistent denial of any meaning in the scenes. They remain bound to the pictures and find it extremely trying to tell a story which departs in any way from the immediate scene. Even so, their story response leave out crucial elements which they have obviously taken into account in telling the story, thus suggesting that, since the examiner already knows the whole story, it would be unnecessary or perhaps self-incriminating to tell too much. The parents of the neurotic children quite often identify the pictures as scenes directly out of their own lives and find it difficult to believe the pictures have not been selected to make it easier for them to relate real life events troubling them in the present.

There were also quite striking differences between the two groups of families in the way each group dealt with the instructions for the tests. The parents of the antisocial children handle the rules so that they make it difficult for the examiner to be helpful to them. They put their questions regarding the test material in such a way that the tester must either disagree, which makes them angry, or accept their distortion of the instructions. They pose rhetorical questions such as: This is right, isn't it? They apparently repeat the rules as they wish to state them and then behave as though these were the instructions given, trying thereby to ally the examiner with their denials. They change an element in the picture and then tell the story as though their version of the scene were the stimulus card. One father observed that the picture was obviously incorrect, that the time was day rather than night, and then told his story accordingly. The parents of the neurotic children plainly had difficulty in accepting the instructions, but they appealed directly for help in clarifying the rules.

A sentence completion test was devised dealing with situations involving limit-setting activities on the part of a parent. The sentences were presented in two ways: first, how the parent would deal with the situation and, second, how the parent of another child might. The parents of the antisocial child are world- or adult-oriented in their responses. They see the issue as one in which the child must conform or else he is flaunting adult wishes. The parents of the neurotic children are more child-oriented in their responses, constantly questioning the parental role and indicating their difficulties in setting limits for a child. The parents of the antisocial children expect little if any differences between their own responses and those of other parents, while the second group could see alternate choices different parents might make. The choice of method was obviously a matter of concern to the latter parents. The parents of the antisocial children mentioned fewer disciplinary or management techniques for a child and those described were used rigidly, irrespective of the situation; the parents of the neurotic child mentioned a wider variety of techniques and these were more precisely attuned to the situation presented by the sentence.

Throughout the psychological testing, the parents of the antisocial children showed no evidence or awareness of anxiety, while the parents of the neurotic group, when anxious, indicated their feelings and asked for help and reassurance.

Similarly, the neurotic children were more overtly anxious; they reached out for help and tried to verbalize their feelings. The antisocial child was more guarded, suspicious and negativistic. He conformed to the demand made upon him, but in a minimal way, with evasiveness and little effort at mastery. The antisocial children used the instructions in such a way that they could not be supported. Like their parents, they changed the rules and then asked, "Isn't that right?" The neurotic child inquired if he could turn the cards, and he could be given permission to do so.

The clinical data from interviews, psychological testing and home visits were analyzed by a modification of the Leary Scales [15] for scoring interactions. These scales provide a framework for describing and quantifying an individual's interaction with one or more people, presenting four basic positions: positive, active and passive, and negative, active and passive. Within each of these categories, there are four subpositions, the total forming a circle of 16 points. The results of the scaling corroborated the clinical findings and brought into focus complementary elements of interaction which had not previously been noted by the interviewers.

The parents in the antisocial group were much more controlling in all situations and with all people (husbands, wives, children, and clinic personnel) than the parents in the comparison group. Their mode of control was predominantly negative and active, as they rejected or criticized the lead of others. These techniques they used almost exclusively. The parents of the neurotic children most frequently sought help from the clinic staff (positive and passive) and withdrew when put on their own responsibility.

With the clinic staff, the antisocial children directed the activity (positive active) and when they could not do so, they withdrew from the situation (negative passive). The mode of behavior was in contrast to that of the neurotic child who searched positively for help but could become openly critical when under stress (negative active).

At home, the antisocial children were markedly negative in interacting with both parents, actively with their mothers, and passively with their fathers. In contrast, the neurotic child was more often quite directly negative toward his father but generally passive with his mother, either searching for help positively or withdrawing if none was forthcoming.

Present Research Study

In January, 1958, van Amerongen and Schleifer began our present three year project,* using the methodology which had been developed during the exploratory phase. In the pilot study, our attention had first been concentrated particularly upon the content of the interviews and testing to understand the familial attitudes toward instinctual gratification and control and to seek out distinguishing differences between families in such patterns and attitudes. As we analyzed our clinical data and scaling results, we found early in the pilot study that we had tapped an important source for immediate observation in the attitudes of the parents and children toward the various clinic staff members.

The reality is that families who come to a child psychiatric clinic are motivated by a wish for help toward change in their child whose problems have occasioned them considerable frustration as they have been unable to alter the child's behavior or control him. The clinic offers them the possibility for a gratification of that wish but imposes in turn certain frustrations which are implicit in the kind of help obtainable from modern psychiatric treatment methods. We therefore have adopted the concept of "help toward change" as the basis of our on-going research.

Thus, the clinical orientation and experience of our research workers are incorporated into the research scheme. All staff members of a psychiatric clinic are professionally trained to assess the psychological status of their patients and to determine through diagnostic measures both the nature of the difficulties and the possibilities of change through our particular way of working. It is relevant not only to the stance of our research staff but to the expectancies of the parents that they have come to us rather than to a family doctor, minister or neighborhood friend and that they have come at some point of crisis in the child's affairs. Our data naturally reflect such factors and our understanding of the behavior of the parents in our setting is clearer because of our familiarity with such situations. In all of our data collecting, we pay particular attention to eliciting facts and observing behavior which tells us something about the way in which each family can or cannot use our kind of help. The nature of the Leary Scaling itself has provided a helpful check upon the particular characteristics of the interviewer, since it deals with modes of interaction, as well as content.

We have wished to maintain the criteria for selection of our research cases which we set up for the exploratory phase. However, thus far, since we began the present study, the families coming to the clinic with an anti-

* Supported by U. S. Public Health Service Grant No. M1795.

social child have varied somewhat from those studied during the pilot investigation. Either the child's pattern of dissocial behavior began at a later date and has persisted no more than a year when the parents sought help or the children have shown repeated episodes of serious impulsive aggressive destructive behavior over several years. They appear as a group to rest on a continuum between the more persistently antisocial children studied previously and the neurotic children, thus giving us an opportunity to isolate more precisely the factors in parental attitudes which may accompany antisocial behavior. The parents' emotional disturbances are less rigidly fixed and the elements making for a cohesive family unit are stronger. The fathers are less passive in relation to their sons and the mothers fall predominantly in the severely neurotic group, rather than that of serious character disorders. However, although subtle shifts in the interviewing and scaling toward the neurotic characteristics have been observed, the predominant modes of interaction and the attitudes toward instinctual gratification and control resemble those of the research group in the exploratory phase.

Discussion

This series of studies was initiated to investigate in various ways the personalities and behavior of children with a pattern of persistent antisocial behavior at an early age. Up until 1956, when the current formal research projects were begun, the work was carried on by busy clinicians with limited resources and time who were persuaded of the practical and theoretical importance of adding to our understanding of this group of children. A happy by-product of the formal research program has been the deep satisfaction derived from the opportunity and the obligation to study systematically and thoroughly phenomena which had engaged our interest for so long.

Although different facets of the problem were approached in each investigation, the line of continuity of thinking from the original treatment project which permitted us to describe children and evolve a means of treating them psychiatrically to the present preoccupation with familial attitudes as an avenue to understanding the emotional climate of the home in which the antisocial young child is brought up has remained unbroken. The earliest scientific contributors to the problem of delinquency saw the importance of the early home environment to the development of the pattern of dissocial behavior. We have been seeking to define by the use of child psychiatric techniques what the significant family influences are and how they are mediated in these young children. The whole group of aggressive destructive young children merit attention if only from the standpoint of the management problem they present to the home, school, neighbors and clinic. However, it is the antisocial young child as the precursor of the adolescent or adult delinquent who has engaged our attention during these years.

It is well known that a large number of antisocial young children from highly pathologic homes are referred in any urban community to psychiatric clinics and casework agencies. They have often been subjected since birth to an endless series of emotional traumata and the gross deficits in physical care, affection, and discipline they have experienced are elicited in even a cursory social history. It has been encouraging that we and others have found in some of these children sufficient capacity for emotional growth so that, with therapy, they have been able to give up the dissocial pattern and find more socially acceptable modes of behavior. However, a detailed study of their family milieu is often difficult to carry out, both because of the parents' unwillingness to cooperate with us and because of the extent of the social and emotional pathology within the family group. What we have learned about less disorganized families has helped us understand more clearly the ways in which the traumatic experiences and unwholesome influences interfere with socialization of the antisocial child brought up in the "typical home of a pre-delinquent." What is often forgotten is that all the children from such a home do not necessarily become delinquent; there are always unique circumstances and specific influences which lie behind this type of adaptation in the particular child.

Investigation of relatively intact families with an antisocial child has enabled us to focus upon more subtle factors in familial attitudes and interactions which go to make up the emotional climate of the home for the individual child. The comments about parents and families below pertain to the better organized group, in which the family is self-supporting, does not live with other relatives, and the child has lived his life with his own parents without significant separations from them. Yet, in each instance, the child by his early grade school years has developed a persistent pattern of antisocial behavior unamenable to the usual disciplinary methods. Here, the usual explanations for delinquent behavior, the broken home, the criminal and/or psychotic parent, frequent placements of the child, dependent economic status do not obtain and we are forced to turn to the subtleties of the emotional lives of child and parents for explanations.

We have reason to believe that if this early pattern remains unchecked, the child will continue into adolescence and perhaps adult life as a persistent delinquent. However, we know from various sources that many individuals with such an early history do not follow a life-long career of delinquency. Among the most interesting questions which we cannot answer as yet are: which ones of such children will so continue and which ones will be able to curb their antisocial behavior at some point? What are the inner changes which lead to the development of adequate controls and what outer influences may be brought to bear which facilitate this process?

In those children who have progressed well in the course of therapy, we can follow the process of emotional growth which leads to the curbing of the antisocial pattern. However, there were five children in Rose's unimproved group who were no longer involved in delinquent activity at the time of the follow-up study: what unperceived role the therapy or other factors unknown to us had played, we could not say. On the other hand, we were able to observe the reversal of the control of antisocial impulses under the impact of puberty in two of the children who had done well in psychiatric treatment. That such children may be particularly vulnerable to a recurrence under considerable emotional or physical stress seems a likely possibility.

The group of individuals who have given us the most frequent occasion for speculating about the spontaneous curbing of the delinquent pattern is that of fathers of antisocial young boys we have seen. Since 1952, all parents who refer a child to the clinic are interviewed jointly in the application interview so that we have had the opportunity to hear the father present his view of the boy's problem at that time. Almost invariably, the fathers couple their depreciation of the seriousness of their son's behavior with the report that they too indulged in precisely the same behavior as boys and they "have turned out okay." In some instances, further acquaintance with the family has unveiled the information that father continues serious delinquent behavior or pursues a course of marked chronic rebellion to authority, indicating that his initial report was somewhat overoptimistic. In the majority of the families studied, however, there was no evidence that the father had continued actual antisocial behavior into his adult life.

The overwhelmingly predominant character structure of fathers of antisocial young children we have seen over the past eleven years is that of a passive, restricted, and hostile man, strongly allied with his obstreperous son, firm in his belief that aggressive behavior of whatever kind or degree is evidence of desirable masculine self-assertion and is not to be curbed. We were repeatedly reminded of the personality patterns of such fathers when we reviewed the follow-up data of the group of 57 and saw the predominance of passive, restricted, relatively unproductive young adolescents among those who were no longer displaying antisocial acts. We can only speculate at this point whether the antisocial pattern is curbed in many instances at the cost of considerable personality restriction, leaving little psychic energy for the development of successful sublimations and achievements or of mature object relationships.

The effect of the father's personality in determining whether the son will continue a pattern of delinquent behavior is an extremely important area to which we hope to contribute as our researches progress. The crucial importance of a strong identification with a criminal father in the maintenance of antisocial behavior was demonstrated in several of Rose's treatment cases. A boy's identification with a father who is not overtly criminal but derives vicarious gratification from his son's delinquency may be a strong determinant for future antisocial behavior.

The most striking and consistent feature of the psychiatric material in the exploratory phase of our present research project was the attitude of the fathers in the antisocial group toward their sons. Several actually used the same phrases in expressing their opinion about their boy's behavior and, invariably, they belittled its seriousness, referring to their own similar activities in childhood. Whatever difficulties they see they explain as due to the mother's unwarranted interference with the son's masculine self-assertion. Both parents indicate that the fathers are markedly indulgent with the boys and take little responsibility for the management of the home or the discipline of the children. Some fathers are away from the home most of the child's waking life and "on Sunday are just too tired to pay much attention to the boy."

The initial impression of the father's faulty sexual identification was supported in subsequent observations in interviews and psychological tests of his confusion about his role as a father, as a husband, and as a man. In some instances, what is most striking is the father's strong narcissistic identification with his rebellious aggressive son who lives out the antisocial wishes the father can no longer express directly himself. The fathers intensely allied with their sons in continual warfare against the woman indicate their homosexual solution of their own oedipal conflicts. Other fathers demonstrate their feminine identifications in their intense rivalry with their wives for the mother's role, but they betray their misconceptions of the maternal function by concentrating upon indulgence and extreme partisanship of the boy. In each instance, the father's own father was largely absent from the home during his childhood or is perceived either as a very ineffectual or an extremely punitive father figure. Whatever differences there may be in the level of maturity or the type of defensive structure the father has attained, his confused sexual identifications are evident. The impact of this emotional reality upon his son is clearly an important determinant of the boy's subsequent development and behavior.

Whereas the majority of the fathers are remarkably passive and unconcerned about their sons' aggressive behavior, the mothers invariably demonstrate the abrasive effects upon their own adjustment of the boys' conduct. The mother's decompensation and regression from a previously more adequate level of functioning has been a common finding in the group of mothers we have seen. Diagnostically, the mothers may be classified in the hysterical group of neuroses, or the well-defined character disorders, or, in a few instances, their problems suggest a psychotic core. However, in each instance their previous defensive structure has been undermined by the impact of a sadomasochistic relationship with their sons so that they are driven back to an earlier line of defense against conflict and anxiety. They do not complain of anxiety but in both psychiatric interviews and psychological tests there is abundant evidence of intense conflict and of massive defensive operations against the resulting anxiety.

In the group of four mothers described by Rexford and van Amerongen,[18] the common problem of intense unsolved oral needs was prominent in women of widely varying personality types. In other instances, the antisocial child was clearly identified with a frightening, undesirable, or ambivalently loved person in the mother's past. Not infrequently, she saw him as the embodiment of male sexuality and aggression viewed in highly colored sadomasochistic terms, and, at times, as her projected perception of her own unacceptable but intense instinctual wishes.

Since our systematic studies of the interactions within the families are still in process, we can report upon these findings only in a preliminary fashion. The analysis of the data collected thus far indicates that the families with an antisocial child present a pattern of interactions among themselves and with the clinic staff which has been remarkably consistent and which has differed significantly from that of the comparison group of families. It appears that we have tapped an area with important implications for understanding the emotional climate of the home and for guiding us in seeking modified treatment approaches. The antisocial child's parents seem to be primarily concerned with the control and suppression of the boy's misbehavior to avoid the criticism of outsiders. They have not welcomed the opportunity to think about the child or to try to understand his feelings and behavior. They want to do something and demand from the clinic staff devices which will magically stop the criticized acts. Their tolerance for thinking and feeling is in marked contrast to that of other parents of similar social and educational background. Their mistrust of and uncommunicativeness with others appears to be echoed in their transactions with one another. They are obviously reluctant to accept help toward change from others and concomitantly find it exceedingly difficult to help their child except by demands that he stop his misbehavior when outside pressures build up that "something be done about the child."

The reactions during the psychological testing of the families with an antisocial child open up ways of investigating further both superego and reality testing functions. Their subversion of the directions and alteration of the TAT stimulus cards have been unique responses consistently displayed. The theme of gauging right and wrong in terms of "what you can get away with," "whether or not you are caught," "what people will say" emerges repeatedly in their test responses. The sentence completion test revealed the same tendencies observed in the interviews to deal with the child by control and suppression, to use only a few management measures rigidly and repetitively no matter how ill-suited or ineffective, and to assume that they after all know best what to do with a child, expecting no disagreement from others.

The Leary [15] scoring patterns have brought out the great preponderance of controlling mechanisms in the interactions of the parents of the antisocial children, with clinic staff, with the child and with one another. Their predominantly negative approach to others, controlling by rejecting, criticizing and opposing, suggests that the child at home may be constantly confronted with the choice of submission to parental demands or outright rebellion against them.

Subsequent treatment of the research families is not a formal part of our research obligations. However, wherever we find or can mobilize sufficient motivation for change and the parents wish to continue at the clinic, we have accepted the families into the regular clinic caseload. We are experimenting with various modifications of our usual therapeutic approaches based on what we have learned in the research investigation and we plan at a later date to assemble this treatment material for scrutiny and publication. All of the families with a neurotic child thus far have wished therapy and have been absorbed in the regular clinic treatment program.

The pattern of persistent antisocial behavior in the early grade school years is primarily a conduct disorder of boys. Although the average proportion of boys to girls referred to a clinic during the grade school years is five to three, relatively few girls are seen because of antisocial behavior. Antisocial behavior in girls appears characteristically in adolescence with the various manifestations of sexual delinquency. Two girls were members of the initial treatment project, one for a diagnostic study and the other for therapy, and one girl thus far has been studied in the research population investigated since May 1956.

Summary

This report summarizes the various studies of antisocial young children and their families carried out over the past eleven years at the Thom Clinic, a child psychiatric clinic in Boston. These investigations have included a psychiatric treatment project, a follow-up study of the original research group, validation studies of the Glueck Social Prediction Scales, a psychotherapeutic study of four mothers, and, finally, formal research projects dealing with the processes of interactions in the families of antisocial young children.

The group of young children, the majority of whom are boys, who present in their early grade school years a persistent pattern of aggressive destructive behavior offer a valuable opportunity for an investigation of the origins and development of the antisocial pattern of behavior. Many adolescent and adult delinquents have a history of such an early conduct disorder. Other individuals with a similar early history do not embark upon a career of crime as they become older. We very much need further information about such pertinent factors as the reasons for the failure of adequate socialization of the young child by the time he enters school, the elements both intrapsychic and interpersonal which militate against his acquiring more effective controls as his entry into the larger community brings him into increasing strife with peers and elders, the forces which may be brought to bear which help him curb the dissocial behavior and those which may promote a recurrence of antisocial acts. These areas may be investigated by the study of young children creating already such problems to the community that their parents are pressed to bring them to an agency for help to change the child's behavior.

Our studies have led us from the area of psychodynamic descriptions of the child's personality structure and appropriate treatment techniques for him to a consideration of the parent-child relationships in these families and finally to a study of the processes of interaction whereby these families deal with one another and with outsiders. It is our goal to acquire sufficient understanding of these processes to enable us to devise more effective therapeutic techniques than are now employed in clinics and casework agencies. We hope simultaneously to make a contribution to the general scientific knowledge of the nature and development of antisocial individuals which may be of value to persons in other professional fields who need a more basic understanding of antisocial behavior to carry out their appointed tasks.

We are aware of the many limitations and of the modest extent of our activities in this area. However, so far as we know, no other clinical group has carried out and reported a series of studies pursued over a number of years with such children.

Bibliography

1. Aichhorn, A.: Wayward Youth. New York, Viking Press, 1938.

2. Alexander, F., and Healy, W.: Roots of Crime. New York, Alfred A. Knopf, 1935.

3. Axelrod and Gluk: Application of the Glueck Social Prediction Table to 100 Jewish Delinquent Boys. Jewish Social Quart. *30:* 1953.

4. Bowlby, J.: Maternal care and mental health. Bull. World Health Organ. *3:* 355–533, 1951.

5. ———: Forty-four juvenile thieves: Their characters and home-life. Internat. J. Psycho-Analysis *25:* 19–53, 107–128, 1944.

6. United States Children's Bureau: Special Juvenile Delinquency Project, Conference, June 28–30, 1954. Washington, D. C.

7. Friedlander, K.: The Psycho-Analytic Approach to Juvenile Delinquency. London, George Routledge & Kegan Paul, Ltd., 1947.

8. Glover, E.: Psycho-Analysis and criminology: A political survey. Internat. J. Psycho-Analysis *37:* 311–317, 1956.

9. Glueck, S., and Glueck, E. T.: Unraveling Juvenile Delinquency. New York, Commonwealth Fund, 1950.

10. Goodrich, D. W., and Boomer, D. S.: Some concepts about therapeutic interventions with hyperaggressive children: Part I. Social Casework *39:* 207–213, 1958.

11. Healy, W.: The Individual Delinquent. Boston, Little, Brown & Co., 1917.

12. ——— and Bronner, A. F.: Delinquents and Criminals: Their Making and Unmaking. New York, The Macmillan Co., 1926.

13. Johnson, A. M., and Szurek, S. A.: The genesis of antisocial acting out in children and adults. Psychoanalyt. Quart. *21:* 323–343, 1952.

14. Kaufman, I.: Three Basic Sources for pre-delinquent character. Nervous Child *11:* 12–15, 1955.

15. Leary, T.: Multilevel Measurement of Interpersonal Behavior, Psychological Consultation Service, Berkeley, California, 1956.

16. Redl, F., and Wineman, D.: Children Who Hate. Glencoe, The Free Press, 1951.

17. Rexford, E., Schleifer, M., and van Amerongen, S. T.: A follow-up of a psychiatric study of 57 antisocial young children. Ment. Hyg. *15:* 196–214, 1956.

18. Rexford, E., and van Amerongen, S. T.: The influence of unsolved maternal oral conflicts upon impulsive acting out in young children. Am. J. Orthopsychiat. *27:* 75–85, 1957.

19. Rose, K. E.: Personality structure and therapeutic manipulation of a young offender. Am. J. Orthopsychiat. *21:* 838–844, 1951.

20. Rose, K. E., and Shriver, M.: The dynamic significance of mother-child relationship in a young delinquent with psychotic mechanisms. Am. J. Orthopsychiat. *24:* 797–828, 1954.

21. Schmideberg, M.: The psycho-analysis of asocial children and adolescents. Internat. J. Psycho-Analysis *16:* 22–48, 1935.

22. Welfare and Health Council of New York City: Conference on Psychiatric Research in Juvenile Delinquency, Princeton, New Jersey, March, 1955.

23. Witmer, H., and Tufts, E.: The Effectiveness of Delinquency Prevention Programs, United States Children's Bureau, Washington, D. C., 1954.

8

A Study of Deviate Sexual Behavior in Children by the Method of Simultaneous Analysis of Mother and Child

By MELITTA SPERLING

THE METHOD of simultaneous analysis of mother and child in which mother and child are treated psychoanalytically in separate sessions (preferably without the child knowing of the mother's analysis) by the same analyst was first applied by me in the treatment of psychosomatic diseases in children, especially ulcerative and mucous colitis, bronchial asthma and some skin disorders.[15, 17, 19, 24, 26, 30]

In the treatment of these children, I found that at a certain phase during their analysis a seemingly unmotivated exacerbation or aggravation of their condition occurred or that their treatment was suddenly terminated with or without a rationalization. I found that these occurrences were the result of an unconscious resistance of the mother to the treatment of her child. In adults, this resistance is manifest as such in the patient and can be handled directly; in children the resistance of the parents may come out through the child in various forms and often cannot be handled directly, that is, through the child alone.

I have found that this crucial phase in the treatment of the psychosomatically ill child is the time when the child, enabled by analysis, is attempting to dissolve the symbiotic relationship with the mother and the mother, because of her own unconscious needs, cannot accept this.[17, 18, 22] Unless the mother can be helped through psychoanalytic intervention to understand and to overcome her resistance, she will not permit this basic change in the relationship. In spite of a very cooperative conscious attitude on the part of the mother, treatment of the child will not succeed. In these children, in whom resistance manifests itself in somatic symptoms which set in with amazing speed, it is essential that this resistance of the mother be spotted and analyzed at once. This can be done best by the analyst who treats the child, particularly in the case of younger children, where I have found that mother and child function as an inseparable unit which can be best understood and treated by one analyst. The shortcomings of the method of collaborative treatment, where mother and child are treated by two different analysts, lies in the fact that the subtle but decisive shades of the interplay between the unconscious of the mother and that of her child are missed even if there are lengthy and frequent conferences between the two analysts or team of workers.[4, 11] Even in the treatment of these children in a clinic, where the handling of the mother was routinely delegated to another therapist, I found it necessary in many cases to treat mother and child myself, at least during certain phases of the treatment.*

The analyst of the child must have the mother's complete acceptance and trust (which can be reliably established in the analytic relationship) if the treatment of the child is to be successful. The conscious attitudes of the mother are completely deceptive and unreliable in these cases. One modification of the method of simultaneous analysis of mother and child is the technique of treating the mother first, at least for a period of time, before embarking upon the treatment of the child, especially in the case of younger children up to eight or nine years of age. I have found that even in the cases of an acute and alarming illness such as ulcerative colitis, where the pressure of the situation is usually intensified by the attitude of the attending physicians urging hospitalization, surgery and other strictly medical procedures, adherence to the method of working first with and through the mother is extremely rewarding. In many cases, the acute symptoms subsided quickly and the children improved so remarkably that there was doubt in the parents' minds whether the child still needed direct treatment. This resistance can be handled very easily once a therapeutic relationship with the mother is established.

The great merit of the method of simultaneous analysis of mother and child, however, lies not in the fact that it represents an essential technical aid in the treatment of certain psychosomatic diseases in children, important as this may be, but that it proved to be a new and extremely rewarding approach to the study and understanding of a very important area of child development, namely, the psychology and psychopathology of the mother-child relationship. This method permitted the immediate observation of the interaction between the unconscious of the mother and her child, and of the ways in which the unconscious wishes of the mother

* Such an example of handling the mother's resistance during this crucial phase of the treatment of the child and then transferring her back to her own therapist in the case of a child with mucous colitis is described in *Psychogenic Diarrhea and Phobia in a Six and a Half Year Old Girl,* Workshop 1952.[24]

were transmitted, received and reacted to by the child as well as of the changes in their mutual responses in the analytic process. With this a new understanding of the etiologic factors and the deep psychodynamics operating in certain psychosomatic diseases of children was gained. I have reported on the successful treatment of ulcerative colitis in children with this method and on my concepts of this illness based upon the insight gained with this method in a series of publications from 1946 to the present.[15, 18, 25-27] This method also made it possible to study and to compare the conditions under which, in a situation of symbiotic mother-child relationship, a psychosomatic disorder occurred and in which situation a psychotic development was the outcome.[27]

In the treatment of children with mucous colitis with this method, it is possible to recognize the specific behavior of the mothers of children with mucous colitis and to compare and to differentiate it from the behavior of mothers of children with ulcerative colitis.[25] The study of a case of allergy and bronchial asthma with this method made it possible to observe in action the pathogenic effects of the mother-child relationship and to resolve them in the analytic process.[17, 26] The study of skin disorders such as pruritis, eczema and dermatitis, but particularly the study of a case of ulcers of the leg with this method, made it possible to understand the symbolic use of the skin and its ulcers by the child and his mother.[19, 26, 30]

My application of this method to the study and treatment of severely disturbed children, whose bizarre, explosive and unpredictable behavior could not be fully understood nor sufficiently influenced in individual treatment, proved to be most fruitful. M. Mahler,* in discussing one of my papers stated, "By studying longitudinally in actual psychoanalytic treatment both partners of the mother-child unit, Dr. Sperling obtained insight into the specific and deep unconscious psychodynamic correlations between the psychopathology of mother and child." In the cases studied by this method, behavior which might have been ascribed to inherited factors could be demonstrated to be a reaction of the child to the mother's unconscious wishes.[21] Similarly, it was possible to understand behavior in children which could have been ascribed to extrasensory perception had it not been studied by this method.[21, 22] My research in this area would seem of particular interest for the understanding of the phenomena and psychodynamics in hypnosis, folie-à-deux, and child psychosis. In some cases, even of older children, where the child for various reasons was not available for treatment, the pathologic behavior of the child could be

* The Neurotic Child and His Mother: A Psychoanalytic Study, The American Journal of Orthopsychiatry, Vol. XXI, No. 3, April, 1951, pp. 363.[22]

remarkably influenced through the psychoanalytic treatment of the mother alone.[20]

In my discussion of the "Case of An Atypical Child," presented by Dr. E. Rexford at the Midwinter meeting of the American Psychoanalytic Association in New York, December, 1948 (Panel on Child Analysis), I expressed my opinion that no permanent therapeutic results could be obtained with these children unless their mothers were treated psychoanalytically, preferably by the same analyst who treated the child, or, even better, were analyzed prior to the treatment of the child.[8] I based my opinion on my findings from the psychoanalytic studies of such a mother concerning the unconscious identification of the child by the mother with either an unconsciously hated and rejected part of herself or an unconsciously hated important object from childhood with whom the mother had not resolved her infantile conflict, and which instead was revived and continued with her child.*

I have been interested for some years in the study of perversions in adults and of deviate sexual behavior in children.[1, 16] There are comparatively few contributions on deviate sexual behavior in children in the psychoanalytic and psychiatric literature.[2, 3, 7] This is rather surprising as severe character disorders and perversions are frequent psychiatric conditions in adults; they are difficult to treat and, from the etiologic and dynamic point of view, still present many problems. In the treatment of an adult exhibitionist, I was struck with the attitude of the parents who had consistently disregarded the manifestations of the perverse behavior of my patient when he was an adolescent, although it had been brought to their attention, until he was apprehended and sentenced to treatment as it were.[16] In every instance of a case of deviate sexual behavior in a child which came to my attention, the child was brought for treatment under much external pressure and with great reluctance by the parents. The parents of these children appeared to be respectable, well-meaning people whose conduct seemed beyond reproach. The behavior of the children appeared almost paradoxically unrelated to that of their parents.

My contribution to this volume deals with a research into deviate sexual behavior of children with the method of simultaneous analysis of mother and child. From the eleven cases of children with deviate sexual behavior treated by me, fragments from the treatment of three cases will be presented to illustrate my method as a technique for research and treatment with its advantages and complications.

* This discussion was erroneously attributed to B. Rank by Ernst Kris in *Notes on the Development and on Some Current Problems of Psychoanalytic Child Psychology,* The Psychoanalytic Study of the Child, Vol. V, p. 32.

Case 1. Treatment had been suggested for six and a half year old Rhoda by the school because of certain behavior observed there. Rhoda had been found, on several occasions, with other girls in the toilet with her panties down, inspecting and touching their genitals. Rhoda had been bringing large amounts of candy to school as gifts for these girls. The candy she bought with money she took from her mother's purse. Rhoda also suffered from persistent enuresis. Her mother had been told that she did not require treatment for the enuresis and that she would eventually outgrow it. Rhoda's parents had separated when she was five years old.

Rhoda was a good-looking, but overweight, bright youngster. For a considerable period of her analysis, Rhoda would play school with me. She would push me, tie me, want to hit me, yell at me, and, in general, treat me very sadistically. Rhoda went to a private school where the teachers were especially considerate. It was obvious that this game did not repeat a school situation. On many occasions she would suddenly jump on me, get on top of me and make movements as in intercourse. Rhoda very cautiously began to reveal some of the activities that had gone on between her and the other children. She had always been the seducer. What she really was interested in, much more than in looking, was to exhibit herself and to be looked at. She also liked to treat the other girls roughly and to hit them over their naked bodies.

After a year and a half of treatment, during which her behavior in school had improved considerably but her analysis did not seem to progress much further, her mother accepted my suggestion to undergo analysis herself. A condensed and fragmentary account of the relevant material as it emerged in the analysis follows.

Rhoda's mother had a very strong, unconscious homosexual attachment to her own mother, from whom she had never separated. Mrs. A. (as we shall refer to Rhoda's mother) had been a very pretty, bright and talented girl, the pride of her mother. Her mother had controlled every one of her steps. As a young girl, Mrs. A. had not been interested in men; she was married at 25, after all her girl friends had been married, to a man whom she supported until he could establish himself. After her marriage she continued to live with her mother, and for some years she had spent her vacations with her mother, instead of with her husband. Analysis revealed that she had established with her husband the relationship which she had with her mother, only now she was taking the role of her mother. She had to know exactly where her husband was at all times, when he would come home, and would anxiously wait for him at the window should he be a few minutes late. She now also controlled her mother, who, after her husband's death, depended upon my patient. Mrs. A., a very soft-spoken woman, respected by everyone for her polite and kind behavior, would lose her temper frequently at home and have violent fights with her mother. During these scenes, both women would be in the nude, and "for an old woman she still has a very nice body," Mrs. A would tell me. After such a scene, they would make up. Mrs. A. was treating Rhoda in a similar way to the way she behaved with her own mother. She would get very angry, yell at her, and hit her, also in the nude, as these scenes would take place in the bedroom or bathroom in the morning or at night. The sadistic and sexually attacking teacher whom Rhoda was impersonating could be identified now with certainty as her mother.

It could be seen that Rhoda was doing actively with other girls what her mother had been doing with her. Rhoda had been very disappointed and frustrated with her mother after the separation of her parents. She had hoped unconsciously to take her father's place with her mother, but, instead, her mother, who at that time was on the verge of a depression and completely preoccupied with herself, was totally inconsiderate and neglectful of Rhoda's needs. She did not spend much time with Rhoda; in fact, she was hardly ever at home during that year. This was the time when Rhoda's sexual aggressive behavior and the display of the scoptophilic, exhibitionist and sadistic impulses in school began.

The mother never admitted to herself and certainly could not have admitted to others how she felt about Rhoda and what was going on between them. She felt repulsion and strong attraction at the same time. She began to realize that she had unconsciously identified Rhoda with herself, although consciously she maintained that Rhoda was the image of her husband and that her unrestrained and impulsive behavior were the paternal characteristics.

In the analysis of the mother it became clear why Rhoda, after a year and a half, had come to an impasse in her analysis and did not make further progress. Mrs. A. felt that, in the matter of self-control, Rhoda was surpassing her. In fact, had she shown more control, she would have shamed her mother, who at that time was not ready to curb her own behavior. Later in the analysis when the mother began to curb this behavior toward Rhoda, Rhoda would often say, "We are getting modest these days," or "You are not kissing me as you used to."

It was found that Mrs. A.'s superego was peculiarly contradictory. On the one hand, it demanded very high moral, ethical and intellectual performance; she had to be very bright, altruistic, loyal and self-sacrificing. But, on the other hand, it permitted an almost complete abandonment of any standards and the acting out of crude sexual and sadistic impulses in reality. Only in the simultaneous psychoanalytic treatment of Rhoda and her mother could this behavior and its unconscious motivations be exposed and its effect upon Rhoda's psychosexual development and especially upon the structure of her superego be observed and understood. It became clear that this relationship with her mother had led to the establishment of a superego which not only did not prohibit, but, in fact, condoned her behavior. Rhoda had a very well-functioning ego; she showed no impairment of the sense of reality or other important and essential functions of the ego. She was very clever in her attempts to keep out of her analysis the significant material and to reveal as secrets, and with much fussing, the less significant behavior. In this respect, she behaved in her treatment like an adult pervert who is unwilling to give up his perversion. Even the enuresis in her case had the quality of a perversion as there was hardly any guilt or shame but, on the contrary, much pleasure connected with it.

I had the opportunity to work with Rhoda analytically again when she was 16 years old and preparing to enter college. The problem which brought her into treatment then was a sudden marked drop in grades in her senior year of high school and feelings of panic, especially during exams. It was found that underlying these symptoms was a conflict of separation from her mother. To graduate meant to go to college and to leave mother. This analysis was very rewarding, particularly because it permitted the evaluation of the effects of the analytic treatment rendered to her and her mother years ago. Significant additional information and insight into the behavior she had exhibited as a young child could be gained. This material, together with other follow-up studies, will be reported at some future date.

Case 2. Jerry was eight and a half at the time he entered treatment. His parents had been aware of his behavior for some time but brought him for treatment only after pressure from his school. Jerry had difficulty with children as well as with adults. He habitually used filthy, obscene language with adults. He was afraid of older boys and boys of his age, but attacked younger children, especially girls. He had an insidious way of doing this, mostly a sneak attack from behind. He would pinch them and poke his fingers into the anal region. On one occasion, he had jammed a pencil into a child's back and had injured the child. He did not pay attention to the school work, being busy molesting children, and consequently he was a permanent visitor in the principal's office. The parents disagreed upon methods for handling him: the father was for strictness and punishment; the mother felt that her husband was too severe and, in fact, believed that he was responsible for the child's behavior. She had resisted earlier suggestions for treatment for Jerry, but now, under pressure from the school, was ready to accept it.

I learned from the mother that Jerry also suffered from allergies of the upper respiratory system, a condition which she thought he had inherited from her. He had discontinued treatment by an allergist because he objected to injections and also because it was ineffective.

Jerry was a rather frail and innocent-looking youngster, with a long mane of hair hanging over his eyes. He didn't like to take haircuts, and so would go without one for months at a time. He had been told that I would treat him for his allergies with a new method, without injections, but would talk and play with him. He was a boy of superior intelligence and he was obviously curious about me and the playroom, and behaved in his first interview in a rather civil way. From the start of treatment and for some time after, Jerry would play only with the dolls during his sessions. He would make clothes for them and even bring some from home which he and his mother had made together. He was using a toy sewing machine, cooking utensils and everything that would interest girls. He wanted to sit very close to me and, in a rather obvious manner, made sexual advances towards me; for example, trying to put his head into my lap and towards my genitals. When he was rebuffed, he would go into fits, use obscene language worthy of a truck driver. He wanted to push me, jump at me, throw things at me. Then again, he would court me by bringing me cookies which he baked with his mother, and even flowers. His behavior alternated between overt sexual advances and abusive behavior and language when he was frustrated.

During the first few weeks of his treatment, there was a noticeable change in Jerry's behavior, particularly at school. It was the first time that his mother had not been called to the school for two weeks straight. However, there was a change now in his behavior in the waiting room. It was almost as if he were putting on an act. When I opened the door, he would begin to call me names, looking at me and at his mother, who sat there with a peculiar smile on her face as if she enjoyed the spectacle. He would run around the waiting room, unconcerned whether there were other people present, while his mother was looking at me to see how I would cope with such behavior. After a few minutes he would calm down spontaneously and storm into the playroom.

He became so abusive and physically aggressive with me that I felt I needed the help of his mother to keep him in treatment. The parents had indicated that they did not want to be involved in therapy themselves. The father had asked for treatment for Jerry upon the urging of a friend in whose judgment he had great trust. The mother had reluctantly consented and expressed skepticism about the advisability of such treatment. There had been such noticeable improvement in Jerry's behavior in school within the short period of treatment (three months) that I felt I could confront the mother with an ultimatum that either she undergo treatment also or I would terminate Jerry's treatment. I had learned from practical experience by this time that the treatment of a child with deviate sexual behavior is difficult and bound to fail unless the significant partner with whom the child has this relationship is willing to release the child from it.

This is a brief account of the picture as it shaped up in work with the mother. She had agreed to the treatment of the child because she did not think it would be possible for me to treat him. Although she was not conscious that this was a design on her part to break up his treatment, she was aware that Jerry's behavior in the waiting room had something to do with her feelings. It could be understood now that his behavior had the meaning of pacifying his mother, as if to indicate to her, "Don't worry; she (the analyst) is not taking me away from you; in fact, you see, I don't even want to go in with her." It also became clear that the mother was releasing her own hostility toward people through Jerry. He verbalized and did to people what she could not allow herself to say or do. This could be particularly well observed in Jerry's behavior towards me. Whenever she experienced an upsurge of resentment and hostility toward me, Jerry would become very difficult and almost unmanageable in the playroom, on various occasions actually hitting me.

The mother felt very frustrated in her marriage, sexually and in every other way. She had always wanted a double bed because she liked to snuggle up and enjoyed the feeling of physical closeness during the night, but her husband wanted twin beds and felt uncomfortable in her close envelopment. She suffered from a sleep disturbance of long standing. After her older son was born, she had wanted her second child to be a daughter, but she felt now that not even a daughter could have been more affectionate and loving to her than Jerry was. He was always with her. Instead of playing with boys, he would spend his time helping her cook, sew, with the dishes, the dinner table, etc. For his fifth birthday she had bought Jerry a baby carriage and dolls because he liked it, she said. She was surprised at my questioning the advisability of such a birthday gift for a boy: "Even if he liked it?" she asked. Jerry still liked and collected dolls to this day. Before leaving for school in the morning, he would always hug and kiss his mother very affectionately and come running home at lunch to repeat the performance and to have lunch with her. She told me that he was in the habit of running over to her and kissing her in the very same way as he observed in love scenes on T.V. She never had any difficulties with him when she was alone with him. The fighting and misbehavior started when there were others around. He would always fight for the seat next to her, and on such occasions had often managed to pull the tablecloth and dishes off when they were invited for dinner or were eating out. People were afraid to invite her because of Jerry.

She could not remember having seen him masturbate. Sexual matters were not discussed in her house; her husband and she were rather prudish people, she told me. There was one thing about Jerry that really bothered her. Sometimes, especially after a losing fight with his brother, she would find Jerry sitting in his room and staring into space. After such a fight with his brother recently, she told Jerry to go to his room and to clean it up. When she came into his room, he just stood there. When she told him again, he just sat down and looked at her as if he were in a daze. He had a very peculiar expression on his face. She got scared and slapped him across the face to "snap him out of it." Her fears concerning his sanity came out more clearly later in her treatment when her own infantile fantasies and fears came to the fore. She, too, would often stare into space unaware of what she was thinking. At times, she would become panicky and find herself shivering and with goose-pimples all over her body without any apparent reason. Much later, when she had developed a strong transference relationship, she revealed that she had occasional visual and acoustic hallucinatory experiences. She also revealed that she had a fear that Jerry could kill her, or kill somebody, or himself. She had fantasies and fears of being sexually attacked. Her own destructive impulses could be dealt with only later in her treatment, which lasted for more than five years.

Her stepmother lived in the same building, but they were mostly not on speaking terms. On occasion, there were violent fights between them, at which Jerry was present.

With difficulty and reluctance, the mother was now beginning to discourage

Jerry's affections toward her. On several occasions Jerry had gone off to school in the morning without kissing her, almost without taking notice of her. He now was not so punctual at lunch time and would spend some time with the other children. This was all very painful to the mother. In the course of having to frustrate herself, she was beginning to expose her husband. She was resentful that she, who had objected to Jerry's treatment, was involved in treatment herself, while the father went free, as it were. She thought that he was too strict and punitive. He liked to tease the children and they were afraid of him. When he was in a good mood, he liked to play with Jerry in certain ways, pinching and biting his behind and, as she put it, practically to stick his nose in Jerry's anus. This type of play was practiced on Jerry also by the father's brother. Sometimes both men would get after Jerry, holding him down on the sofa and squeezing and pinching him playfully.

During this phase of treatment, Jerry began to show some phobic concerns regarding his mother. He became very anxious about her standing too close to the track on the subway, or about her walking downstairs and falling or hurting herself. He also complained that she didn't kiss him the same way she used to.

Jerry was still playing with dolls in his sessions, but he was less careful with them now. Once he tore off the head of one doll and wanted to rip her between the legs. While doing this, he told me that his mother had three girl's names ready for him. If he had only been a girl, he could have been Susan. To the interpretation of his hostile impulses toward his mother, he responded with outbursts of temper and verbal attacks upon me. He had fantasies of cutting my throat; he would put me into a bathtub so the blood would not drip on the floor. He would get my jewelry even if he had to cut off my ears for the pearls or my finger for the ring. He played out these fantasies with a doll, cutting her neck and stabbing her. He broke a little doll which he had liked very much into pieces.

He began to discuss the sexual differences with me. Boys, too, he said, have two holes, one in the back and one in the penis. He drew figures of male and female, making hair in the back of both. He erased it and said, "It is being cut off; when there is hair, bones can be moved even if there is only one hair." He had one such hair, he told me, and the doctor gave him something yellow over his face and cut it off. This happened when he was five years old, he said. "From the penis too, the skin is cut off," he explained, "or else urine couldn't come out. It would fill up and up to the throat and one would choke from it." These fantasies were in part an elaboration of his reaction to a tonsillectomy when he was five years old and to the death of a little boy in the neighborhood around that time. This boy supposedly died after an operation for spina bifida. These fantasies were of particular interest in connection with his allergies, but this subject cannot be dealt with here.

He was gradually losing interest in dolls. He joined the Cub Scouts and was playing with other boys. It was still very difficult for him to renounce gratification of the pleasures which he had so freely enjoyed with his mother. He began to show interest in books and particularly in painting. Upon his own request, he joined a painting class and actually enjoyed it and did very well in art work.

Through the treatment of the mother, some changes in her relationship with Jerry had been effected. It now became obvious that Jerry's relationship with his father was a highly pathologic one and that, for successful treatment, this would have to be changed also. Both Jerry and his father derived too much overt gratification from their physical contacts in fighting and teasing. In my limited contacts with the father, I had to be direct in forbidding him (with little success) this type of play with Jerry. It was possible, at the time when Jerry was eleven years old, to get the father into psychotherapy with the therapist who treated Jerry's brother.

In Jerry's case, both parents used him for the gratification of their own infantile sexual (perverse) needs. To the mother, Jerry had to substitute for the unsatisfactory husband, giving her the cuddling, kissing, physical proximity and all the attention and time she wanted, but did not get, from her husband. He also had to make up to her for the daughter she longed for. He used to bake, sew, and clean house with her and accompany her on her shopping trips.

Jerry knew exactly what his mother unconsciously expected of him. He behaved neither like a boy nor like a girl, nor was he very childlike. His mother hated men, but she also hated women and she did not like children because they required too much care. He was what she would have wanted to be. She had always been very self-conscious and timid. Although she was a bright and good pupil, she could never speak up in school nor anywhere else. She could not even ask questions. She had always been painfully aware of this shortcoming, but she had not been aware that she made up for it in an exaggerated way through Jerry. He said anything he felt like saying to people to whom she could have never opened her mouth. For this, she really admired him and he knew it. He was dependent upon her for sexual gratification and provocative with his father, whom he feared very much. Under these circumstances, this was the most satisfactory arrangement for him. In this way, he managed to have both parents busy themselves with him and oppose each other. At times when the parents were getting along well, they would go off together and leave Jerry to care for himself, often for the entire day. His mother, who was mostly very indulgent toward him, could also be very cruel with him at times. Such an attitude is typical for the dominant partner in a perverse relationship. In the analysis of the mother, it was found that she had a masochistic sexual perversion and she required for sexual gratification, pinching and hitting of her buttocks. At a later date in her analysis, the mother realized that she actually instigated fights between Jerry and his father because it gave her pleasure to see them both fight over her.

Jerry had not established a definite sexual identification. In this way, he could be the love object for both parents. The hate and contempt which he had for his mother were covered up by a compensatory overevaluation of her and turned against, and released, on other women. In the simultaneous treatment, it could be seen clearly that as long as the mother was maintaining this "love" relationship with him, the hatred and destructiveness were deflected from her and directed toward other people. For example, he once sprayed toilet water into the eyes of the maid when he was really angry at his mother. His mother suffered from an eye condition and was very sensitive about her eyes, which would become inflamed readily. He once "accidentally" killed the parakeet which belonged to his mother and which he liked too. He would damage and set fire to furnishings, cut upholstery, and so on when he was angry at his mother. She was spared aggression and treated with physical affection by him. The hate for the father was less repressed and only thinly covered up by the fear of him. These feelings expressed themselves in his behavior toward men; he liked to provoke them and often played nasty tricks on them; he once got the F.B.I. looking for his father's friend.

There was no superego conflict in his case. He had no guilt feelings about his behavior, nor did he have a wish to change it. His superego did not demand renunciation of his instinctual gratification nor ask him for control of behavior. Such behavior was not only permitted, but approved of, by the parents, especially the mother. In order to be free of internal conflict, he had to turn his aggression and hatred out and towards external objects. Every improvement in his relations with other people made for internal conflict, bringing back the hate to the superego, the incorporated parental images. This could be observed particularly clearly during one phase of his treatment when he had a positive relationship with me and did not release his destructiveness, but was repressing it. This was the time when he developed neurotic symptoms, such as phobias and nightmares.

His ego was not weak at all. He was very clever, almost shrewd, in manipulating people when he wanted to and when it served to gain the pleasures he desired. His sense of reality was not impaired nor was any essential function of the ego.

Case 3. Mrs. B consulted me about her thirteen year old daughter, Joan, who was a behavior problem. Joan was very critical of her mother, particularly in the presence of her mother's friends. It was obvious that the mother was using this difficulty with Joan to get treatment for herself. It was also obvious that she was afraid to admit, even to herself, that she was in need of pychiatric treatment. She had experienced a severe anxiety attack a year prior and now had a recurrence of this anxiety. She suffered from acute anxiety of panic proportions; she was afraid to be alone in the house; she was fearful to go near the window, and her sleep was very disturbed. She felt as if she were losing her mind. At times, when she was very anxious, she had experiences of a hallucinatory character. She would see her mother, who died when the patient was an adolescent of 15 years, sitting on the bed, coming after her, and grabbing her from behind. She blamed her father for her mother's death. One night she and her mother had surprised the father in bed with the patient's older sister. Her mother, who had suffered from TB, died shortly after that.

Mrs. B's marriage was unsatisfactory. She complained about her husband's impotence but gradually came to recognize that she was frigid and only wanted foreplay and to stimulate her husband without gratifying him sexually. She had several friendships with women who obviously had strong homosexual leanings. She thought of having extramarital relationships with men, but she really wanted only to tease them. She claimed that the only satisfactory relationship was with her younger daughter, Judy, aged nine at the start of her mother's analysis.

For an entire year she had managed not to bring up her daughter, Judy, in the analysis. Gradually, with the development of a more positive transference and with the help of dreams, the relationship with this daughter was brought into the analysis. She began to reveal some of the activities between her and Judy which she had wanted to keep from my knowledge. Judy, by that time ten years old, was still coming into her mother's bed every morning after her father left and often would sleep with her mother all night. On such occasions, the father had to leave the bedroom and sleep in Judy's room. Judy liked to pet and kiss her mother's body. She had a certain way of doing it. Her mother told me that Judy would start from the top and go down to the bottom, petting and kissing her mother's vulva and then repeat this performance from the bottom up to the top. She would often tell her mother: "I don't want to get married when I grow up. I don't want a man to make sis with his penis into my vagina." Judy, who was a rather stout girl, according to her mother, liked to pull up the fat from her belly playfully, lifting it like an apron, and invite her mother to lick her vulva. The mother, who frequently had sensations of an imaginary penis, experiencing these sensations in that part of her body where she thought the penis should have been, on several occasions, when taking a bath together with Judy, hallucinated a penis also on Judy's body.

It was very difficult for her to curtail these activities with Judy. She felt rejected by her older daughter and by her husband. The only person from whom she received sexual gratification was Judy. Judy was the only one who really loved her, she felt. She was fearful of what analysis would do to this relationship; she could not afford to lose her. There was no chance of getting Judy into treatment. Even the slightest suggestion that Judy would require treatment was, at this point, totally unacceptable to her mother. After two years of analytic treatment, she could not yet discourage outright Judy's sexual approaches. Occasionally she would say to her, "Not today, I have a headache."

Nevertheless, there were definite changes in the behavior of her children. Joan became more amenable toward her mother, while Judy became more difficult. Judy began to have temper tantrums and, in a way, she was now behaving with her mother as Joan had before. At this point, the family had moved and Judy became friendly with a girl next door. Judy, who used to spend most of her time with her mother, now became inseparable from this girl. She became increasingly difficult and critical of her mother; she complained about the food, the house, her mother's appearance. The mother came close to a depression. She related that the change in Judy's behavior was so obvious that outsiders commented on it. She realized that she, herself, had become more critical of Judy and that she was jealous of Judy's girl friend. She felt that Judy had replaced her with this friend and she suspected that the girls were having a homosexual relationship. She complained that whenever this girl visited Judy, the door to her room was kept closed. This was a source of great irritation to the mother since there had previously never been closed doors between mother and daughter. One day, when both girls were in Judy's room and the mother wanted to enter, Judy called out, "Don't come in!". The mother walked in and found the girls in a very suspicious position on the bed. At this point, she would have wanted immediate treatment for Judy, but it was obvious that Judy would not accept any suggestion for treatment. In fact, the mother still found herself at a loss at how to make such a suggestion to Judy. She discovered, in her analysis, that her wish for Judy to be treated was not genuine, but that she wanted to break up the friendship between the two girls and to win Judy back for herself.

Judy was now twelve and a half years old and preparing to leave for camp with her girl friend. Shortly after, her mother called me from camp requesting an appointment for Judy. Judy and her friend had been expelled from camp for offensive behavior; they had been abusive to the counselor and camp director. Under the pressure of the situation, Judy had consented to see me. It was obvious that Judy was not ready for treatment; she felt indignant about it and considered it an imposition and intrusion into her private life. I saw her twice and tried to convey to her the feeling that the treatment was not a punishment for bad behavior, as she felt, nor something to be coerced into. I knew that I would have to wait for her and hoped that, through the continued analysis of her mother, Judy would eventually find her way into treatment. Later in her treatment, the mother, when analyzing her fears of insanity, recognized that she, too, had not been ready for Judy's treatment at the time she had brought her to me.

There was mental illness in the families of Judy's parents, a fact the mother was concealing from Judy. One day, to the mother's surprise, Judy asked her some questions about a relative who was in psychiatric treatment. At first, the mother wanted to evade the subject, but, realizing the implication, she managed to talk about it frankly. Judy asked how long this relative had been in treatment and whether it was helping him. The mother told her that she thought it did and that he was in his second year of treatment. Judy asked, "How long do you think it would take me?" When the mother said that she didn't know, but that it would probably take some time, Judy replied, "Why don't I start now?" Judy was fifteen and a half years old when she started psychoanalytic treatment with me.

Summarizing briefly the important aspects of this case, the fact that it took six years for Judy to get into treatment deserves some explanation. It is obvious, even from this very fragmentary report of the mother's analysis, that she had to be considered at least as a borderline case. It took over a year of treatment for her to get ready to talk about her relationship with Judy to me. It took another two years of treatment until she could get herself to discontinue the overt intimacies with Judy, and, even then, it was very difficult for her to tolerate the ensuing hostility from Judy and the threat of losing her as a love object.

As long as she had been willing to maintain this relationship with Judy, she not only permitted Judy these sexual gratifications without guilt but, at the same time, Judy's hatred against her mother (for being seduced by her and made dependent upon her for these gratifications) was kept in repression and was overcompensated for by the overt "love" relationship. This (pregenital) hatred and destructiveness, previously vented toward others, became now directed towards the frustrating and "unfaithful" mother who was withholding the gratification which she had offered before. The handling of this hate is a difficult technical problem in the treatment of these children which requires the full cooperation and understanding of the parent with whom the child has had this relationship. If the child alone is treated, the parent may not be able to accept the turning away of the child and may become very cruel to the child. This happened with Jerry before and even for some time after his mother began treatment.

The change in the behavior of Joan toward her mother could be attributed to the change in the relationship between the mother and Judy. Joan had often referred to them as the "lovers." The role of the father in such a family setting seems to be a typical one. If he is not an active partner in the relationship with the child, as in Jerry's case, he is conspicuous by his absence. In Rhoda's case, the father separated from his wife when Rhoda was five years old, but actually he had left Rhoda's mother for another woman shortly after Rhoda was born. Judy's parents had not lived together sexually for many years. In fact, there was hardly any family life in her home. The father would eat out with his business associates and the mother would have the two girls eat separately, preparing special dishes with great care for Judy. She realized, during the treatment, that she didn't want her husband home and did not want to feed him. Whenever she had to prepare a meal for him, she would burn or spill the food or have some mishap. According to the mother, "A dog deserved more consideration." This hatred for men and the right to exploit and abuse them was taken over by her daughters. Joan married a man whom she could treat as her mother treated her father. Judy had an opportunity to work through her feelings about men in her analysis, which I plan to report together with other follow-up studies.

Discussion of Etiology, Dynamics and Therapy

Freud, in his first concept concerning the etiology of hysteria, postulated the occurrence of actual sexual traumata as an etiologic factor.[5] He later revised this concept by accepting fantasies, fictitious traumata and psychic reality as sufficient etiologic factors.[6] The concept of the traumatic etiology of the neuroses, although generally accepted, appears to be somewhat neglected in the clinical practice of psychoanalysis, where it is difficult and perhaps not always possible to establish the causal connection between trauma and illness. It appears to me that too much room has been left to the workings of fantasy life *independent* of experiences in external reality and to inherited factors in the etiology of the neuroses. I am referring here particularly to the Kleinian school of thought.[12] An over-emphasis on inherent factors in ego development also seems to me to constitute a similar danger of overlooking the role of actual experiences in ego and superego development.[10, 14]

While the instinctual life follows certain innate patterns of development in the child, it is a known and accepted fact in psychoanalytic theory and practice that these patterns of instinctual development in the child can be continually influenced and modified by the experiences of the child with his emotionally important objects (his parents), that is, through and by his object relationships. My investigation into deviate sexual behavior of children has been focussed particularly on this aspect. One of the reasons which prompted Freud to give up the seduction theory of hysteria is of interest in connection with this study: Freud spoke of his astonishment at being asked to believe that all his patients' fathers were given to sexual perversions.[6] It is difficult to assess correctly the etiologic value of certain childhood experiences in the lives of perverts from reconstruction from their analyses, especially if striking experiences of seduction are absent. But even if such experiences are found, we still question which factors promote the development of a perversion in one case and of hysteria or neurosis in another case and seemingly undisturbed development into full genitality in many others. In this study, we are particularly concerned with defining those factors which encourage the development of deviate sexual behavior in children and which favor or determine that specific component instincts will take the lead.

In the simultaneous analysis of Rhoda and her mother, it was possible to establish with certainty that Rhoda's behavior was directly related to actual experiences and her relationship with her mother. It was also found that the onset of her behavior problems in school occurred at the time when she was disappointed in her mother and afraid of losing her as she had just lost her father (through separation). In identification with the lost object, she would have wanted to take his place with her mother. Disappointed in her mother, she turned toward other children as the active seducer, identifying herself with her mother in this aspect. Without this insight, her behavior could have been easily interpreted merely as an expression of her inner fantasy life and the significance of the specific relationship between Rhoda and her mother as the causal factor could have been overlooked.

Rhoda's deviate behavior manifested itself in a display of exhibitionistic, scoptophilic, and sadistic tendencies. There was also a marked tendency toward homosexual development, with a wish to take the male role. In the analysis of her enuresis, it was brought out that she unconsciously identified urine with semen and that she had fantasies of making babies for her mother by wetting. In her sexual games, she was always Bluie (the boy) while her partner, even if she was much older than herself, had to be Pinkie (the girl). In the analysis of her mother, it was found that these were exactly her perverse interests (exhibitionistic, scoptophilic, sadistic, and homosexual) and in the simultaneous analysis it could be observed that and in which ways the mother stimulated specifically these partial instincts in Rhoda.

The manner in which Rhoda managed to keep out of her analysis certain activities between her mother and herself clearly indicated that she was aware of their sexual nature and that she sensed that analysis would interfere with them. This propensity of the child with deviate sexual behavior to protect the parent or older partner of this seductive relationship I have found with such consistency in the treatment of these chilren that I have come to consider it as typical. Only if for some reason the parent or older partner discontinues this relationship and the child is frustrated may the disappointment with the "unfaithful" partner express itself in hostility and abusive behavior toward this partner with a need to expose her unfavorably. From the technical point of view, these phases can be handled best if both partners are treated simultaneously. If only the mother is in analysis, this phase can be handled rather well, especially with younger children, as the withdrawal of these gratifications or the "weaning from the perverse relationship," as I would call it, can be done gradually and be replaced by a healthier and more genuinely affectionate motherly attitude. Even with older children, through analysis of the mother alone, the relationship between them can be improved to such a degree that the child eventually will accept direct treatment. This was demonstrated in the case of Judy, who, without the lengthy analysis of her mother, could not have been gotten and certainly would not have stayed in analysis. If the child alone is treated, this phase of the treatment when the child makes an attempt to free himself from his relationship may be dangerous for various reasons. It is the most frequent cause for failure of treatment because the mother (or parent with whom the child has this relationship) will not permit it and with some meager, or even without any, rationalization will withdraw the child from treatment. The mother, in such a situation, can become very cruel toward the child, and this may lead to serious destructive (self) acting out of the child. To some extent, this was the case early in Jerry's treatment when the mother became quite cruel with him, and later on when the father's increased sadistic attitude toward him became a serious obstacle in his treatment, leading to much acting out and temporary interruption of it.*

Furthermore, analysis of the child alone does not reveal and certainly does not eliminate the pathologic attitude of the parent which has these particular effects upon the child's superego structure. The conduct of these mothers is usually exemplary. This was particularly true of Rhoda's mother. And yet Rhoda was stealing from her mother, wetting herself during the day and night, was overeating and manifesting the deviate sexual behavior described. In addition, she had a great need to cling physically to adults, especially women. This lack of instinctual control as well as the clinging to objects were very characteristic traits of her mother. Mrs. A. had overcompensated her very strong unconscious homosexuality with an exaggerated interest of a physically absorbing nature in men. The oral quality of her object relationship required the physical presence and preferably physical union with the object. She could not be alone. This need to reassure against object loss and make up for the lack in object relatedness by seeking close bodily contact was very apparent in Rhoda also.

Since, in my opinion, deviate sexual behavior in children is dynamically a disturbance of the superego resulting from the internalization of certain unconscious parental attitudes, I consider it an essential therapeutic requirement in the case of children to modify the unconscious attitudes of the objects from whom this superego is derived.† My material has amply

* Adelaide M. Johnson and S. A. Szurek have made similar observations in the treatment of children with antisocial behavior. In *Genesis of Antisocial Acting-Out in Children and Adults*,[11] they stress the need for collaborative therapy. They state that otherwise the guilt mustered up by the child in individual treatment will be dissolved by the unconscious permissiveness at home. They stress treatment of the significant parent and state that if this permissiveness is on a conscious level, treatment is usually impossible, and they consider treatment of the child alone in serious acting-out cases as dangerous. Cf. in this connection also B. Bettelheim, *Truants from Life*.[4]

† I am referring in this connection particularly to the work of O. E. Sperling on the parasitic superego in *Interpretation of the Trauma as a Command*,[32] and his concepts of the split in the superego in the *Psychodynamics of Group Perversion*.[34] I have re-

demonstrated that these (more or less) unconscious perverse needs of the parent(s) present an irresistable temptation for the child and an insurmountable resistance in the treatment. If the "perverse relationship" is the only way in which the child can be close to the parent and receive gratification, he has no choice and this becomes the child's mode of object relationship.

The actual physical and emotional dependence of the child upon his parents makes for a transference in child analysis which is in some aspects different from that of adults. Only one of these aspects can be discussed within the framework of this paper but this one is essential to an understanding of the therapeutic goals. The child knows what the analyst expects of him, namely, to give up the deviate behavior, just as he knows what his parents and particularly the parent with whom he has this relationship expects of him, namely, to continue the deviate behavior, even though the overt actions and verbalizations of this parent may not seem to indicate this. For a full cure of the child, which entails the reconstruction of his superego, it is essential that the analyst and the parents of the child see eye-to-eye on this matter; otherwise, the child will only be in conflict about whose leadership to follow.* One outcome in this situation, if the unconscious needs of the parent have not been changed, may be a superficial compliance on the part of the child without a basic change in the structure of his superego. This situation in treatment is analogous to the situation when the parents of the child do not see eye-to-eye on the important issues of sexual adjustment. Just as the parents themselves have to be in true agreement concerning the important goals for the child, so have the parents and the analyst of the child to be united in their endeavors. I have found simultaneous analysis of mother and child to be an essential therapeutic technique in achieving this necessary unity.

One other advantage of simultaneous analysis of mother and child should be mentioned: it can be more goal-directed, especially with the mother, and focus on her relationship with this child. The objection might be raised that this is not in accordance with the rules of analysis. In these cases, however, the relationship with the child is the most

---

ported similar observations concerning the superego structure in the treatment of children with pavor nocturnus type 1 in *Pavor Nocturnus*.[31] Cf. in this connection also *Psychoanalytic Observations of Deviate Sexual Behavior in Children*, a paper which I read at the Mid-Winter Meeting of the American Psychoanalytic Association in December, 1953, and J. Arlow's report on the panel on *Perversion*,[1] as well as W. Gillespie's *The Structure and Aetiology of Sexual Perversion*.[9]

* Cf. in this connection O. E. Sperling's *Some Observations on Failure of Leadership*.[33]

pathognomonic feature of the mother's personality and consistent analysis of this aspect not only does not preclude but enhances the progress of analysis. The fact that the mother is aware of why she and her child are in analysis with the same analyst works as a stimulus for the analysis.

The question concerning the technical difficulty of having the mother in analysis simultaneously without the child's knowledge has come up. As far as the mother is concerned, there may occasionally be some difficulty in regard to her reliability on a conscious level, especially at the start of analysis. In such a case, or if the mother appears too sick to begin with, it is advisable to start with the mother alone and treat her, at least until a reliable therapeutic relationship has been established. If it is not possible to stimulate enough of a sincere wish in the mother to help her child so that one can rely on her, the chances for the child are poor. In Jerry's case it would have been preferable to work with the parents first, but to insist on this seemed too risky as it was obvious that they were uncooperative and looking for an easy way out. His treatment was fraught with difficulties and interruptions. But then again his prognosis, in view of the family situation, was a very unfavorable one from the start, and his development was leading into criminal psychopathy. He is now 15 years old, in treatment, has maintained himself in school, has stayed at home and out of the courts. This, in his case, has to be considered as a satisfactory result so far.

In the 16 years that I have been working with this method, I have never had any difficulty in relation to the child. I have explained this phenomenon to myself on the basis that the changes in the mother conformed with the child's experiences in his analysis and therefore did not create any difficulty, conflict or confusion but, on the contrary, facilitated the progress of analysis by narrowing the gap between the attitudes of the mother (parents) and that of the analyst.

Bibliography

1. Arlow, J.: Perversion: Theoretical and therapeutic aspects (Panel Report). J. Am. Psychoanalyt. A.: Vol. II, 1954.

2. Bender, L., and Paster, S.: Homosexual Trends in Children. Am. J. Orthopsychiat. *11:* 730–743, 1941.

3. Buxbaum, E.: Exhibitionistic onanism in a 10-year-old boy. Psychoanalyt. Quart. *4:* 161–189, 1935.

4. Bettelheim, B.: Truants from Life: The Rehabilitation of Emotionally Disturbed Children. Glencoe, Free Press, 1955.

5. Freud, S.: The Etiology of Hysteria (1896). *In* Collected Papers, vol. I, pp. 183–219. London, Hogarth, 1946.

6. ———: On the History of the Psychoanalytic Movement (1914). *In* Collected Papers, vol. I, pp. 287–359. London, Hogarth, 1946.

7. Friend, M. R., and others: Observations on the development of transvestitism in boys. Am. J. Orthopsychiat. *24:* 563–575, 1954.

8. Gardner, G. E., Panel: Report from the James Jackson Putnam Children's Center, Boston, The 1948 Midwinter Meeting. Bull. Am. Psychoanalyt. A. *5:* 33–36, 1949.

9. Gillespie, William H.: The Structure and Aetiology of Sexual Perversion. *In* Lorand, S.: Perversions, Psychodynamics and Therapy. New York, Random House, 1956, pp. 28–41.

10. Hartmann, H.: Ich-Psychologie und Anpassungsproblem. Internat. Ztschr. f. Psychoanal. u. Imago *24:* 62–135, 1939. *Also in* Rapaport, D.: Organization and Pathology of Thought. New York, Columbia University Press, 1951, pp. 362–396.

11. Johnson, A. M., and Szurek, S. A.: Genesis of antisocial acting-out in children and adults. Psychoanalyt. Quart. *21:* 323–343, 1952.

12. Klein, M.: The Psycho-Analysis of Children. London, Hogarth, 1933.

13. Kris, E.: Notes on the development and on some current problems of psychoanalytic child psychology. Psychoanalyt. Study of the Child *5:* 24–46, 1950.

14. Rapaport, D.: The Autonomy of the Ego. *In* Knight, R. P.: Psychoanalytic Psychiatry and Psychology. Vol. I, pp. 284–258. And paper read at Anna Freud Meeting at Clark University, Worcester, Mass., Sept. 21, 1957.

15. Sperling, M.: A psychoanalytic study of ulcerative colitis in children. Psychoanalyt. Quart. *15:* 302–329, 1946.

16. ———: The analysis of an exhibitionist. Internat. J. Psycho-Analysis *28:* 32–45, 1947.

17. ———: The role of the mother in psychosomatic disorders in children. Psychosom. Med. *11:* 377–385, 1949.

18. ———: Problems in analysis of children with psychosomatic disorders. Quart. J. of Child Behavior *1:* 12–17, 1949.

19. ———: Analysis of a case of recurrent ulcer of the leg. Psychoanalyt. Study of the Child *3/4:* 391–408, 1949.

20. ———: Indirect treatment of psychoneurotic and psychosomatic disorders in children. Quart. J. of Child Behavior *2:* 250–266, 1950.

21. ———: Children's interpretation and reaction to the unconscious of their mothers. Internat. J. Psycho-Analysis *31:* 1–6, 1950.

22. ———: The neurotic child and his mother. Am. J. Orthopsychiat. *21:* 351–364, 1951.

23. ———: Psychoanalytic aspects of discipline. Nervous Child *9:* 174–186, 1951.

24. ———: Psychogenic diarrhea and phobia in a six-and-a-half-year-old girl. Am. J. Orthopsychiat. *22:* 838–848, 1952.

25. ———: Psychotherapeutic Techniques in Psychosomatic Medicine. *In* Bychowski, G., and Despert, J. L.: Specialized Techniques in Psychotherapy. New York, Basic Books, 1952, pp. 279–301.

26. ———: Psychosomatic Medicine and Pediatrics. *In* Wittkower, E., and Cleghorn, R.: Recent Developments in Psychosomatic Medicine. London, Pittman & Sons, 1954, pp. 381–396.

27. ———: Psychosis and psychosomatic illness. Internat. J. Psycho-Analysis *36:* 320–327, 1955.

28. ———: Observations from the treatment of children suffering from nonbloody diarrhea or mucous colitis. J. Hillside Hospital *4:* 25–31, 1955.

29. ———: Reactive schizophrenia in children. Am. J. Orthopsychiat. *24:* 506–512, 1954.

30. ———: Equivalents of depression in children. Paper read at the Annual Meeting of the American Orthopsychiatric Assoc., March 5, 1958, to appear in the J. Hillside Hospital, April 1959.

31. ———: Pavor Nocturnus. J. Am. Psychoanalyt. *6:* 79–94, 1958.

32. Sperling, O. E.: Interpretation of the trauma as a command. Psychoanalyt. Quart. *19:* 352–370, 1950.

33. ———: Some observations on failure of leadership. Psychoanalysis & Social Sciences *4:* 83–93, 1955.

34. ———: Psychodynamics of group perversions. Psychoanalyt. Quart. *25:* 56–65, 1956.

9

On Focal Symbiosis *

By PHYLLIS GREENACRE

We are indebted largely to M. Mahler [8, 9] for the description and the development of the concept of symbiosis, a relationship of mutual interdependence, usually between the mother and the young child, which if prolonged and intense, may distort and narrow the margin of developing autonomous reactions of the infant, who is sucked too much into the mother's reactions. Neither party to this close and inevitably ambivalent relationship can be ordinarily free and resilient in relationship to the outer world, and the maintenance of this too tight little mother-child unit may have far-reaching and sometimes disastrous effects on the child's subsequent development.

Certain related observations had previously been made by Rado [10] in his paper on the anxious mother, and by many others (especially Deutsch [3]) in considering certain gross disturbances of the female castration complex involving the use of the child as a phallic equivalent by the mother, which in its extreme might result in a practical appersonation of the child by the mother. Mahler's work, however, not only outlined and defined the general condition more clearly, but, focussing chiefly and systematically on the effect on the child, has furnished an organization of the clinical observations, these being most useful for further investigations of adult symptomatology as well. It goes almost without saying that, at the very least, separation anxiety and the invasion of the libidinal development by overly strong problems of hostile aggression, as well as a predisposition to untoward homosexual influences in the later childhood or young adulthood, are to be expected in those individuals for whom a moderately severe degree of prolonged symbiosis has existed in infancy. In the most severe cases there is naturally an impairment of the sense of identity and a severe invasion of object relationships and even of the sense of reality.

* From the Department of Psychiatry of the New York Hospital and Cornell Medical College, New York.

The state of focal symbiosis has been much less clearly delineated.* The present paper, primarily a clinical report, will deal with two clinical situations in which the rise of this peculiar relationship and the vicissitudes following it could be fairly well seen. One was an adult patient, under analysis for a number of years, concerning whom the understanding of the nature and sequence of the events was achieved from classical analysis by its work with the different forms of memory, resulting in extensive reconstructions. The second consists of direct observation of a focal symbiotic relationship between two children, which in the natural course of events might have resolved itself quite normally and satisfactorily but having been suddenly and tragically interrupted, was followed by a spreading kind of "chain reaction" affecting the rest of the children in the family.

I would conceive of a focal symbiosis as being an intensely strong interdependence (usually between mother and child, but sometimes, as in my cases, with people other than the mother) which is limited to a special and rather circumscribed relationship rather than a nearly total enveloping one. Probably it represents most frequently an area of pathology of the adult member of the symbiotic pair which is then projected onto the child with focussed anxiety or conviction of a corresponding disturbance in the infant. For example, I recall one such situation in which a mother with an isolated but severe phobia concerning blindness subjected her young child to a daily examination of the child's eyes over a period of months. In this particular instance, the mother's phobia had been dormant until re-precipitated and legitimatized by a rather slight trauma to the child, which then permitted the whole intense "beam" of the mother's phobia to be played out on the child, with scant insight on her part into its pathologic nature. Quite frequent are situations of the absorption of one parent or the other in the bowel habits of the child to such an extent as to produce an extraordinary pull between parent and child on this particular subject.

Probably masturbation fears and their derivative phobias are the most frequent generators of the circumscribed anxious drives of the adult

* By *focal symbiosis* I mean a condition in which a symbiotic relationship exists in respect to the functioning of a special organ or body area. Usually the individuals participating in this symbiotic relationship are of uneven development: parent and child, older and younger sibling, or even stronger and weaker twins. The focal symbiosis represents the special site of emotional disturbance in both members of the symbiotic pair. But it is ordinarily manifest in the weaker or smaller partner, who remains functionally dependent in this specific area on the active response of the other partner, far beyond the maturational period at which the special function would ordinarily become autonomous.

toward the child which result in limited or focal cords of attachment between adult and child. In this connection, one sees such extensions of anxious concern quite occasionally from the father, even when the mother does not participate in them. Paternal generation of symbiosis is fairly likely to be focal, i.e., topical, probably partly because the father is less frequently with the child. But whether the focal symbiosis is derived from the mother or father, it may be a little later in its development than are the consequences in the case of the chronically and generally anxious mother who swathes the infant in her limiting care from birth onward. It would seem probable, too, that in limited or focal symbiotic relationships, there is often a peculiar union of the child's special need with the parent's special sensitivity, and that the total personality of either parent or child may not be as much involved as in the severe cases of symbiotic psychoses described by Mahler.

In presenting the clinical reports, after these introductory remarks, I shall make no attempt consistently to unfold the life development in terms of the chronology and problems of treatment, but will present it more as the story of the evolution of the disturbance as seen retrospectively from the remembered and reconstructed events and emotional reactions.

Case 1. The patient was in her early thirties, the mother of two young daughters of five and seven, and on the brink of a divorce at the time she first consulted me. I had been suggested to her by her children's pediatrician because of her obvious chronic anxiety about her children. She was a handsome woman whose appearance somewhat suggested a dissatisfied or angry goddess, rarely smiling, often showing a kind of imperious but stormy beauty, and again rather disheveled, windblown and resentfully clinging. That much could be seen readily from her appearance and manner in our first interviews. As I began work with her, I was struck by rather marked and at first puzzling discrepancies in her behavior and attitudes. Obviously sensitive and thoughtful, she showed unusual sense, skill and determination in her plans for herself and her children and a kind of decisive aversion to her husband, but with almost no bitterness and actually a very reasonable considerateness. On the other hand, when she approached any topic having to do with a conscious appraisal of herself as a woman, whether as mother, housewife, or of her attractions and the possibility of her marrying again, she would quickly lapse into a childish pleading or tempestuously angry state, comparing herself in frenzied fashion with some particular person and demanding reassurance that at some time in the future she might expect to be as beautiful, as learned, as popular or win out in some particular way over all rivals.

It was obvious that this patient suffered from compulsive fantasies of perfection in any or all spheres. What was most striking, however, was that frequently her disturbances assumed real tantrum proportions. Especially in premenstrual and menstrual states, they often were converted into reality demands of absurd proportions or were presented in their negative form. For example, she would wail, "And will I always have to be younger than my sister, Edna!" (the oldest of her sisters). These islands of absurdity were embedded in an otherwise rather reasonable and sensible character, and were not seen with any humor, even in intervals between their occurrence.

When tantrums occurred, they generally emerged in characteristic form. The patient would seem quiet and possibly brooding, and would either be disinclined to talk or would speak in a monotone, with a controlled, almost studied approximation of indifference. Then gradually approaching the hidden sensitivity, but in a very concealed way, she would either ask me some unreasonable question or pick on some trivial and seemingly inconsequential point in something which I had said, and begin a kind of quibbling and questioning of what I (or some person about whom she had been reporting) had said. On this pivot, her compulsive questioning would continue until it reached almost frenzied proportions in which there was a demand for an absolute answer. I soon came to recognize that these were substitutes for, or at least closely related to, the demands for the reassurances about her own perfection along the lines already spoken of. The form of the tantrum with its slowly mounting tension and its pitch of demand for discharge revealed its relation to an orgasm and indicated its probable derivation from repressed masturbation. A further characteristic was the fact that the patient seemed unable to get a discharge for herself. The great urge was to provoke me to some evidence of anger. If she succeeded in any degree, she generally subsided somewhat for the time being, but might begin again the next day, either on the same subject or utilizing some parallel situation. I thought at first that these tantrums were possibly derived from wishes to be spanked or beaten, which had been perpetuated in this disguised form since childhood. Although the patient showed many anal characteristics, the fixation was more phallic in its content and the tantrums reproduced with an interesting precision the main disturbance of her young childhood.

The patient was the fourth of six children in a family which, on the father's side, had enjoyed the prestige of esteemed public service for many generations, and on the mother's side was known for wealth, generosity and ample living. The father, a lawyer by profession, had retired when rather young; he was a careful and kindly man, much concerned with matters of justice and public welfare, and always regretful of the harsh competitive tactics of his professional colleagues. The mother, on the other hand, was an outgoing, sociable and rather picturesque person, who enjoyed her series of babies but was less mindful of them once they were weaned. Later in her life her interest in young things turned to the breeding of dogs and to the building of houses in various parts of the country, which she would occupy for a time before her restlessness brought about a new venture. Of the six children, only the oldest was a boy. Of the two girls after the patient, one was born in the second half of her second year and the other when she was eight years old.

My patient had shown some disturbances from an early period and had been treated by various psychiatrists and analysts intermittently since adolescence. Her manifest disturbance seemed indeed to have begun much earlier. Some months after the birth of her next younger sister, she developed an habitual masturbation and wakefulness at night. This seemed to have its roots in her watchfulness and primitive jealousy of the mother's nursing the baby. But her nocturnal restlessness brought further stimulation through her awareness of primal scene activities. Her masturbation troubled her father in the extreme; and after some months, he undertook to devote himself to this child in order to get her over the habit, while the mother's attention was focussed on the baby. His care of her involved his sitting with her each night, talking with her one way and another, and admonishing her not to touch herself whenever her hand went in the direction of her genitals. He would stay with her until she finally dropped off to sleep. After some months, in order that his care might be more assiduous, he had the child's crib moved into the dressing room adjoining the bedroom which he shared with his wife. Her wakefulness continued and he was alert to her restlessness and would frequently come to her to quiet her.

A deep and tender bond developed between father and daughter. She never had any doubt that she was his favorite child. This special love, however, was based largely on her suppression of her masturbation, which finally involved a genuine denial of any sensitivity in the clitoris. This absence of clitoral awareness still existed at the time the patient first came to me. The specially paradoxic element of the relationship was that the attachment clearly was sexual in nature but demanded the practical elimination of the main area of sexual stimulation and discharge and the development of a premature, overly strong superego which in turn became somewhat sexualized. The first appearance of clitoral feeling came spontaneously and dramatically after an analytic session. At this time, certain matters of the father's estate, his death having occurred a few years earlier, had to be discussed between the patient and her brother who was executor of the estate. The patient's scrutiny of certain accountings had brought her to a conclusion different from that of her brother. She assumed that she must be wrong although she could not detect her mistake. When I remarked that I wondered why she seemed automatically to assume that she was wrong and he was right, she was immensely surprised and reacted with a clitoral tingling which was bewildering to her.

The patient has had since early childhood a series of fantasies of a sleeping beauty type, involving the idea that she would ultimately be carried off into a romantic marriage by the Duke of D.......... There were several variations on this theme but on the whole the pattern was rather rigid. The fantasy seemed to have begun in early latency and to have gotten its coloring from a period when at around five to six the family had spent a year abroad, most of which was spent in England, ending with a period in Belgium and France. These fantasies had all the appearance of masturbation fantasies, which had become detached from the physical act and served as consolation fantasies whenever she was distressed or anxious. They were the complementary parts to the tantrums in which she doubted her beauty, her ability, her intelligence and her ability to be anyone at all. At times, she would cry and say, "I have no *I*. Will I ever be anyone and have an *I*?" On the other hand, once when I remarked that she might have envied the prettiness of an older sister, she replied quite simply, "Of course, I shouldn't really be worried about whether I am as pretty as my sisters. I have always been considered the beauty of the family."

It seems that during the period in England, the little girl had somehow gotten into sexual play with her brother, who being six or seven years older than she, was then a boy of twelve or thirteen, just at puberty. In this sexual interest she would seem to have been the fascinated, for the most part passive, participant in his exhibitionistic performances involving his showing his genitals, sometimes urinating and again masturbating. Whether or not she had been permitted a more active participation of touching or whether this was only a very strong desire could not be determined. Before the trip to England, during the time of the relinquishment of her clitoris, she had regressed to an interest in her own bowel movements, with fantasies concerning their power and great interest in flatus. This latter was perpetuated in a screen memory of herself letting out a cloud of brown smoke from the rear in an impressive way, very much like Daumier's strutting officer. The contact with the brother seemed, however, to reinstate the phallic interest, and she practically took on his organ as her own possession. A fragmentary memory, seen at first only through dream associations, combined the brother with the famous urinating boy of the Brussels street fountain. In Paris, when the brother became acutely sick with an appendix, an emergency operation was done, and this threw her into a panic since she associated the penis with the appendix and felt vaguely as though she had been responsible for this disaster.

On their return to this country, the brother soon was sent away to preparatory school some distance from the suburban community in which they lived. During latency there was again a regression to anal interests. She played mostly with tomboyish girls who ridiculed boys and told or acted out childish scatological jokes. At one time the chauffeur's son exposed himself in her presence, but she thought that he had only testicles and no penis. Later it became apparent that if boys had penises, the penises were really only stools which amounted to little anyway.

The birth of her youngest sister, when she was eight, brought a new focus of distress with a revival of jealousy of the baby, mixed with intense resentment that the child was not hers. At this time the oedipal jealousy was less evident and the wish to have the baby as her own seemed much more a real phallic envy of the mother.

In another year, however, she was beginning to show the body changes of early puberty. She had an isolated memory from a little later time of her brother, home from school on a holiday, enticing her into a situation of his examining and admiring her breasts. It seemed from subsequent analytic productions that the examination had been mutual and had involved a recurrence of the brother attachment which had begun in the oedipal period. Soon afterward when he, a well developed adolescent, began to show interest in special girls, she was intensely jealous, felt abandoned and "used" by him. From this time until the beginning of the analysis, she had been extremely distant though not actively hostile to him. The fantasy of the Duke of D.......... who would eventually awaken her and marry her obviously referred mainly to the brother.

When her menses came, she was away at boarding school, a strict and pretentious place with many snob standards. Her conscious reaction was of pride and great pleasure that she was now so grown up. She felt lonely, wanted very much to have boy friends but seemed totally unable to do so. A severe florid compulsion neurosis broke out, with fear of dirt, of touching, ideas of having sinned and ritualistic defenses against this anxiety. The anal masturbatory interest which had early followed the relinquishment of clitoral interest and the fascination with flatus as showing the power of illusion reappeared in a symptomatic form with an intense desire and overwhelming guilt at the thought of smoking cigarettes. During much of her adolescence and until her marriage in her early twenties, this neurosis appeared with fluctuating severity. It was partially in abeyance in a period in her late teens when she found some satisfaction in painting, for which she had real talent. At this time, too, she was seeing an uncle in a repetition of her early experience with her brother. Although she was interested in painting, she was frequently repelled by fellow art students whom she considered socially inferior and essentially dirty, like the chauffeur's son. She would then abandon her painting for a time in a state of mind which looked like snobbishness but was really an extension of her mysophobia into social relations and attitudes. The attachment to the father remained extremely strong. He was a heroically spiritual figure with whom no other man could be compared. There was one experience (whether true or an intense fantasy was uncertain) which consisted in her meeting him in the hall near her bedroom when she had gotten up unexpectedly at night and his having kissed her in a lover-like way.

She married in her early twenties, a man of little distinction, of great wealth, and of uncertain potency. He worshipped her and surrounded her with great luxury, but he could not fulfill her ideals of the Duke of D.........., who was handsome and virile. A stillbirth relatively early in the marriage precipitated a florid outbreak of her extreme compulsion neurosis, associated with intense guilt feelings and an obsessional fear of having hurt or killed a child. There were subsequently two children, for whom she had a considerable maternal, though narcissistically heavily burdened, love. After the birth of these children and with the suggestion of an outspoken therapist that her husband might have homosexual tendencies, she had suffered a kind of chronic panic herself with marked sensitivity on the subject of homosexuality. While this was initially focused on her husband, her own touchiness about lesbianism was extreme. The force of her reaction to her father's death, which occurred just before she obtained her divorce, seemed almost muted, so nearly spiritual had he become and so completely had the oedipal problem been deviated and degraded in her relation to her brother.

This young woman's actual relationship to men showed a repetitive pattern.

During the course of her analytic treatment, she was generally fearful that no man would ever again pay attention to her and she was blatantly jealous of all love affairs and marriages which she saw in statu nascendi. Her situation and her own attractiveness were such, however, that men quite occasionally sought her out. At the beginning of such a relationship, she daydreamed constantly about the man and showed a sore-tooth sort of sensitivity to his slightest reaction, which at once became magnified in her fear lest he would drop her or find her wanting. If the relationship developed and the man sought a consummation of his sexual interest in her, she hastily withdrew with the panicky conviction that he thought her a dirty, common woman, which was then followed by resentment at having "been used" by him. If he then became discouraged and withdrew, her fantasies again became active and she would quite paradoxically show an exquisite pain at his neglect of her. This pattern gradually became modified during the analysis, as she gained more insight and more sense of herself as an individual, which permitted then a sense of the man as a separate person, not so much under the shadow of the demand to use him and the reciprocal fear of being abused by him.

It should be emphasized concerning this patient that the longer I worked with her, the more I became aware of potential and partially developed gifts (probably in part constitutionally determined) which had been stunted and mutilated by her severe neurosis but which still showed, even through her troubled states. She had an artist's awareness of the outer world, and in her better periods reacted with an exquisite perceptiveness to people and surroundings. Her painting, which developed in spite of its being discarded from time to time as though it were no more than a dirty and disgraceful smearing, was said to show some merit. Her use of language was unusual. At first, due to the invasion of her thinking by obsessional doubts and needs for precision, her speech showed an habitual slowness which could be exasperating. At times, when I too was among the group of the dirty, despised and inferior, she would begin to talk French or would use somewhat stilted French phrases as though to show me the distance between us, but this also probably dated from her early experiences in France. Again, this tendency might be reversed and there would be many slips, malapropisms, and the language of uneducated maids and kitchen help. But withal, her language always had an interesting quality of vivid perceptiveness and picturesqueness with an unusual capacity for expressing nuances of feeling. Once when out of a desperate feeling of lack of education and know-nothingness, she took some courses in literature and writing at one of the universities, she was surprised to find herself receiving some recognition and being regarded as showing some embryonic ability as a writer. Her taste in literature was unerringly good.

This case has been given in this much descriptive detail in order to follow through the effect and manifestations of the early symbiotic relationship with the father, which expressed itself paradoxically in a tender loving attachment and in the negation of an essential developing function, viz., the participation of the clitoris in the organization of the child's sensori-emotional life. The suppression of this was followed by a regression to anal interests with stool retention and smearing, which did not last long and in turn was relieved by an intensified interest in the brother's phallus, compensating thus for her loss of her own clitoris. There was an actual appersonation of the phallus, mediated largely through vision but with strong desires for touching and sucking. This was later to form the basis of an illusory phallus possession, alternating with periods of a sense of complete loss and degradation: "I am nobody." "I have nothing." "Nobody will ever pay any attention to me." These dejected feelings came fairly regularly with the menses, which were also looked upon as evidence of fecal smearing and loss of control. The premenstrual tantrums with their provocativeness followed very closely the pattern of the child's frustrated and seemingly diffused erotic feelings for which she could get no discharge except very incompletely and vicariously through the brother's discharge.

At the time of the major working through of the disturbances of the pubertal period, the patient went through a state of some days' duration in which she felt alienated from herself as though her head and its thoughts were very far away. There was no definite feeling of unreality of the external world, though she was preoccupied and disinterested in events of the outer world. One might describe the condition as a partial depersonalization with a sense of her thoughts lacking significance and being poorly possessed by her. She could only describe it as a little like being drunk.

Case 2. The second clinical situation involved a little girl who at fourteen months suffered the sudden and complete loss of her only sibling, a boy of four and one half years. The little girl was at that particularly charming period when just after learning to walk there appears a quickening and unfolding of all of the sensory responses. It is a period which, in its capacity for exhilaration, is somewhat like the phallic phase, to which it has been compared and described as a forerunner, the total body seeming to take on a new animation and responsiveness.[7] It is a time when children are still in, or at least, just beginning to emerge from a stage of normal symbiotic relationships and the introjective-projective responses are still preponderant. I have several times seen little ones of this age go into states of fantastic primordial exhilaration while watching the dancing and leaping of flames of a bonfire.

By chance, I had had an opportunity to go for a walk with the little girl almost as soon as she was able to manage more than a toddler's exploration of her own household. I had been entranced by her vibrant response to her surroundings. She laughed as she walked along, stopping now and then to touch and smell weeds and flowers, to squat down on the sidewalk to peer at and run her small hands over an area where wide cracks had appeared in the cement; or again to seat herself gravely on the steps of a water power plant while, with her head cocked to one side with comical intentness, she listened to the pumping of the water inside the building and registered her answer in the slight rhythmic swaying of her body.

Two weeks later the older brother died, suddenly and with no warning symptoms. As far as she was concerned, he was there playing with her in the morning and then was gone. She was too young to understand, and at the most it could only be said that he had "gone bye-bye." While she certainly must have reacted to the grief around her, the main symptom, which appeared on the second night after he was gone and continued for some time, was insomnia with nocturnal restlessness and especially difficulty in going to sleep at night. She was at first obviously expecting him to return and would run to the door when she heard little boys playing outside. Something in her behavior then made the mother realize that she was probably missing the body contact with him and kinesthetic satisfactions that their evening play together had involved. They had been wont to romp together on the floor at her bedtime, very much in the fashion of playful puppies. On the advice of a friend, the little girl was given a large soft teddy bear to play with and cuddle. This seemed to help the immediate symptom in that she went to sleep more readily. But the situation became intolerable to the parents. On a visit to them, I realized that the child's persistent and uncanny efforts to animate the bear and convert him into the lost brother presented such a grim caricature that it could not be accepted, and the mourning struggle had to be continued in other ways.

Slightly less than a year later, another child was born, a little girl, a somewhat premature and very quiet baby. Three months before the birth of this baby and eight to nine months after the death of the older child, the little one showed quite distinctly some memory of the lost brother. On one occasion when she had to be separated from the father for about two weeks and was told that he was now coming and would arrive very soon, she looked up in a puzzled way and gave the name of the lost brother. She was twenty-two months old and not yet forming sentences. When the father actually did arrive, there was an appreciable delay in her welcome to him, followed by a quick break-through of joyous recognition, after which she did not want to let him out of her sight.

When the little sister was about ten months old and the older one was approaching her third birthday, I again saw the children for a period of time. An intense relationship had grown up between them. The older child, who was now gay, animated and extremely playful, had somehow made the younger one her captive audience. What ever she did, the baby watched gleefully and patty-caked her hands with enthusiastic fascination. She seemed in a state of happy bondage to the older one. This continued for some months. Then with the older girl's going to kindergarten, the little one was inconsolable. When she was about two and a quarter years old, a third little girl was born. The second one turned then to this baby as soon as the baby had reached an age of appreciation. The bondage in their case was neither so intense nor so sustained and the suffering of separation for nursery school which also arrived in the course of time was less devastating than it had been with the second girl. The chain reaction had become attenuated.

But the oldest child, who had gone through a season of elation in the reinforcement of herself in the applause of her sister, had become again a sober child, inclined to be overconscientious and anxious, to suffer from vague aches and discomforts, and to seek body contact for solace.

Discussion

The emergence of the concept of symbiosis would appear to have come about through a combination of certain trends in psychoanalysis, which in themselves represent a return to interests apparent in the earliest decades of Freud's researches. I refer especially to concern with the psychoses and, closely related to this, the examination of biologic and even specifically physiologic aspects of psychological reactions. It was probably necessary that a purely psychological approach be developed in the intervening years. But it prepared the way for a re-examination of the influence of variations in physical maturation phases on the earliest appearances of the psyche. Work along these lines has then proceeded with promising fruitfulness. These trends have inevitably joined forces with these growing out of child analytic work, with its concomitant interest in the direct observation of infants. Somewhere in the setting of this background is the further outgrowth of a special interest in childhood psychosis. The very notion of this would have been anathema forty years ago, when it was thought that the earliest evidence of psychotic development could be detected only after puberty and it was considered a psychiatric truism that psychotics, especially sufferers from dementia praecox (how rarely we hear this terminology anymore!) are "those who founder on the rocks of puberty." Although there were admittedly a few examples of psychoses already well established in pre-puberty periods, these were looked upon as freak developments.

There is still considerable controversy concerning the relative prevalence of psychotic symptoms in childhood, and even more question concerning their essential sources. The natural tendency is to hold the parents, especially the mother in her closest of all relationships to the child, responsible for the pathogenic developments in the child. One has only to realize how consistently the mother in her brooding and breeding of the child is blamed by the grown-up child himself for all the physical as well as emotional ills which have beset him and by girls for the fact even of their biological sex itself to realize also how deeply rooted is the fantasy of the omnipotence of the mother to provide everything and consequently her culpability in case of any failure. Along with the strength of this strong fantasy, it is also true that the *mother is* the person of paramount importance in the first months of life and that disturbance in the mother-child relationship in the first eighteen months does seem to endanger the subsequent psychic health of the child (Spitz).[12] Further, it is obvious that both parents may communicate elements of their own neuroses to their children, especially during the pre-school years. Rado's beautiful description of the beach scene with the anxious mother and her five year old boy whom she continually released to play in the water and then drew back again by the checkreins of her own anxiety strikes one with such familiar resonance as in itself to be convincing of the strong invasion of the child by his mother's neurosis. Certainly the recent book by S. Brody on *Patterns of Mothering* is a monumental recognition of the work done and expected to be done in research on interaction between mother and infant.[1]

Against this background, then, it is of interest to note the appearance of Mahler's concept of symbiosis, first presented in relation to the psychotic child, in a paper which compared and contrasted autistic and symbiotic infantile psychoses. The work of Kanner [4-6] and other observers [2, 11] had already described the autistic child as representing a special kind of disturbance in the child, apparently endogenous in origin and not dependent on the mother's attitude; the latter, however, may become disturbed in secondary reaction to the apparent alienation of the infant from her. Mahler's conception, presented first in 1951,[8] as already mentioned, was more clearly etched out in later papers, especially one published in 1955 with Gosliner.[9] A symbiotic relationship between mother and child is a normal one during the early months but, ordinarily, gradually gives way during the period extending roughly from twelve-eighteen months to thirty-six months to a stage of separation-individuation.

There are, however, according to Mahler and Gosliner, certain constitutionally predisposed children who do not and cannot make this shift normally. In contrast to the autistic child, the one predisposed to symbiosis shows a need for a prolonged clinging to the mother which is stronger than the aggressive, outward pushing autonomous drives normally developing at this time. It is the child's defect, rather than the mother's disturbed character, which then sets up the vicious circle of intense, prolonged symbiosis between mother and child which may cause such severe after-effects in the child. Even a well-poised mother may be seduced by such a melting child into too strong a reciprocal and anxious reaction. But if the mother or nurse contributes her own pre-formed neurotic reaction to the child or is especially narcissistically gratified by the infant's response, it is conceivable that the symbiotic partnership is that much more intense and prolonged. The tendency, however, has frequently been to underrate the part played by the infant in establishing this bond.

The case presented in this paper lies somewhere between that of the anxious parent appersonating the child and that of a truer pathologic but focal symbiotic relationship due to disturbance in the child.

The patient does not seem to have been one of those extraordinarily clinging infants without sufficient body-image demarcation encountered in severe general symbiotic relationships. She was probably an overly-sensitive and perceptive child in whom pregenital phase drives are readily and intensely aroused early. It is noteworthy, however, that her disturbance culminating in a focal genital symbiotic relationship with her brother was developed in two stages. She was robbed by her father's tender ministrations and sought restitution through the brother. The loss of clitoral awareness created a deformation of her body self-image and the diminution of the essential organizing influence in her ego development, affecting also her sense of identity. In addition the special need, like a vacuous area with a centripetal restitutive pressure, resulted in a strengthening of the introjective-projective capacities operating in this particular focus. A phenomenon probably related to this clinical observation is described in Mahler's 1952 article in which she notes that a "peculiar hypercathexis of one part of the body is often encountered in symbiotic psychotic children. It seems to occur in those cases of symbiotic infantile psychosis in which parental psychopathology is rather pronounced." She notes that this often corresponds to the type of overstimulation which occurred during the symbiotic relationship. It is further stated that in some instances a high degree of countercathexis is established and the symptom is a negative silent area, rather than a positive one. All this is of some interest also in investigating the nature of cathexis itself, a term now used entirely in the restricted psychological sense.

Bibliography

1. Brody, S.: Patterns of Mothering. New York, International Universities Press, Inc., 1956.

2. Despert, J. L.: Schizophrenia in children. Psychiat. Quart. *12:* 366–371, 1938.

3. Deutsch, H.: The Psychology of Women: A Psychoanalytic Interpretation. Vol. 2: Motherhood. Pp. 294–332. New York, Grune & Stratton, 1945.

4. Kanner, L.: Autistic disturbances of affective contact. Nervous Child *2:* 217–250, 1943.

5. ———: Early infantile autism. J. Pediat. *25:* 211–217, 1944.

6. ———: Problems of nosology and psychodynamics of early infantile autism. Am. J. Orthopsychiat. *19:* 416–426, 1949.

7. Loewenstein, R. M.: Conflict and autonomous ego development during the phallic phase. Psychoanalyt. Study of the Child *5:* 47–52, 1950.

8. Mahler, M. S.: On child psychosis and schizophrenia: Autistic and symbiotic infantile psychoses. Psychoanalyt. Study of the Child *7:* 286–306, 1952.

9. Mahler, M. S., and Gosliner, B. J. L.: On symbiotic child psychosis. Psychoanalyt. Study of the Child *10:* 195–215, 1955.

10. Rado, S.: An anxious mother. Internat. J. Psycho-Analysis *9:* 219–226, 1928.

11. Ritvo, S., and Provence, S.: Form perception and imitation in some autistic children. Psychoanalyt. Study of the Child *13:* 155–161, 1958.

12. Spitz, R. A.: The psychogenic diseases in infancy—an attempt at their classification. Psychoanalyt. Study of the Child *6:* 255–279, 1951.

10

Some Observations on Children Hospitalized During Latency*

By LUCIE JESSNER †

THIS PAPER stems from observations on children hospitalized ‡ with serious, prolonged illness during latency.

In psychotherapy of children between the ages of six and ten, it became obvious that long-lasting illness brings challenges usually not occurring until adolescence for the healthy child. Illness draws attention to the body, altering the body- and self-image. It may shake the belief in the power and protection of the parent, with a consequent return of repressed pre-oedipal fantasies, arousing severe anxiety. Thus, the child is pushed forward to cope with tasks beyond his age. At the same time, he is curtailed in motor expression and mastery of the outside world, which are relevant devices leading to the consolidation of ego functions in latency. The ensuing helplessness can throw him back into infantile anxieties and ego-alien regressive longings. Defenses against anxiety and regression result. From the economic aspect this means that premature excitation interferes with the developmental process.

This report deals only with three areas of the effect of illness: the alteration of ego functions, the change of body image, and the threat of losing the love object.

(A) EGO FUNCTIONS

(1.) *Heightened sensitivity and perception of the body and its functions.*

In the healthy child, during latency and following the period of intense curiosity and explorations of excretory and sexual organs—more directed

* Partially read at American Psychoanalytic Association Meeting, San Francisco, May, 1958.

† This study was in part supported by a Research Grant (MH-66) from the National Institute of Mental Health (USPHS).

‡ Mass. General Hospital, Boston, Mass. or North Carolina Memorial Hospital, Chapel Hill, N. C.

toward others than oneself—the body is taken for granted. This relative unconcern usually persists until pre-puberty. In health the body plays during latency a major role only in narcissistic concerns about the size and strength of the genitals in a comparative and competitive way, and in castration fear and penis envy. Illness enforces awareness of physiologic events which are otherwise not registered. This evokes repressed infantile experiences. Particularly the inside of the body, the gastrointestinal tract, joints, etc., becomes invested with more oral, anal and oedipal fantasies and animistic concepts of the enemy within, elaborated in the terms of later childhood. For example, John, an eleven year old boy with chronic liver disease and recurrent abdominal swellings, was on a rigid diet. He mentioned that a tornado blew the roof off a diner nearby and hurt two people. He imagined a man coming out of the diner. The man must have thought it was something he ate. "If you ate something, came out of the diner and then something happened, wouldn't you think it was because of something you ate?" he asked the psychiatrist.[1] This indicates a confusion of forces in the outside world with forces from the own inside.

Incorporation and ejection become magic feats. "I must have eaten something when I was very little," is a common theory of children with gastrointestinal disturbances. The contents of the abdomen become unbearably malevolent and dirty. Several children with ulcerative colitis ate soap and toothpaste to clean their insides. One of them, Jimmy, who will be discussed later, after discharge from the hospital chose to become a taxidermist. He practiced eviscerating birds, squirrels, etc., replacing the dirty content with a clean stuffing, thus preventing decay, and also conquering his fear of death by providing immortality. There is a striving for static conditions as a defense against the frightening awareness of constant change.

(2.) *Awareness of reality.*

Certain concepts, i.e., illness, death, heretofore kept abstract and at a distance, inapplicable to oneself, become immediate experience. The former defenses, (e.g., "This cannot happen to me" or "Only old people die,") against the frightening meaning of these words cannot be maintained in the same way as before. The healthy child can gradually prepare himself for grim events through dealing with his own dangerous impulses in play, in fantasy, and in language. There is usually an expectation that the outside world reciprocates in a similar "make-believe" fashion. Illness and its vicissitudes are likely to shake the fundamental distinction between fantasy and reality on which the child in latency relies and which he uses to ward off anxieties stemming from magic wishes. Destructive impulses, formerly enjoyed in games or stories, suddenly become actualities and frequently lead to projection, serving as a defense against uncontrollable forces from within. For example, one boy with ulcerative colitis wondered whether the medication his grandmother had given him was poison. He spoke of food that kills fish and people too.

(3.) *The mastery of outside and inside.*

(a.) The child's control of the outside world and his inner impulses during latency is achieved to a large degree through action. Motor activity expresses feelings and discharges tensions and aggression in a more or less acceptable way. Also, unacceptable emotions are experienced in a motoric way, rather than by awareness of feeling. Helen Keller recalls, speaking of herself in the third person before she acquired language at the age of seven: "There blazed up in her frequent fierce anger which I remember not by emotion but by a tactual memory of the kick or blow she dealt to the object of that anger." [6] Interfering as it does with the use of the body for these purposes, illness may lead to complete anaclitic regression, to a panicky discharge or to counterphobic defenses. Denial of illness, counterphobic and paranoid defenses against fear of death were evident in an eleven year old colored boy hospitalized for chronic rheumatic heart disease with acute exacerbation (rheumatic fever) necessitating bed rest. He was referred to psychiatry because he refused to stay in bed, managed to get up in spite of cuff restraints, ran up and down the ward, throwing a bottle at a nurse, etc. The patient claimed he didn't know why he had to be in a hospital. He did not feel very ill, and his mother had told him that he would die if he did not stay in bed, but he thought that the nurses were trying to kill him with injections. He got particularly enraged when a nurse had him take his pants down to give him an injection in the buttocks. He thought a male attendant hated him and wanted to harm him, to which he associated that an uncle once had tried to kill him. He dreamed of ghosts who attacked him because he tried to kill a man. He was extremely upset to see girls in the nude on the ward because it excited him. The threat of death, conveyed by his mother, had aroused the child's fear. Enforced bed rest, depriving him of any motor discharge, increased the fear to a pitch of panic. He tried to ward it off by denial and counterphobic activity. Doctors and nurses interfered with his defenses and aroused his rage. His own hostility increased his expectation for retribution and mobilized guilt feelings. Libidinal impulses, stirred up by the sight of nude girls and by the homosexual implications of an injection into his behind, heightened the inner turmoil. Discharge of tension through attack was curbed by hospital personnel so that his main defense consisted in projection, i.e., paranoid ideas.

For a detailed discussion of the relevance of motility I refer to Bela Mittelmann's paper, 1957.[7]

(b.) His body is not his own possession anymore; mother, nurses and doctors manipulate it.[3] This aspect is relevant, not only because of the decrease in mastery but also for its sexual implication. A frequently seen defensive maneuver is the child's playing out being doctor on a doll (for the libidinal meaning of the doctor game I refer to Ernst Simmel's article, 1926).[5]

Another defense consists in the possessive and often cruel "care" some children devote to a healing wound or scar. Several children with burns tore their bandages off or scratched the lesion underneath it, thus creating a major surgical problem. A pain or an itch may become a precious part of the body which the child may be most reluctant to give up. One boy with dermatitis sang to himself: "I want a new mummy, a new nurse, and a new itch." Scratching, with or without itching, thus serves not only masochistic gratification but is used also to recapture or strengthen feelings of one's own identity and mastery of the body, turning a passive experience into an active one.

One of the most constructive defenses observed consists in the identification with nurse or doctor, sharing their power and transforming cruel impulses into constructive helping action (reaction formation).

(c.) The loss of control over body *function* is fearfully equated with the loss of control of impulses. This is particularly critical for the obsessive, overcontrolled child. For example, a meticulous girl of ten went into a panic, followed by withdrawal from people and from her former interests and ambitions, after an enema was given. She regarded the enema as a penetration into her body.

(d.) Certain controls, e.g., reaction formation against exhibitionistic and voyeuristic tendencies, are broken down by the environment through lack of privacy, undressing and manipulations in front of others. For instance, the order that urination and defecation belong to the bathroom is reversed when the child is confined to his bed.

(e.) The transition the child has made from pleasure to reality principle may be disturbed through the illness: in serious illness, immediacy is often a dominant theme. The counterpoint to this is that some tensions remain unrelieved due to the nature of the illness.

While the adult may be able to wait for the goal of "health," this state has no attractive value for the child. In latency, health becomes conspicuous only by its absence. The child, except for the hypochondriacal and the obsessional one, will want to have a pain taken away or to have something fixed, but he does not concern himself with his future health in a realistic sense.[3]

In regard to the body, the child in latency does not acknowledge physical causality but adheres to a moral one in which punishment follows a crime and being sick means being bad, with more elaboration than in earlier childhood, during which causal connection is predominently magic. The fear of consequences of masturbation are heightened, and pleasures heretofore permitted, e.g., eating, may become forbidden for medical reasons. They require added controls and acceptance of frustration, thus reviving early conflicts about oral aggression. In this way, previously conflict-free areas of the ego become conflictual.

The change from the familiar world where the child to a high degree knew what to expect threatens his sense of acquired mastery and leaves him to experiences which are not mitigated by realistic anticipation, sometimes arousing a flood of mutilation fantasies. Parental figures change during illness: they are more controlling than usual, but also more controllable by complaints and demands.

Paul Schilder's statement: "Our tendency to live in the world of reality leads us to neglect what is going on in the field of sensations," [8] seems particularly true for the child in latency. Illness, with its sequelae of limited transactions with the outside world and of increase in bodily sensations, reverses this tendency.

(B) Self-Image and Narcissistic Concerns

(1.) The attack on the intactness of the body through injections and operations, the intrusion into privacy and secrecy through physical examinations,* the change from individual clothes, which formed part of the ego-image, to unfamiliar, anonymous hospital garments are narcissistic amputations and insults. Being suddenly different from class- and playmates, with the concomitant loss of group identifications, further alters the self-image. The actual impairment of ego strength through fever, metabolic disturbances, etc., enhances feelings of lost identity and continuity in the child.

(2.) A change of the self-image to "a bad egg," "rotten," "a piece for the garbage pail" may occur. For example, a nine year old boy was referred

* William Carlos Williams [11] describes in a short story his battle with a sick little girl during a diphtheria epidemic. The child denied to parents and physician having a sore throat and fought with all her force against an inspection of her mouth. She finally was overpowered. "And there it was—both tonsils covered with membrane. She had fought valiantly to keep me from knowing her secret."

for psychotherapy because he was a severe feeding problem on the pediatric ward. At age five, his cowboy suit had caught fire, resulting in third degree burns of both legs and buttocks. He was hospitalized for most of the following years, and received 25 skin grafts, 75 blood transfusions, and several courses of penicillin. At age seven, he stopped learning and became disinterested in everything except coffins, hearses, and death. He was considered mentally retarded. An I.Q. showed average (100) intelligence with greater potentiality. It was possible to work through with him his conviction that he was doomed to die. In other cases the defense consists in a vehement denial of signs and symptoms of the illness in order to maintain the former self-image.

(3.) One specially vulnerable aspect is a derivative from concerns about masculinity. Enforced passivity, dependency, and submission are equated with lack of manliness and are terrifying to the boy according to the degree of his unconscious female or bisexual identification. Castration fear increases. Passivity also revives infantile anaclitic wishes, which are ego-alien for either boys or girls. The outcome of this conflict may be surrender to the regressive wish; or the defense against it may take the form of turning passive suffering into active self-destruction.

(4.) A further change in self- and body-image may stem from the libidinization of the diseased organ or the symptom. An example will illustrate this point: Betty Lou was dealt a blow on her right hip by another child when she was seven years old. Severe pain at the right iliac crest persisted and led to hospitalization. A low grade infection of the hip-joint was assumed; she was treated with penicillin and became symptom-free. During the next eight years she was hospitalized several times for a recurrence of the same complaint. Physical examination was negative. In psychiatric interviews she connected the pain in her hip with her father, a man of violent temper. He had knocked holes in the wall with his fists, had beaten her, and recently had taken her to a local M.D., to have her virginity tested. Whenever she got excited about her father's rage, her hip hurt her; occasionally, she also fell down and felt a numbness in the region of her hip. This hysterical conversion took the form of a repetition of an actual trauma and was used for symbolic expression; the conflict between incestuous wishes for a cruel attack from her father and the struggle against it crystallized around the once-injured part of the body. Illness thus may provide the "somatic compliance" which facilitates a conversion reaction as a "solution" to an already on-going conflict.

Another girl was hospitalized for four months at the age of eight because of rheumatic heart disease and chorea. She recovered. During the next six years she was hospitalized five times because of choreiform movements of the extremities; no evidence for rheumatic heart disease or chorea was found and the cardiologist diagnosed her condition as "psychosomatic." The patient, a shy, sensitive and reticent girl, was completely dependent on her mother's extreme and jealous care. The mother had divorced the patient's father when the child was three years old, and had later acquired a much older husband with three children of his own. The repetition of the symptoms granted permission to regress into infantile closeness with her mother.

(C) The Threat of Losing the Love Object

(1.) Libido, otherwise radiating to people, concentrates on the self during illness, as Freud[4] has stated: ". . . the sick man withdraws his libidinal cathexes back upon his own ego, and sends them out again when he recovers. 'Concentrated is his soul,' says Wilhelm Busch of the poet suffering from toothache, 'in his molar's narrow hole.' Here libido and ego-interest share the same fate and are once more indistinguishable from each other."

(2.) The image of the parents changes. This is true even visibly; the parents standing at the bed seem overpowering to the child who has to be supine. Sitting next to, especially below the high hospital bed, they look peculiar. While they can leave, the child has no come or go. The child's previous self-assertive independence, with the freedom to leave and yet return for the protection and support essential for his security, is no longer possible. More important, however, is the change in his image of the parent. Vestiges of the all-powerful protector, to which the child is still entitled, are demolished. Sometimes, parents are obviously helpless and anxious. Even if this is not the case, their incapacity to rescue or to protect becomes painfully clear. Some children then conclude that the parents, at least by omission, caused the illness in order to take revenge or to punish. Thus, the parent may turn into an archaic, devouring monster, retaliating for the child's own murderous impulses. Identification with the parent becomes tenuous under these conditions. The possibility to borrow strength from the parent, so essential for the child's ego development in latency, may decrease in illness. On the other hand, through awareness of the parents' love during illness, the child may obtain needed narcissistic supplies at this time of depletion.

In the child's struggle to maintain the bond to a beloved person, it seems to me, lies the crucial point for the outcome. Loneliness, not so much outer as inner loneliness, due to the withdrawal of object cathexis, invariably ensues. This can result in paranoid or melancholic attitudes. An example of a paranoid reaction, alternating with a depressive one, is Jimmy, ten, hospitalized for ulcerative colitis, which began six months after his mother's remarriage two years prior to his hospitalization. He was convinced that nurses and doctors would put him to sleep forever because he was a nuisance. He stated his grandfather died while asleep from a sedative given by his doctor. From the interview material, it was evident that his suspicion was displaced from mother and stepfather, whose marriage he disturbed, to nurse and doctor. During one blood transfusion he screamed and kicked off four nurses who were trying to hold him. As an explanation, he told me he saw an air bubble coming into his vein, a sign that he was to get a "mercy killing." His associations revealed his impulse to kill his stepbrother and father. He refused to take medications because "the doctor prescribes something," e.g., opium. The patient then cannot live without it and is completely in the doctor's power. The doctor then raises the price, until the patient has nothing left. The paranoid fantasy revealed the nature of Jimmy's transference to me, namely, the fear of becoming dependent on a mother who would destroy him. Projection alternated with turning aggression against himself. "If I had my way, I'd starve myself to death. Nobody wants to die," was one of his characteristic remarks. Before Thanksgiving he decided to "eat turkey, even if it kills me." In the course of therapy he finally was able to renounce his possessive dependency on his mother, to accept the stepfather and to identify with him. This may lead to a new, realistic acceptance of the parents and a reorientation toward life.

Another example for a child's struggling through psychosomatic and depressive afflictions to a reconciliation with "the good object" is Dorothy, referred because of a suicidal attempt at age eleven. At the age of two, she had run after her older sister through a pile of smouldering leaves. Her sister came through unscathed but Dorothy stopped and screamed in terror for her mother, who did not immediately realize what was happening. As a result, the patient sustained third degree burns of her feet and had to stay in bed for several months. She became a fussy eater, started to soil, and gradually developed diarrhea. At age four, ulcerative colitis was diagnosed and led to several prolonged hospitalizations, the latest at age eleven, following a suicidal attempt which led to referral for psychotherapy. She was at this time depressed and apprehensive, complaining of a fear from way back of something about to happen. She wanted somebody to watch her all the time. During interviews she continuously played doctor for a doll, Patty Ann (Ann being the patient's middle name). The doll wore a bandage on her stomach because the doll had crossed the street with her mother and a car came at them. The mother saved Patty Ann's life by throwing her away from the car, so that she only got a bruise. "A bruise" was also the patient's word for the lesions in her colon. Injury to the outside of the body was always interchangeable with one in her abdomen.

In another interview, Dorothy said that mother and father used to keep dangerous things within Patty Ann's reach when she was a baby. Once Patty Ann got some matches to play with, but her father took them away just in time. Patty Ann, however, might have swallowed some little toys which should have been bigger, so they could not be swallowed. (At some later time, two objects the doll had swallowed had to come out.) Dorothy had told Patty Ann's parents that they were careless and would have a lot of misery if Patty Ann died.

This complaint, made by many children, that mother should have prevented one from doing something bad illustrates the latency child's plea for reinforcement of superego strength from without. Indeed, the modification of the archaic superego and the incorporation of parents is not complete at this stage and depends on continuous interaction with authoritative figures.

Dorothy's associations showed the inclusion of the incident of burns at age two with her present illness. The thread running through all interviews was the bitter disappointment in the parents who had failed to prevent her from doing something bad and consequently from dying. She fluctuated between her own guilt feelings and hostility against her mother, the latter seemingly being the most unbearable emotion.

In the course of psychotherapy, intestinal bleeding and bowel movements decreased and her suspicious, resentful attitude changed to a trusting and affectionate one. It was noticed that at times of stress, e.g., before an x-ray check-up, Dorothy would rub her stomach with her hand. She commented that this made her fear and pain "go away," and she recalled that her mother used to do that for her when she was little and couldn't eat or had a pain in her stomach or felt like going to the bathroom. Thus, the patient treated herself as her own baby. The reliving of memories of her mother's care and tender feelings for her, the incorporation of the good mother, seemed the most relevant feature in her improvement.

She progressed well, with only one bowel movement a day, until the time when she felt her psychiatrist (male) preferred a fifteen year old roommate, a sister figure, to her. Dorothy cried that nobody cared for her, snatched a drug from the lab, and tried also to strangle herself. This episode was followed by a refusal to eat and frequent diarrhea. After this experience was worked through, the patient again was able to maintain a lifeline by recapturing her feelings for the mother of her pretraumatic infancy.

Discussion

The material presented suggests a number of questions.

(1.) How was the child before he fell sick? Several of the children here described had psychosomatic disorders, which indicates that unsolved conflicts contributing to the genesis of the disease existed before illness became manifest. The affliction, in turn, brought on new experiences the child had to cope with. The cycle of dynamic and biologic forces before, during, and after illness is a most fascinating topic; however, it is one which goes beyond the scope of this paper. So does the predisposition of an organ for later pathology, when physical symptoms first occurred at a time of critical conflict, which Felix Deutsch[2] has pointed out.

Also, children in whose illness psychologic factors are not so manifestly involved react to the event, of course, in an individual way; this is largely determined by their previous level of anxiety, their emotional ties, and the degree of their maturity. Whether previous traumatic experiences have or have not been integrated is another relevant factor.

(2.) Is there any difference between the effect of illness and that of any other potentially traumatic event during latency? There are common features in any anxiety-arousing experience, such as regression and alteration in defense mechanisms. However, illness has its specific impact through the cathexis of libido on the body, through the weakening of ego functioning as a direct sequel of the physical illness, and through the restraint of motor expression and interaction.

(3.) Is there any difference between the reaction to illness during latency and during later periods of life? Regressive reactions, especially depressive and paranoid ones, can certainly be observed in adult, chronically ill patients. Children in latency, however, are in many respects less armored than adults, as I have attempted to show; judgment of reality, e.g., knowledge of illness, is still incomplete, the relationship to the parents is not yet free from archaic vestiges; they depend on parents to borrow strength for ego functioning and for stabilizing superego demands, and they need motor eloquence to satisfy aggressive urges and to gain mastery.

Summary

I have attempted to describe the experiences of the sick child in latency. The impact of illness consists of a change in the child himself, his orbit, and his atmosphere. The sequelae of this challenge for the ego may be transient or result in long-lasting regression, a masochistic pattern of life, an illness-prone condition, a withdrawal of libido from the world, depression and self-devaluation, aggression and denial of sickness; but it may, indeed, also lead to growth. Emmy Sylvester [10] pointed out in a paper in 1954: "There are three principal ways in which a child who has met a disrupting event may attempt mastery of the trauma: he may deal with it in fantasy, talk about it, or translate the injury he has suffered into action." With this statement, I certainly agree, but I would like to add that mastery, at best, would lead through a kind of grief reaction, an acceptance of a loss—a loss of narcissistic and early parental images, to a reincorporation of the loved object and the readiness for a new life-size relationship to oneself and the parent, i.e., the vicissitudes of the child's object relations. Anna Freud [3] has described two ways for the patient to react to the heightened demand of the ill body for libidinal cathexis. One way is to claim a surplus of love and attention from the mother. The other way of reacting consists in a withdrawal from the object world and a concentration on the body and its needs, which she calls a beneficial process. I believe that these children of the second type, those who turn their faces to the wall, are going through a grief reaction. Through such an integrative process, illness may not only spur maturation but also widen the horizon, heighten sensitivity, and bring forth a greater depth of feeling, capacity for empathy and for sublimation.* It may be "the beginning of the love affair with the world which seems to be an obligatory condition in the development of great talent or genius," which Phyllis Greenacre[5] speaks of. It does not seem accidental that so many great artists, scientists and political leaders have experienced "childhood illness that so strangely began with a number of profound and grave transformations." † We are reminded of Freud's statement: "Here experience speaks with no uncertain voice." [12]

Bibliography

1. Blom, G. E.: The reactions of hospitalized children to illness. Paper presented at the 26th Annual Meeting of the American Academy of Pediatrics, October 7, 1957.

2. Deutsch, F.: Thus speaks the body: Some psychosomatic aspects of the respiratory disorder: asthma. Acta med. orientalia *10:* 67–86, 1951.

3. Freud, A.: The role of bodily illness in the mental life of children. Psychoanalyt. Study of the Child, *8:* 69–81, 1952.

4. Freud, S.: On Narcissism. The Standard Edition of the Complete Psychological Works of Sigmund Freud. London, Hogarth Press, 1953. Vol. XIV: 82 (1914–1916)

---

* "Les malades se sentent plus près de leur âme" (The sick are closer to their soul). Marcel Proust.

† Rainer Maria Rilke: The Notebooks of Malte Laurios Brigge, New York, 1949.

On the History of the Psycho-Analytic Movement, Papers on Metapsychology and Other Works.

5. Greenacre, P.: The Childhood of the Artist. Psychoanalyt. Study of the Child, *12:* 47–72, 1957.

6. Keller, Helen Adams: Teacher: Anne Sullivan Macy, p. 42. Garden City, Doubleday, 1955.

7. Mittelmann, B.: Motility in the therapy of children and adults. Psychoanalyt. Study of the Child, *12:* 284–319, 1957.

8. Schilder, P. F.: The Image and Appearance of the Human Body. London, K. Paul, Trend, Trubner & Co., 1935.

9. Simmel, E.: The "doctor game," illness and the profession of medicine. *In* Fliess, R.: The Psychoanalytic Reader, Vol. 1, pp. 291–305. New York, International Universities Press, Inc., 1948.

10. Sylvester, E.: Developmental truisms and their fate in child rearing. *In* Senn, M. Z. E.: Problems of Infancy and Childhood, pp. 9–37. New York, Josiah Macy, Jr., Foundation, 1954.

11. William, W. C.: The Use of Force. *In* Warren, Robert Penn, and Erskine, Albert: Short Story Masterpieces, pp. 538–542. New York, Dell Publishing Co., Inc.

12. Freud, S.: Analysis Terminable and Interminable (1937). Collected Papers, Vol. V, p. 335. London, Hogarth Press, 1953.

11

On the Meaning of Play in Childhood Psychosis*

By RUDOLF EKSTEIN
and
SEYMOUR W. FRIEDMAN

VICTOR TAUSK'S CLASSIC CONTRIBUTION *On the Origin of the "Influencing Machine" in Schizophrenia,*[17] despite its now partly outdated conceptualizations, continues to stimulate many investigators in our field through its richness of ideas. The nature of Natalija A.'s "influencing machine" was then understood primarily in terms of paranoid projections. Tausk speaks about the "infantile stage of thinking, in which a strong belief exists that others know of the child's thoughts." He suggests that "a striving for the rights to have secrets from which the parents are excluded is one of the most powerful factors in the formation of the ego, especially in establishing and carrying out one's own will." He speaks of "the loss of ego boundaries," a concept which is frequently used in the work of Federn, and suggests that "this symptom is the complaint that 'everyone' knows the patient's thoughts, that his thoughts are not enclosed in his own head, but are spread throughout the world and occur simultaneously in the heads of all persons. The patient seems no longer to realize that he is a separate psychical entity, an ego with individual boundaries." We recall that the ego concept here does not derive from the tripartite model of psychic organization and is used somewhat loosely in terms of the self-concept.

Freud[17] discussed Tausk's contribution in a meeting of the Vienna Psychoanalytic Society, and he "emphasized that the infant's conception that others knew his thoughts has its source in the process of learning to speak. Having obtained his language from others, the infant has also received thoughts from them; and the child's feelings that others know his thoughts as well as that others have 'made' him the language and, along with it, his thoughts, has therefore some basis in reality." Freud's

* Read on the occasion of Anna Freud's visit to the Reiss-Davis Clinic for Child Guidance, Los Angeles, California, on March 30, 1959.

comment, as well as Tausk's discussion, would have to be considered an oversimplification of the genesis of paranoid projections were we to try to understand this discussion against the background of more modern concepts of psychic organization rather than against the then prevalent theoretical frame of reference.

Natalija A.'s "influencing machine" represents a regressive phenomenon within a psychic organization which is characterized by rudiments of a mature psychic apparatus. Her fantasy of the "influencing machine" constitutes a restitutive element, the psychotic's attempt to reconstruct [2] the dramatic past and to describe inner experiences which run parallel to the infant's lack of developed capacity for differentiation of self from object, his struggle to maintain a world of omnipotence while at the same time growing toward awareness of self and objects. During this stage, primary narcissistic omnipotence, as it prevails in a comparatively undifferentiated psychic organization, shifts at times by means of narcissistic projection onto the object, which then is experienced as giving thoughts or knowing all thoughts, and as thus influencing the other. The "influencing machine" characterizes the fluctuation of fantasies of omnipotence from self to object and back to self, a struggle which attempts to restore symbiosis, and to thus overcome fragmentation of the body image and to restore the "oceanic feeling," the oneness with mother, in which she has the executive function of the controlling ego.

These newer assumptions which attempt to describe the development of the psychic organization before individuation has taken place were expressed in those early years in terms of the *content* of fantasies, and only later were attempts made to infer from the content the *state* of the psychic organization. For example, Freud [17] also suggests when discussing Tausk's contribution that "the significance of the mode of burial of Egyptian mummies," that is, that the mummy is placed in "a case resembling the human body suggests the idea of the return to 'mother earth,' the return to the mother's body in death." He suggests that "as a compensation for the bitterness of death, man takes for granted the bliss of existence in the uterus." The fantasy of the return to the uterus is "then an atavistic one, a pre-formed fantasy;" and as such, "this fantasy appears symptomatically in schizophrenia as the pathological reality of the regressing, disintegrating psyche. The mummy returns to the mother's body by physical, and the schizophrenic by psychical death."

The "psychical death" of the schizophrenic constitutes an attempt actually to restore an early unity which is to give safety but usually fails to do so, since the symbiotic experience often signifies the threat of loss of identity, the fear of being devoured and of being dominated by the other.

The "influencing machine," then, represents both the wish to return to an undifferentiated, symbiotic phase and the lonesome struggle against the loss of precarious identity.

As we trace the literature for contributions in which psychotic mechanisms of childhood are described and pay attention particularly to the use such children make of machines,[2, 6, 11, 14] we face a variety of problems of a different order. These children, particularly of younger age, have of course never advanced to states of maturity characteristic of the pre-morbid adjustment of Natalija A. Rather, we find in them personality organizations which frequently will be better understood in terms of psychotic fixations rather than in terms of psychotic regressions. In this regard, we must remember that the application of these dynamic processes toward the characterization of the essential nature of the state of personality organization of psychotic children is more a way of speaking, a convenient shorthand generalization, as it were, for a complex situation, rather than a scientific conclusion still to be determined by more valid evidence. For these processes merely refer to the importance of developmenal factors in the evaluation and understanding of the various problems of psychosis in childhood and stress the need to make qualitative as well as quantitative distinctions between the psychotic processes of adults and children, and between the psychoses of younger and of older children.

Thus, in the very young children of pre-school age, we find ego fragmentation, symbiotic and autistic conditions, an extremely impaired capacity for reality testing, and primitive precursors of object-relationships which characterize their specific adjustments. The dynamic considerations which more appropriately define the dimensions of the play of psychotic children are derived from factors which characterize the archaic structural aspects of the developing ego. Significant and relevant components of the ego organization which determine the patterns of psychotic play concern the concepts of distance as a function of defense, the vicissitudes of impulse organization during the development from primary to secondary process control, language development and object relationships, the problem of identity, and the adaptive functions of the ego, especially its motoric and synthesizing functions.

Similarly, qualitative differentiations can be made beween the play of neurotic and psychotic children, for example, in the play of acting-out children[4] in which acting-out, play action, and play serve the functions of recollection, mastery of conflicts, and the search for identity. But in the play of the psychotic child, the functions of mastery, pleasure, and motoric expression are less important as the end products of ego development, interesting us more, rather, as diagnostic indicators of the functional state of the ego and as the means of communication about the conflictual problems confronting the ego in its particular developmental state.

The foregoing considerations have been among the many subjects dealt with in the enormous body of literature which has accumulated during the last decade and which has been described and integrated by the authors of this paper and their co-worker, Bryant.[3] More recent publications deal with the relationship of play patterns and diagnosis in childhood psychosis.[9, 10, 16]

The purpose of this paper is to study the play of such children in order to find answers to two sets of questions. Their play constitutes the royal road to an understanding of certain aspects of the available psychic organization. The understanding of the structure of available psychic organization can then be used in order to develop techniques which should prove of help therapeutically. The child's play, the royal road to his unconscious,[8] can be considered the dominant language of the child, and thus his most powerful means of communication with the therapist.

The word "communication" must be understood in terms of the available psychic organization of the child, just as must the word "influencing." Even the assumption that the play be considered a substitute for free association in the treatment of the psychotic child needs amplification, since the effectiveness of language, of interpretive work,[1] depends upon the nature of the psychic organization, the available capacity for differentiation of self and non-self, and the fluctuating state of affairs concerning object relationships. Consequently, we need to raise questions as to what communication and interpretation really mean when psychotic "transference" prevails. We would like to ascertain how psychotic play could teach us to make contact with such children, a problem which engaged the attention of the authors in an earlier paper.[5] And we wonder how it might be possible to develop "sending power" [7] in profoundly psychotic children in spite of the deficits in their psychic organization. One also might wish that Natalija A. would be able to teach us how to develop "influencing machines" for those autistic and mute children who possess only a rudimentary capacity for play, the nature of which is very different from the play of children within the neurotic range.

An analogue of Natalija A.'s "influencing machine" was experienced by a five year old boy for whom all noises were felt to be intrusive, penetrating tormentors who, by gaining entrance into his body, could simultaneously discover his secret, forbidden wishes and destroy him. Upon hearing loud noises he would cringe and cower as if in pain, whimper in terror and in mounting panic and instantly clap his hands over his ears as if to block out the hideous, frightening sounds that would attempt to invade his head. For this psychotic boy, the threatening noises and sounds were equated with the frightening voice of his enraged father threatening to send him away if he were naughty again. And like Natalija A.'s "influencing machine," they represented a monstrous but impersonal delusional force which this boy had introjected in order to achieve symbiotic union with the omnipotent father, at the same time that he struggled against introjection of the father's violent image and enraged voice which would have separated him from home and the needed father.

While the "influencing machines" of both Natalija A. and this psychotic child dealt with their common struggle around the conflicting wishes toward symbiosis and individuation, one essential difference between them lay in the capacity of their respective egos to internalize and stabilize parental introjects. In a sense, Natalija A., having internalized the object, could create a completed machine which could function without the external physical object and could derive its driving power from the force of her delusional fantasy. The psychotic child, not having succeeded in internalizing the introjected image of the omnipotent father, could create only a precursor of the "influencing machine" which could not yet function independently of the real, external object-voices and sounds around which he wove a delusion of the ambivalently viewed father who could both destroy and protect him within the same fantasy. Reality is the "nutriment," as Piaget puts it,[13] for the ego of the child without which the inherent patterns cannot be mobilized.

The successful achievement of identity depends upon the ego's capacity to internalize its introjects or it never comes to fruition, as in the severely psychotic child. Waelder [18] has suggested that the play of the child can be understood as fantasy woven around external objects. Although he refers to physical objects which the child employs for his play activities, he nevertheless assumes a capacity for differentiation between outer and inner world, a primitive form of thinking which, however, has moved toward a more mature developmental stage. Natalija A.'s "influencing machine" might be considered such an external object around which she weaves fantasies, the nature of which, however, is of such a kind that no differentiation is possible between her own body image and the fantasy image of the "influencing machine" in the hands of her alleged tormentors. Winnicott's [21] conception of the transitory object provides us with intermediate stages of object formation in which part objects may also become the hub around which delusions may be woven by the child's ego.

Of the small psychotic child it often may be said, then, that when he weaves fantasies around external objects, he frequently cannot identify these external objects as being a part of the outside world. We might paraphrase Waelder and suggest that the play of the psychotic child is explicable as hallucinatory and delusional fantasy woven around external objects. The adult psychotic, having in the past once internalized but having later lost the introjected object, can create a psychotic fantasy through autistic thought processes without the help of actual external objects. The psychotic child, never having been able to internalize the object adequately, must weave hallucinations and delusions around external objects which are not experienced by the child as differentiated from the internalized object. Abortive attempts at differentiation between internal and external objects, just as is his interrupted struggle toward individuation and identity formation, are regularly followed by regressive moves for the maintenance of symbiotic union with the parental object. The psychotic child's play so very frequently characterizes the conflictual struggle, which is to maintain symbiosis and to wipe out the difference between himself and the outside world, in order to avoid painful insight and to remain one with the world.

This brings to mind the play of the psychotic child who had to twirl constantly and who reacted with violent displeasure to attempts to interrupt her twirling. She suggested that she did so because she wanted the world to be confused and topsy-turvy, so that the world would be exactly as she felt within herself, and so that she would not need to sense that she was different from others. No doubt, this child could make such an observation only at the point when her symptoms no longer completely possessed her, after she had started to experience her symptoms as an alien part of herself and therefore needed to rationalize them in order to make her symptoms egosyntonic.

We are indebted to Williams [20] for the example of the psychotic girl whose play so vividly demonstrates the need of the child to maintain her sense of oneness with the outer world. This psychotic girl, who was treated intensively and presented in an unpublished study, started treatment in the early latency period. Her outstanding play activity during a long period of treatment centered around her fascinated love for incinerators, which this child attempted to control by magic gestures and to which she was endlessly attracted. During many therapy hours her fantasy life was woven around one special incinerator which, perceived as a representation of the maternal introject, provided her with longed-for warmth and protection. The incinerator, as the representation of the fragmented maternal introject, separated the negative, engulfing, and threatening aspects of the maternal object from the positive, nourishing, and protective components of the maternal image. The child's endless play around the incinerator and her fascination with it contained both the precursors of obsessive mechanisms as well as related instinctual derivatives, witnesses to the ceaseless but unsuccessful struggle of the rudimentary ego to establish a stable, adaptive and defensive organization.

In this example, the psychotic child used a mechanical object to which to attach psychotic thought processes, while in situations that are characteristic of a somewhat higher psychic organization, actual persons are used as the nucleus of the psychotic fantasy.

The situation existent in the case of Natalija A. might be considered an intermediate stage as she utilizes actual persons in combination with fantasied "influencing machines." As another example, illustrative of another state of ego organization, we think of the "space" child whose pure psychotic fantasy concerning the "time machine" [2] later attached itself in the transference situation to the person of the psychotherapist as the patient made progress toward a higher ego organization. In this latter example, the psychotherapist became the representative of an intruding but persistent reality around whom the patient carried out his struggle for the establishment of boundaries between inner and outer reality experiences. Still another example, provided by Wexler,[19] concerns the play of a psychotic boy who repeatedly threw a ball in fantasy to another child while he actually remained on the periphery of the play group. He fantasied himself joining the group at the same time that he remained uninvolved and isolated from it. By means of the ball which in fantasy he threw at the actual child, this psychotic boy made contact in fantasy with the playmate as he combined the fantasied physical object, the ball, with the fantasy of making contact with an actual object.

The discussion which was predominant in 1919 concerned the *meaning* of symptoms, a meaning which was sought for in the origin of symptoms. This question of historic origin has been enriched recently by questions concerning the nature of the psychic organization of which the symptom is but a sign, and concerning the nature of techniques that must be developed in order to bring about therapeutic change.

The case illustrations which we propose to use can serve as a few among many models for the type of thinking necessary in order to reconstruct the psychic organization characteristic for the child, and in order to develop modes of intervention which are derived from a better understanding of the nature of the psychotic child's "communications," his play activities. We wish to call attention once more to the necessity of having to clarify what we mean when we speak of communication during psychotherapy with a psychotic child. Within this context, we must differentiate between that aspect of the communication which is derived from the child's activity and the alternate pole of the communication which refers to the therapist's interventions. Psychotic play activity, if understood properly, might yield those insights necessary for a fuller understanding of the process of communication as well as of a number of other mental processes which hopefully will enrich our understanding of the psychic organization. This in turn might enable us to develop more effective therapeutic techniques which could further the development of the patient's psychic organization.

Robby was almost five years old when he was brought for psychiatric treatment. For the past two and a half years he had posed the most difficult management and discipline problems to his parents, who felt themselves caught in an impregnable trap created by his incomprehensible behavior and wild emotional outbursts. They complained of his severe temper tantrums that erupted with volcanic fury at the slightest frustration and sometimes with apparently trivial provocation. They felt desperately helpless that they could not reach him or make themselves understood to him, and they were deeply concerned and frightened over his failure to mature along normal developmental lines, thus leaving them with the fearful expectation that he would be diagnosed as an organically damaged child for whom there was no hope of cure or improvement. Robby's father particularly despaired that the child's intellectual development would remain permanently retarded, and he found himself inextricably enmeshed in his own struggle between his despair for the boy's future and his own violent rage toward his son when provoked by Robby's uncontrollable behavior. The one area in which the parents found a glimmer of hope, i.e., Robby's agile motor development, proved to be a mixed blessing for them. For although Robby's precocious motor development gave them the one ray of hope that he was not a retarded child, it also provided the most excruciating provocation for their anger and helplessness, since they could not prevent Robby from using his motor skills and his singular mechanical aptitudes to dismantle the doors, locks, and mechanical appliances in their home. At sporadic times the parents frantically felt that they could only stand by in paralyzed impotence and watch their house literally become dismantled, piece by piece, as Robby, in his frenzied, excited forays, would leave the doors hanging loosely from their hinges, the moldings separated from the walls, the carpets torn up to expose the bare floors, and every object, sufficiently loose as to become vulnerable to his prying tools, torn from its moorings. Robby's parents feared that his infantile verbal and language development meant that he was hopelessly mentally retarded. Robby's language consisted of a very few words, which were difficult to comprehend and consisted mainly of bizarre sounds and fragments of words to which only his parents, eager to understand him, could attach meaning.

For the first few months of psychotherapy, Robby did not display the unusually frantic behavior that plagued his parents. At worst, his play was fragmentary, impulsively interrupted, but never impetuously frantic. From fragmentary house-building with blocks, Robby slowly turned his interest to the door stoppers in the therapist's office. Quickly, all other play activities were pushed into the background as Robby became obsessed with collecting every door stopper within his visual and tactile reach. His speech would rise in an excited crescendo as he would gleefully repeat the phrase, "want a door stopper" and impulsively pounce with either hand or foot upon every door stopper accessible to him. He would tug and pull, jump and pounce upon the door stoppers, until he would either break them off or unscrew them from the wall. He carried a large collection of door stoppers of every variety with him, and at one time posed a difficult problem for the therapist when he would run through the corridor of the medical building in which the doctor's office was located, dashing into every office and pouncing upon the door stopper until he was apprehended and removed. With lightning speed he would dash away from the therapist, and, at one foray, he burst into a strange office, quickly broke off the door stopper and slammed the door against the wall, cracking the plaster and leading to a socially difficult situation for all concerned.

The interpretation that Robby was looking for a stopper that would stop him from breaking down his house when he couldn't help himself from flying open like a door and breaking the wall eventually diminished his compulsive, frantic need for the door stoppers as both therapist and parents assumed more effective forms of external control for him. But as he slowly gave up his need for the door stoppers and yielded to the authority of adults as stoppers of his lightning impulsivity, Robby's compulsive preoccupations then centered around a collection of screwdrivers and doorknobs which he skillfully and with lightning rapidity removed from every available door. At home, in the therapist's office, wherever there was a door, no doorknob was safe from his frantic clutch. With one swift movement of the screwdriver, he could remove a doorknob before he could be stopped. In his repetitious chatter the one word "knob" formed the nucleus of his verbal expressions.

During part of the phase of his compulsive attachment to doorknobs, Robby's father was absent from home for several weeks. Robby's need to dismantle doors and to remove the doorknobs heightened in intensity until his mother found herself desperate and unable to cope with his impulsive destructiveness. Prior to one therapy hour, the mother told the therapist that Robby had had quite a scare. He had suddenly burst into the kitchen where the mother was working and in wild excitement threw his screwdriver into the air, cracking the ceiling fixture so that part of it came tumbling down to the floor, crashing between Robby and his mother. Robby dashed in wild panic from the room while his mother dashed after, both to comfort and to scold him. As she angrily took the screwdriver away and threatened him with its loss forever unless he learned to refrain from using it as a dangerous weapon, Robby went into a wild hysterical panic and he could not be comforted for two hours until, in spent exhaustion, he lapsed into a tormented sleep.

When Robby arrived for his therapy hour, he quickly dashed to the therapist's drawer where his favorite screwdriver lay waiting for him. Following his familiar pattern, he quickly went to the playroom and removed the doorknobs and the plates from two doors in the playroom. The therapist had been interpreting to Robby his need for the doorknobs as his need for mamma who left him with the therapist whom Robby called Friend. For many weeks Robby had gone through a ritual of demanding numerous kisses from his mother when she left him, whereupon, with reassurance that she would return, he would immediately dash to the doors with the therapist's screwdriver to dismantle the doorknobs. This would leave Robby with a smile of satisfaction, mischievous cunning, and an almost ecstatic pleasure in which the therapist could feel Robby's great relief from his anxiety over the mother's leaving. As the time approached the ending of the hour and the mother's expected return, Robby went through the ritual of replacing the doorknobs with the help of the therapist's interpretation, insistence, and encouragement that now he could put the knobs back and leave them with Friend since mamma was now coming back to take Robby home. At this point in this particular hour, Robby became quite anxious and repeated with almost tearful pleading that he needed the doorknobs and did not want to put them back. "Why put doorknob back?" he cried in repetitious, frantic excitement. "Don't want to put doorknob back," he threatened in a defiant gesture. Trying to allay his anxiety, the therapist told Robby that he knew that mamma had taken the screwdriver from him and that he was very frightened that he would be without his screwdriver and could not have his knobs. Maybe he was even more frightened without his knobs when his daddy was away, especially since mamma had taken his screwdriver away. Robby confirmed this interpretation by displaying mounting anxiety and by more intensely repeating his pleas for the knobs. The therapist told him that he knew that Robby needed the knobs in order not to be afraid that mamma would leave him and sometimes he needed the knobs so that he would not be afraid of mamma. But Friend wanted to help him so that he would not have to be afraid and he would feel big and strong even without Friend's knobs. Although Robby listened and betrayed a fleeting, satisfied smile, he maintained his insistence that he must have the knobs and could not put them back, repeatedly asking why the doors needed the knobs. When it became clear to him that he could not take the knobs with him but would have to replace them on the door and leave them with Friend, his anxiety mounted into panic proportions as he looked at Friend and in a terrified whisper confessed, "Don't want to be a girl."

Robby's strange, repetitive play, the compulsivity of which was also characterized by uncontrollable passion, moved through a number of phases which permit conjecture about the nature of the process which took place. The first phase of the game concerned the ceaseless removal of door stoppers, the prevention of the locking of doors, the deeper purpose of which was to fight against isolation, against separation, and to secure access to the parental figure. Availability of mother had to be fought for through the struggle for the open door. The removal of the door stoppers could be understood as an expression of his uncontrollable impulsivity, no holds barred, and thus his telling the world, his therapist, about the deep conflict between his uncontrollable impulsivity which had to be stopped and governed, which threatened him with the punishment of isolation and separation from the protecting and nourishing mother, and his deep wish to be reunited with her and to keep the doors, the access to her, open. One could hardly think of a better symbolic representation of the struggle between the autistic and the symbiotic position. The removal of the door stopper portrays the eruptive quality of his impulsive life which then actually threatens accessibility to the parent who is driven away because of the child's lack of control, lack of boundary between self and non-self, and the ceaseless, passionate yearning for unification. The constant threat to the home, the literal physical annihilation of the inside of the home, destroys the very basis for emotional security which such a child needs, and is characteristic, and certainly a symbolic presentation also, of the state of the personality organization of the child, in which boundaries between different psychic organizations and identity of separate functions cannot be maintained. The regressed and fluctuating ego of this child is deprived, if we may use the metaphor of the play, of its door stoppers, its doors, its walls, and its separate entities. The struggle against walls and doors, motivated by the wish for unification, for togetherness with mother, actually achieves the opposite and threatens the very foundations of his life.

While the first phase of the play characterizes the archaic conflict, the regression to a state of uncontrollable impulsivity, the second phase of the play aims at restitution, at the solution of conflict after psychotherapy had developed toward a new phase. The removal of the door stoppers, the removal of all controls, is followed by the passion to remove doorknobs from all available doors, to collect them and to keep them; they assumed for the child the meaning of a *quasi fetish*. This play took on different meaning at different points, and at times maintained different meanings at the very same moment. Whenever the child found himself in a phase where higher functions of personality organization were available, where there was some availability of object and self differentiation, the knob symbolized parts of the mother or the father which the child wished to make accessible to himself. By holding on to the knob he had access to the open door, and he could maintain the connection between himself and the parent. At most moments, though, as is expressed so clearly in the child's frantic and terrorized plea that he did not want to be a girl, the knobs refer to his own body. It would be incorrect if one were to see in the knobs only symbolic representations of the male genitalia. The dominant meaning of these knobs referred to his inability to maintain a clear body image. The loss of the knobs, identity with the loss of the mother as an accessible object, as an introject that could be maintained, referred to the threat of loss of identity, a threat particularly powerful whenever separation was threatened.

Each ending psychotherapy hour, when he had to give up the knobs of the office doors, created a new threat for him, the separation from the therapist, and the necessity to take along the quasi fetish. The function of the fetish is not only to replace the lost love object, but, and therefore our suggestion to speak of quasi fetish, to secure narcissistic cathexis, so that the body image could be maintained and precarious identity insured.

The external knob, not unsimilar to the function of "influencing machines" as described earlier, is the external object around which delusions and inner perceptions concerning body and self-identity are woven.

If our interpretation of the play is correct, we should be able to draw conclusions for therapeutic technique. In this instance the use of the quasi fetish for symbolic representation and symbolic gratification becomes a part of the therapy. The therapist cannot treat the doorknob simply as a utensil but has to think of it as part of an important ritual without which communication cannot succeed. Zulliger [22] made use of a talisman which he gave to his girl patient as symbolic representation of the father image. Sechehaye [15] made use of symbolic gratification in the case of her schizophrenic girl patient. The use of the knob here, above and beyond the verbal interpretations as they are possible, insures communication and contact with the child.

The ritual which developed about leaving time, when the knob was finally returned to the therapist, as was the screwdriver which was used in order to control the different knobs, became for the child the symbol of security. It was as if the two had agreed that the means of control were safe as long as they were left with the therapist, and that the child would trust the therapist in terms of accessibility and in terms of a guarantee for restitution. As long as he is with the psychotherapist he borrows, as it were, the strength of the therapist by taking his doorknobs, the guarantee of parental supply. When he leaves he is willing to restore the therapist's wholeness, and feels secure in the knowledge that the continuing process is guaranteed. In the cases described by Zulliger [22] and Sechehaye,[15] a talisman or a gift of an apple is given the patient, but in this case the quasi fetish is returned to the psychotherapist, a form of undoing of the fantasied destruction of the therapist, the child's first indication that he aims to master the problem of impulsivity and will replace the primary process with higher mental functions which will make available to him a new capacity for delay.

During an interim phase of this play the child would bring old, beaten-up doorknobs from home and try to exchange them for the new, shiny doorknobs of the therapist. This gesture of trying to exchange what was old and nearly destroyed for what was considered new and good seems to be the symbolic representation of an attempt to get well by introjecting the therapist and to get rid of introjects from earlier phases of life which were experienced as damaged, powerless, and undesirable.

The compulsive behavior of the play of this child differs from compulsions on a higher level of development through the fact that it is accompanied by unbridled affect, that it is dominated by uncontrollable impulsivity. One might suggest that the obsessive-compulsive in the neurotic range is characterized by a compulsive ego. In the case of this child one is tempted to speak of a compulsive id which dominates the situation. This manner of speaking, though, is inexact unless one remains aware of the nature of the comparatively undifferentiated psychic organization.

Three months later, Robby's therapy hour had assumed a new compulsive and ritualized form. Every hour would start with his bursting into the therapist's office, his hands filled with an odd assortment of tools, followed by an anxious ritual of bidding good-bye to his mother with demands for more and more kisses, gradually decreasing in intensity as he seemed more reassured that mamma would return for him. He would dash to the drawer for the screwdriver and urgently remove the doorknobs in the therapist's playroom with obvious relief and satisfaction in his prowess, and then quickly explore the office for more available doorknobs and loose hinge-pins. These he would quickly remove if he were given freedom to do so, then gather up his screwdrivers and tools which he would store in Friend's pocket as he would exclaim, "Want to go out," and lead the way into the corridor. There then followed the familiar trek along the corridor as Robby would compulsively touch the doorknob of every office door, almost happily walk down the stairway with one hand in the therapist's hand and out into the alley where Robby would look for abandoned pipes, bulbs, hinges and doorknobs that had been thrown away in the piles of rubbish conveniently left by workmen who were remodelling offices in nearby buildings. The therapy journey would lead to a parking garage in which Robby had come to know the location of every door and of every doorknob. At the doorway to the stairs leading up to the various levels, Robby would inspect the door which for a long time was without its knob which Robby at one time had dismantled and had thrown away into the alley rather than have it taken away from him. Finding the knob missing, he would rapidly ask where the knob was. And on being told that Robby had thrown it away, he would smile with a satisfied, cunning expression on his face, and with that would lead the way to the second level where he would inspect the doorknobs of the door leading into the garage. Noting that the knobs were present, he would immediately proceed to the third floor where one knob was still absent as a result of his prior activities, and demanding that the therapist hold the door open, he would wrap his legs around the door and hold on to the protruding part of the lock as he would swing back and forth and emit a loud excited shrill, "EEEEE," and rapidly ask where the doorknob was. When told that Robby seemed happy that the doorknob was gone but that maybe he was really frightened to see that there was no doorknob after he had thrown the doorknob away, he would give up swinging on the door, slam it shut with great gusto, and proceed down the stairs into the alley. The therapist would interpret to Robby that he seemed happy to see the doorknob gone but that every time he saw a doorknob missing, it must make him think that the same thing would happen to him. And without his doorknob Robby was afraid that he had no mamma, no daddy, and no Friend. Robby would characteristically respond with a satisfied smile and place his hand in the therapist's as they would walk together to a new building which had recently been finished and in which an office was undergoing completion. Here, Robby found a windfall of doors, doorknobs, wooden paneling, molding, and building equipment of all kinds.

One door that had not been fixed to its hinges but was leaning against the wall became the center of Robby's frantic compulsive activity of removing its doorknob. As he deftly and swiftly removed the doorknob and looked for other knobs to place in his collection, the therapist turned to him and remarked that Robby seemed very happy when he could have his bright, shiny doorknob. It must make him feel very strong and big so that he would not have to be afraid that he would be left alone. A pleased smile crossed his face as he went on to explore the pile of rubbish in the room for more doorknobs and hinges. As the time approached to leave the office and return to the therapist's office, Robby went through a struggle of returning the doorknob at the therapist's request. With the therapist's interpretations that he knew how hard it was for Robby to leave the doorknob on the door when Robby thought he needed it to make him feel like Robby and to make him feel as big as Friend and as daddy, Robby went through an obsessional struggle with the doorknobs, almost replacing them and then quickly removing them, until the therapist remarked that he knew how hard it was for Robby to leave the doorknob with the door, Robby didn't like to see that the door had a better doorknob than Robby had. And Robby was afraid to return the doorknob because he was always afraid that he would not have his knob and that he would have no one to belong to, while the doorknob belonged to the door. For a moment Robby seemed satisfied as he replaced the doorknob, but as he started to walk away, he quickly removed the doorknob with one quick stroke of his screwdriver and a tug of his hand. He stood still as if transfixed. He looked at the therapist and rapidly repeated the question, "Who took doorknob off? Who put knob in Robby's hand?" The therapist remarked that Robby needed Friend to tell him that Robby took the doorknob and that Robby had put it in Robby's hand. Robby needed Friend to tell him what he did, because Robby did not know Robby, and he did not know what Robby did. But now he could put the knob back and Robby could go back with

Friend to the office, to Robby's and Friend's house, where mamma would be waiting for Robby.

When Robby seemed at first unable to return the knob, the therapist suggested that maybe he would be able to help Robby put it back and Robby quickly remonstrated that he would do it. And as he quickly returned the knob, he said, "Friend, I fix it."

On the trek back to the office, he followed the familiar path of going down the stairway into the basement of the building, where more doors and knobs were quickly explored, given up after a struggle, and into the alley leading to the parking garage and up the back stairway of the building. Here, Robby, on hearing loud noises, would suddenly close his ears and appear frightened. The therapist would remark to him that the noises frightened Robby whenever he thought that he was bad, and that the noises would jump out and carry him away from mommy, daddy and his home. Sometimes Robby felt like the knobs that he took from the doors, alone and not belonging to mommy and daddy, and when he took the knobs he was afraid that daddy would scold him and make big noises like the noises that he now heard. Apparently satisfied with this interpretation, Robby would remove his hands from his ears and place his arm in front of his eyes as he put one hand in the therapist's hand and again blindly lead the way up the stairs, but with the assurance that the therapist was shadowing him from behind. In this manner he would reach the therapist's office. He would dash into the office and inquire in a loud questioning voice, "Where mama?" Upon mama's arrival he would happily entwine his legs around the door and, with one hand on each knob of the door, would swing back and forth in gleeful excitement and then, on his mother's request, would pick up his screwdrivers and other paraphernalia and bid good-bye to Friend as he would rapidly dash down the hall to the elevator.

In this play sequence which took place several months later and repeated itself hour after hour for many weeks, we find a new development in the ritualistic play around the doorknob. First of all, we realize that the patient can cope with the threat of the psychotherapy situation only if he can control it through the ritualistic play. The compulsive control of the doorknobs, the collection of these doorknobs, guarantees his mastery over the object and reduces anxiety. The meaning of the play is, of course, overdetermined inasmuch as his control of the doorknobs guarantees him both accessibility and an avenue of flight. He can get to the object without having to be afraid of it, and can leave it at will. The doors, physical symbols of the object, are deprived of their controlling mechanism and thus can be controlled by the child.

His collection of doorknobs, combined as it was with the passionate glee of victory, could be compared to the trophies of head-hunters, who, in collecting their trophies, not only master the enemy but also incorporate his virtues and his strength. These trophies are not only the sign of victory but a protection against deep-seated anxiety.

As the play continues Robby struggles with the therapist, but actually attempts to resolve his inner struggle about control. Hour after hour as he incorporates aspects of the psychotherapist who continues to show him the meaning of the play, he gathers strength and can be compared to a head-hunter who feels that everybody is afraid of him when noticing all his trophies of victory. The child therefore can discontinue this attack, and may even be able to discontinue the exhibition of his trophies.

This struggle concerning the incorporation of introjects as it is exhibited in the play with physical objects leads him to the beginning of individuation. As he incorporates the therapist, or rather the therapist's well-meaning and helpful intentions, he can raise the question as to "who did it." The loss of body function may be caused in the mind of the child by the threatening, castrating, negative introject, which creates a paralyzing fear, which, if recognized and given up, may lead to the restoration of function. It is during this period of the hour that the child, in raising the question, permits the therapist to help the patient see that he (the child) himself took off the doorknobs from the door, thus destroyed the function of the door, tried to undermine the functioning of the therapist, symbolically destroyed him, and even though he expects retribution he also finds out that he may safely ask the question since separation and individuation have now become a less frightening task.

As he understands that he himself is the one who takes the doorknobs off, and as he starts to sense his own will, the first recognition of individuation, he is overwhelmed by fear, and as the play, the ritualistic repetition of the hour, proceeds week after week, he finds himself confronted by terrible noises, as frightful as the vengeful chorus of the Erinyes. He interprets the noise of the tools, actually the acceptance of the therapist's earlier interpretation as to "who did it," as voices of doom and of danger. He tries to deny their existence, shuts his ears, but nevertheless works through on this level his extreme fear of annihilation, of the destruction of his body, and of his individuality. Again, the interpretive and reassuring voice of the therapist, who permits individuation but does so at the speed of the child, helps the child to take one step further in his development.

It should be pointed out that this part of the therapeutic process is worked out in play action and in a language in which the third person is used instead of the "I" and "thou." It is as if the therapist spontaneously recognizes the psychological need of the child who cannot take full responsibility for what he does and cannot yet accept full individuation. The expression of the conflict through the use of third person language is characteristic for interpersonal relationships in which there is no clear-cut separation, in which the way toward identity is still characterized through incomplete recognition of the "I" and "thou." But as the confidence of the child is restored, he accepts some of his newly gained individuality, and also accepts the therapist, expressing trust in the psychotherapist by means of denying his own capacity to find the way back. He closes his eyes, and as he pulls toward the goal he holds on to the therapist whose control he thus wants and to whom he wants at the same time to express that he is pulled by blind forces.

In the ending phase of this ritualistic game the child acts out not only the rediscovery of the object, the finding of the mother, but also the restoration of the object now that the anxiety has dwindled, and as he holds on to both doorknobs which he has restored to the door and as he gives passionate expressions of joy for his mother's return, he restores the unity with her on a different basis of mastery which permits him to seek out the object without having to destroy its function. The head-hunter has given up his fear and turns with joy to the source of love.

We believe it ought to be stressed that in this phase of the play activity we find not only the emergence of individuation but also the emergence of language. It may be suggested at this point, and Piaget has given us many instructive examples, that the development of language mirrors the development of the psychic apparatus. Thus, we find that originally it was only the compulsive play activity which helped us to understand the conflict and the psychic organization which tries to master it. Now, at this stage of the psychotherapeutic process, the child also has available language, primitive as it may be and as fixated as it may be at an early stage of language development; he comes nearer to a stage where the acting-out fantasy is replaced in part by verbal fantasy. Waelder's formula of the play as a fantasy woven around physical objects is now applicable since the first inroad has been achieved against the destructive force of compulsive and fragmented activity determined by hallucinatory and delusional processes.

Earlier, we referred to Freud's discussion of Tausk's paper. The present situation in the case of Robby may be taken as further illustration of Freud's comment. The boy, who does something with the doorknob and who, because of his illness, does not know what he has done, turns to the psychotherapist, who, in understanding the play activity, reads his mind as it were, and literally gives him the thought and therefore gives him language and the knowledge of his deed. Terrifying anxiety did not permit him to know that he could be an individual or that he was the one who had done it. It would be worthwhile to discuss this material in terms of superego and ego development. The question of the child as to "who did it" indicates the emergence of the precursors of superego formation, and of beginning delay mechanisms, but at the same time it refers to the exploration of reality and to the wish to master reality. His wish to know who has done it establishes new ego strength as well as superego function. It has been suggested elsewhere that the precursors of reality testing can be found in primitive, early superego injunctions. This kind of reality testing, rather than making use of a more advanced ego organization, takes recourse in the early parental "who did it" and its implied injunctions and threats of punishment.

Nick was almost thirteen when he was brought for psychiatric treatment. He had been profoundly disturbed, in the parents' recollection, ever since he was three years old, when the birth of his sister apparently precipitated the acute onset of his illness. The severe disturbance never resolved itself in the ensuing years of Nick's life. The parents characterized his difficulty mainly in terms of retarded intellectual development which they attributed to a birth injury but which was never medically established. The mother was convinced that Nick was doomed to an incurable illness for which there was no real help but only those futile gestures of medical treatment which parental conscience and duty required her to arrange for him. Although there had always been an open question regarding the etiology of Nick's disturbance and there was ample reason to suspect some organic brain damage, it was clear from an evaluation of Nick's illness that he had been psychotic for many years, and there was reason to believe that his intellectual retardation was more in the nature of a pseudo stupidity than a genuine organic type of dementia. At the age of thirteen, Nick displayed a grotesque masochistic compliance in relation to his peers, which manifested itself in bizarre ways. He had long become known to his schoolmates as a clown who would do the most ridiculous things to make other boys laugh. Nick never saw humor in these situations but only a desperate need to comply with the tormenting provocations of his peers and to offer himself as a helpless victim of their abuse and ridicule. Nick described these situations with an air of remoteness about them, as if he were talking of the exploits of another boy rather than of himself. Actually, he did in fact speak about a dissociated part of himself. A favorite pastime of his schoolmates was to gather around Nick and to shout various orders to him to humiliate him. When they would order, "Nick, piss on the wall," Nick would immediately comply by urinating on the wall. When the boys would shout at Nick, "Shit in your pants," Nick would go through the motions of having a bowel movement and would sometimes be so compliant as to succeed in defecating in his pants. When the boys would torment him with the command to kiss their shoes, Nick would get down on his hands and knees and obediently kiss the shoes of his tormentors. Nick's parents were confused and greatly mystified by his behavior, since to them it seemed that his most cardinal difficulty was that he never obeyed them. They felt that the most difficult thing about him was his negative attitude toward them in which he seemed never to accept their authority and which often manifested itself in a most provocative way in constant clownish attacks on his younger sister.

Although they vaguely recognized that there was much that was immature in his development, they were never really aware of his illness. They only complained of his badness and the aggravation that he aroused in them. Nor did they realize to what extent Nick suffered an invisible panic lest he be deserted and abandoned. For Nick literally forced his mother to do his bidding at all times lest he become aware that he no longer controlled her and therefore had no assurance of her continued presence and attachment to him.

During many early therapy hours with Nick, the therapist felt the extent of the unbridged chasm that lay between himself and Nick. Nick would withdraw to a corner and read the therapist's medical books or ply him with a number of questions related to the manufacture of drugs used in psychiatric treatment. Nick wanted to know how sodium pentothal was made and why the therapist did not use it on him. He carried a pharmacy manual with him and repeatedly asked the therapist whether he knew what the drugs were for, and continually plied him with inquiries as to why the therapist used no drugs. He brought numerous books with him that he obviously could not understand and perhaps could not read. He gave the impression at all times that he was interested only in what was useless to him, and he seemed to imply in his behavior that he felt that he could expect from the therapist only what was useless, just as all his life he had received only futile gestures of help from the many different types of treatment he had undergone in his pediatric and allergy care. In his unguarded moments he broke out in bizarre clownish behavior in which he attempted to shadow-box with the therapist in such a manner as to convey the deepest anxiety and the most pathetic kind of humor that would inevitably lead to his ridicule and humiliation.

On one occasion the therapist remarked how much Nick would like to be a tough guy but was having a terrible time as he was always so afraid of everyone. Nick liked being called a tough guy and said, "That's my name." The therapist told him that it was fine with him that Nick wanted to be a tough guy and maybe he even wanted to be the leader of a gang. Nick thought this was a great thing and when the therapist offered his services to him in the gang, Nick, now christened Tough Guy, referred to the therapist as Red.

Tough Guy and Red formed the nucleus of an invisible gang which had no apparent purpose for its existence. Tough Guy, as the leader of the gang, had no desire to be a criminal. But he needed Red to accompany him on his explorations through the streets of Beverly Hills, first to discover the whereabouts of the residences of famous movie stars, and then to trace a familiar route along the streets of Beverly Hills, apparently in search of nothing. But as Tough Guy and Red pursued their aimless wandering, Tough Guy cautiously confessed to Red that he had heard that Nick was having a lot of trouble. He heard that he must have many disorders. He even heard that Nick had shit in his pants at school. He hated Nick; he thought he was crazy. Red said that he too had heard about

Nick. He heard that he had many troubles and that he was looking for someone to help him but that he never could find anyone who could understand him. Tough Guy snorted and said that he hated Nick anyway. Red said that he heard that whenever Nick heard that anyone hated him, he got plenty scared because he couldn't stand being hated. He especially got in trouble when Tough Guy hated him. He really wanted Tough Guy to like him. Tough Guy said that he could never like Nick because he was so crazy. He even kissed the boys' shoes when they told him to. Red said that maybe Nick had to do this because he thought that the more he did crazy things, the more he made the other boys laugh at him and the more he thought they liked him. Tough Guy looked vacantly at Red, and suddenly the vacant and incomprehensible look on his face faded slightly, and a faint smile of recognition with genuine feeling appeared as he turned to Red and said, "Red, you're a good psychiatrist."

Red turned to Tough Guy and snorted, "Do you mean like that crooked quack, Friedman?" Nick laughed cautiously and asked Red if he knew Friedman. Red said he had heard about him. He had heard that Friedman was one of the biggest crooked quacks in Beverly Hills. Tough Guy turned to Red and said, "Red, do you know what that Friedman does?" Red said he thought Friedman probably did a lot of crazy things. Tough Guy said he had heard that Friedman sent big bills to Nick for his treatment. Red said he had heard about that too, and then snorted in disgust, "That dirty, crooked quack, Friedman. He's a crooked crook. He pretends to be a doctor and is supposed to cure Nick of his disorders, but all he does is sit in his office and doesn't even give Nick any medicine to cure him. He just sends him big bills and makes Nick's parents pay out all their money so that there is nothing left for them."

Tough Guy looked at Red with questioning but vacant eyes. His suspiciousness of Red was quite apparent and the look of incredulity remained with him as he seemed to become more embarrassed and anxious. Timidly, he said, "Friedman's all right, Red. He's a nice guy." Red again snorted in disgust, "If you want to think he's a nice guy, that's for you to think, Tough Guy. But all I ever hear about Friedman is that he is supposed to treat Nick, but all he does is make him pay so much money that Nick thinks that there is nothing left for his family. He just talks to him, doesn't give him any medicine, and doesn't cure him. He just keeps him coming and sometimes he doesn't even see him in his office. No wonder Nick always disappears as soon as he comes to see him. He would probably get more help if he joined our gang than if he came to see that quack, Friedman."

Tough Guy said, "Yeah. Maybe you're right, Red." And then he musingly remarked, "But I don't want Nick in this gang. He does crazy things. He has a lot of disorders. I hate him."

This case material illustrates the case of a psychotic boy with possible organic involvement whose behavior is quite typically schizophrenic. The case illustration is of special interest to us since it refers to the adaptation of a technique which was described by the authors previously[4] in a paper which dealt with the treatment of a delinquent boy. We discussed there in detail the special meaning of acting-out during the psychotherapeutic process and paid attention to the problem of play-acting, which was in part future-directed. In this previous case the therapist, as is also true in this case, offered himself as a member of the gang. He won access to the inner life of the child, but we become aware of a variety of differences in the two cases which we want to spell out in detail.

In the earlier case, stemming from the patient's primarily neurotic adjustment, both therapist and patient played but one role, the role of the gang member, "boss and doc," while in this particular play sequence we find that each has two faces as it were, so that one may have the feeling at times that four persons are involved. It is not only the child who suffers from a "split personality" but also the doctor, who is perceived by the child literally as a Dr. Jekyll and a Mr. Hyde, only the names chosen by the child differ from those Robert Louis Stevenson chose for his dual hero. "Red" and "Dr. Friedman" characterize the two parts of the therapist to whom the child relates his problems.

In becoming "Tough Guy," the patient strives for the ego ideal and for support from the therapist, actually the "Red" part of the therapist, while at the same time he tries desperately to keep out his pathologic counterpart, the masochistic child who has no identity of his own and lives on borrowed identity, usually the disgracing "orders" of his contemporaries. This despicable part of himself is matched by the despicable part of the therapist who is experienced as not helpful, as charging too much. It seems to thus express what the child does not want to have true but what he might hear the parents say about the therapist as they express discouragement about the slow treatment, the lack of visible success, and about the tremendous expense involved in order to help their child. The negative version of the therapist is also the projection of the parents' own negative attitude toward the child, and thus is experienced by the youngster as the hated parent who is to be kept out of the therapy just as he attempts to keep out of the therapy the hated child-patient. This seems to maintain the collaboration of the positive aspects of patient and psychotherapist, and thus provides a vivid example of schizophrenic ambivalence.

One could look at this situation as one of a divided identity struggle. The therapeutic situation can only be maintained by the forceful seclusion of the other aspect of the personality. It is as if Dr. Jekyll is not allowed to know about Mr. Hyde but finally comes to the point where he might be able to go through life with the identity of Dr. Jekyll and with the added knowledge of a role belonging to Mr. Hyde who is to be kept out of the treatment situation.

It is interesting that our metaphor actually could be understood in reverse, since what is accepted consciously are the negative aspects, if we were to look at these in terms of contemporary values. The conscious value of the patient is complete obedience and masochistic pleasure. The rejected value which is rescued in the sanctuary of the psychotherapy situation is the one of the strong boy, the "Tough Guy," who then in turn is supported by something in the therapist's personality which is experienced by the patient as forbidden, as a secret to be kept from the parents, while the positive notion of him, the psychiatrist with the doctor's title, is experienced as unwelcome and unacceptable to the child.

One might well wonder how the psychotic illness of this child must have looked when he was five years old, in comparison with the way it appears at the age of thirteen. One may very well wonder whether the child might not have utilized, instead of schizophrenic play acting, the use of physical toy objects as demonstrated in the example of Robby. We would like to make the point that prevalent modes of expression will depend upon the stage of development and that the schizophrenic process will find different expressions at different times of the child's life. It is as if the disease process makes use of different channels in the ego organization as they become available because of certain maturational processes which, though distorted, nevertheless are age-bound, that is, follow a chronologic sequence.

It has often been assumed in the case of the adult personality, and this would be a convenient assumption, that the psychotic process would find similar expression regardless of age. This example permits us to raise the question concerning certain quantitative and qualitative differences in the psychic organization of the psychotic ego, which, if correctly understood, would suggest appropriate methods of communication with the sick child rather than force us to be satisfied with a mere abstract understanding of the disease process.

Summary

Influencing machines, inventions of machines which are to control perpetual motion, frequently play a part in the inner life of certain adult schizophrenics. Physical objects which are utilized by children as toys, as transitional objects, as they slowly develop the capacity for adult thinking, seem to be the infantile equivalent of these machines. The play of psychotic children indicates a special use of physical objects which are the external crutches, as it were, on which to support the delusional and hallucinatory ideation which characterize the inner life of such children. Certain qualities of the psychotic play of children, such as stereotyped repetitiveness, fragmentation, condensation, and other characteristics are striking and outstanding features, the observation of which permits inferences about the nature of the psychic organization of the patient. In this communication, a number of case illustrations are used in order to utilize the play as a springboard toward an understanding of the fragile and fragmented ego organization of these children, and thus to be better equipped for the development of rational treatment techniques for this patient group.

Several questions are raised concerning certain elementary processes which characterize the psychotic child's ego. These questions indicate the desirability for formalized research into the nature of the psychotic child's play, research which would require the study not only of different stages of the illness but also would inquire into the nature of the ego organization and its changes when certain maturation takes place. Peller [12] has provided us with a similar study of play patterns in normal development. Such research would contribute toward increased flexibility in the approach to these children rather than reliance on older formulae which may be useful for initial contact but fail us in different stages of the therapeutic process. Psychotic play, then, constitutes the royal road not only to unconscious mental process and conflict but to an understanding of primitive ego organization and its developmental course in childhood psychosis.

Bibliography

1. Ekstein, R.: Thoughts concerning the nature of the interpretative process. *In* Levitt, M.: Readings in Psychoanalytic Psychology. In publication.

2. ———: The space child's time machine: On "reconstruction" in the psychotherapeutic treatment of a schizophrenoid child. Am. J. Orthopsychiat. *24:* 492–506, 1954.

3. ———, Bryant, K., and Friedman, S. W.: Childhood schizophrenia and allied conditions—A review of the literature: 1946–1956. *In* Bellak, L.: Schizophrenia: A Review of the Syndrome. New York, Logos Press, 1958.

4. ———, and Friedman, S. W.: The function of acting-out, play action and play acting in the psychotherapeutic process. J. Am. Psychoanalyt. A. *5:* 581–629, 1957.

5. ———, and ———: A technical problem in the beginning phase of psychotherapy with a borderline psychotic child. *In* Gardner, G. E.: Case Studies in Childhood Emotional Disabilities, vol. 2. New York, American Orthopsychiatric Association, 1956.

6. Elkisch, P.: Significant relationship between the human figure and the machine in the drawings of boys. Am. J. Orthopsychiat. *22:* 379–385, 1952.

7. Erikson, E. H.: Childhood and Society. New York, W. W. Norton & Company, Inc., 1950.

8. Erikson, E. H.: Studies in the interpretation of play: 1. Clinical observation of play disruption in young children. Genet. Psychology Monogr. *22:* 557–671, 1940.

9. Loomis, E.: Play patterns in the schizophrenic and mentally defective child. Unpublished manuscript.

10. ———, Hilgeman, L. M., and Meyer, L. R.: Childhood psychosis: 2. Play patterns as non-verbal indices of ego functions: A preliminary report. Am. J. Orthopsychiat. *27:* 691–700, 1957.

11. Mahler, M. S., and Elkisch, P.: Some observations on disturbances of the ego in a case of infantile psychosis. Psychoanalyt. Study of the Child *8:* 252–261, 1953.

12. Peller, L. E.: Libidinal phases, ego development and play. Psychoanalyt. Study of the Child *9:* 178–198, 1954.

13. Piaget, J.: The Construction of Reality in the Child. New York, Basic Books, Inc., 1954.

14. Rank, B.: Adaptation of the psychoanalytic technique for the treatment of young children with atypical development. Am. J. Orthopsychiat. *19:* 130–139, 1949.

15. Sechehaye, M.: Symbolic Realization: A New Method of Psychotherapy Applied to a Case of Schizophrenia. New York, International Universities Press, Inc., 1951.

16. Shugart, G.: The play history: Its application and significance. J. Psychiatric Social Work *24:* 204–209, 1955.

17. Tausk, V.: On the origin of the "influencing machine" in schizophrenia. Psychoanalyt. Quart. *2:* 519–556, 1933.

18. Waelder, R.: The psychoanalytic theory of play. Psychoanalyt. Quart. *2:* 208–224, 1933.

19. Wexler, M.: Personal Communication.

20. Williams, M.: Personal Communication.

21. Winnicott, D. W.: Transitional objects and transitional phenomena. Internat. J. Psycho-Analysis *2:* 1–9, 1953.

22. Zulliger, H.: Child psychotherapy without interpretation of unconscious content: A theoretical exposition of pure play: The use of a child's talisman as a psychotherapeutic agent. Translated from the German by R. Ekstein and J. Wallerstein. Bull. Menninger Clin. *17:* 180–188, 1953.

12

Countertransference Phenomena in the Treatment of Severe Character Disorders in Children and Adolescents*

By JAMES T. PROCTOR

THE MANY DIFFICULTIES in the technical management and therapy of severe juvenile character disorders are often discussed and are admittedly weighty. However, it is the thesis of this paper that the anxieties, hostilities, fears and actual countertransference phenomena engendered in those dealing with the juvenile character disorders are very important factors which are given too little overt attention. Further, the reality problems are often used by the proposed or actual therapist or therapeutic team in the service of counterresistance or countertransference.

The considerations and observations I want to discuss have been learned in a hard school. They are derived from direct and often painful personal experience as a therapist, from personal analysis, supervision of the therapy of child psychiatric residents and the child psychiatric team, as well as from supervision of the larger hospital team and environment when such children have been hospitalized. The cases themselves, eleven males from seven through sixteen years of age, vary from three with a mental structure approximating that of the psychotic, to two less malignant but still severe neurotic character disorders. The other six cases lie between these extremes. These cases have been managed on both an in-patient and out-patient basis, with therapy ranging from intensive (therapy seven times a week with numerous other brief contacts), through less intensive therapy with a minimum frequency of once a week. The patients have been in treatment from thirty to three hundred and fifty hours.

The factors to be discussed apply to some extent to all therapy, but to a much higher degree to the therapy of the severe character disorders. This is because the countertransference problems become progressively greater

* Presented in a shorter form at the 1958 Annual Orthopsychiatric Meeting, New York.

with the impulsivity or "acting" potential and the degree of narcissism. The more severe cases show marked ego scatter, a vehement repetition compulsion and extensive introjection of terrifying pregenital objects. They also utilize the concomitant defense mechanisms of narcissistic omnipotence, projection and denial. Consequently, they manifest an ambivalent, notably hostile, vacillating and unreliable transference. When these factors obtain, the therapist and others in contact with the patient are placed under unusual stress and defend themselves vigorously (counter-resistance) or regressively react to the patient as a part-object from their own earlier life experience (countertransference). That is, those in close contact with the patient may regressively identify with his aggression or some constituent of his archaic superego, his id impulses or even some psychotic fragment within him.[5] The patient's narcissistic omnipotent defenses are particularly provocative and therapists frequently identify with (and simultaneously defend themselves against) the patient's omnipotent system, indicating the unconscious wish to be even more omnipotent than the patient.

Billy, a thirteen year old boy in early puberty, was initially hospitalized for ten months and seen daily for most of that period. He was referred because of his inability to live in several foster homes during the preceding year, running away, stealing, lying, enuresis and an equivocal delusional system about his mother. There was also some question whether he had visual hallucinations about mother. Early in treatment he briefly played out with dolls the fantasy of an orderly manually exploring a nurse's genitals and the orderly's hand being bitten by the vagina. During this excursion he set aside the doll representing the therapist, but placed the doll astride a desk pen in such a fashion that there was a phallic protuberance equal to the size of the doll. When the therapist pointed out that the therapist-doll had certainly been given a large phallus, Billy responded, "You're always acting like you've got a big dick." The therapist had consciously decided, for various therapeutic considerations, to demonstrate his own ability to compete with Billy in activities as ping-pong, checkers, chess, etc., but when confronted with Billy's countertransference interpretation it became clear that unconscious megalopenile fantasies had been evoked, as noted above. Billy's interpretation was admitted openly as being correct and his anger about the matter explored.

The term countertransference will be used as the reverse of transference, those grossly regressive, relatively fixed patterns determined by infantile object relations which are transferred or projected on the therapist and, consequently, lead to the therapist being reacted to as the past object rather than as a real person. In countertransference the therapist transfers to the patient in the same regressive way, except, as noted previously, there is a striking tendency in these cases to react to or identify with the patient as a part-object. However, in the following discussion, I will also use the term countertransference in the broader sense to include all emotional responses and reactions of the therapist toward or about the patient. This is done as the more general emotional responses and reactions are seldom clearly separable from countertransference phenomena in the pristine sense. The two tend to blend inextricably. Beneath the thin layer of ego function and reality testing, countertransference and counteridentification are constantly operating, so that under stress irrational responses are always at least incipiently present and must be dealt with in greater or lesser degree. Neurotic distortions rising from counterresistance and countertransference are often rather silent, but can result in the patient's being refused therapy, therapeutic stalemate or termination. Such eventualities perpetuate and reinforce the patient's previous negative experiences for the protection of the therapist's psychic equilibrium.

The reality difficulties are certainly pronounced in dealing with the severe character disorders but are usually not insurmountable. In the following discussion, the difficulties, vagaries, trials and tribulations of therapy with such character disorders will be emphasized. The rewards and personal satisfactions which can be derived by the therapist are also considerable, but these are mentioned here only in passing.

However, from any vantage the severe character disorders are very difficult cases to treat and perhaps are the most trying of all, including the overt psychoses. They demand considerable time both in the short-term and long-term sense; we often have poor (or no) family or community support; the patients frequently make vigorous and at times insatiable demands on us for money or other real gifts and manifestations of love; we are often criticized for the patient's acting out and delinquencies; or, at the least, this superego threat arising either from within ourselves or stemming from others is ever present. Also, the personal strain involved in the more difficult cases, the possibility and even probability of personal attack, destruction of personal and other property are significant factors with which we have to contend. The overt psychotic has largely given up his object relations and withdrawn, but the severe character disorder maintains very ambivalent object relations, continually assaulting the object (including the therapist) to obtain the supplies he needs. In the first place these patients begin therapy already in an acting out state, directing libido into extratherapeutic channels, which, if seen in the course of therapy of a neurotic or other less severe disorder, would seem to imperil treatment. It may well be that after mature and objective consideration the reality difficulties are greater than we are willing to accept or can tolerate, in which case we may decide that we cannot involve ourselves.[4] However, this situation should be relatively rare.

More often, the individual therapist or group or others in any sort of therapeutic contact with the patient (I will refer to all of these people as "therapists") will rationalize their counterresistance by stating they cannot work with a given case in view of the difficult reality circumstances. Frequently, the poor prognosis of such cases is pointed out, although the best statistcs we have (as quoted by Glover[7] from the Institute for the Study and Treatment of Delinquency in London) indicate that with a well-motivated and trained therapist and team, we can expect a cure in 32 per cent of delinquent cases, with major amelioration in another 30 per cent. It is probably true that most therapists do not achieve such results. An important factor is that the therapist and staff often approach such cases in a state of resistance. Before even seeing the patient they are prepared to refuse the case or to accept early failure and termination. The therapist is threatened by and resistant to even empathizing with the patient and his aggression, stealing, lying and underlying motivations long enough to formulate an adequate diagnosis and prognosis. Empathy, that transient, trial identification, is frightening as it tends to elicit guilt, superego censure for the trial identification, which includes identification with the patient's unbridled aggression and chaotic sexuality. It is as though to accept tentatively the patient and withhold punishment is to condone the patient's impulsivity. A lack of empathy or understanding of these patients is frequently due to negative countertransference on this basis. The therapist may also identify with the patient to too great an extent and project superego censure away from them both.

In supervision, even with relatively advanced residents and junior staff (some of whom have been analyzed) there is a frequent tendency for the therapist to see such patients as "bad." Their behavior is thus judged in moral terms (superego censure) which blocks adequate understanding of the id-impulse, ego-defense system and so blocks treatment. Also, in diagnostic studies there is a tendency to formulate a more bleak therapeutic responsiveness and prognosis than seems warranted.

A fourteen year old male patient was circumstantially suspected as the arsonist in a major and several minor fires. The police called the therapist to obtain a confession from the patient. An interview with another patient was interrupted to ask if the therapist knew the suspected arsonist's whereabouts, as another fire had started (the suspect was with the police). There was open discussion of the impropriety of bringing such "acter-outers" to a small college town even for treatment, and allusion to the citizens' probable ire. The patient-suspect's teacher called to determine if it was safe for him to be in her class and his landlord called to determine if it was safe to have him in residence. The social censure of the patient and his therapist was overt. It seemed to the therapist as though society at large held him personally responsible for the patient's alleged acting out. While the therapist protected the patient in a therapeutically realistic way, he over-identified with the patient and adopted one of the patient's chief mechanisms: identification with the aggressor. The therapist then, upon little or no provocation, defensively attacked even close associates. This elicited abrupt censure for the hostility, which in turn activated an emerging awareness in the therapist of his own defenses.

The sexual seductiveness of these patients is remarkable. As a part of seeking objects and supplies, they often overtly and aggressively, as well as covertly and symbolically, directly seek heterosexual relations, homosexual contact or perverted sexual activity with any available object. They not infrequently make direct genital assaults, or at least gestures, at times with knives or other weapons. This behavior is, to say the least, frightening and activates any unresolved oedipal conflicts and castration anxieties. This promotes marked defensive maneuvers or counterattack. Even if the therapist has been carefully analyzed, he must learn to recognize, accept and live with his basic, residual and probably irreducible oedipal-castration anxieties, to prevent such defensive maneuvers.[3, 8] Also, every person working with such patients must be encouraged to deal with his irrational fears of violence which are aroused and need to be conscious. Some of these factors are fairly often recognized and discussed, but we must constantly be on guard against therapeutic distortions arising from the therapist's defensive maneuvers against activated oedipal material. Therapists are apt to rationalize their countertransference problems by explaining them on the basis of the less toxic "narcissistic injury," when in fact the distortions are positive or negative oedipal in origin.

Billy's initial therapist left after working with him for some three months. By that time Billy and his violent and provocative behavior were well known to everyone in the department. There was considerable difficulty in finding another therapist for him, various reasons being given: poor prognosis, inability of the therapist to withstand the social criticism about Billy's behavior, his ego fragility and the threat of a fulminating psychosis, etc. These factors were important considerations, but, as Billy was engaged by his second and long-term therapist, other factors became apparent. For example, during the first interview with the second therapist, Billy was frantic. It is difficult to describe his vacillations and alterations in mood and the way he related to the therapist. He bounded about the room on top of the furniture, leaping gazelle-like from chair to couch to desk. He lay on the couch, sat in a chair, assumed a fetal position on top of the desk, all in as little time as it takes to tell. He called his therapist a headshrinker and spontaneously produced fantasies of decapitation with pills being pushed into the stump to shrink it away. He bit the therapist. He deftly grasped the therapist's feet, lifting them over his head while the therapist was sitting in a swivel chair, thus completely rendering the therapist helpless in this precarious position. Billy seductively grasped the therapist's genitals and subsequently swiped at them with a rubber knife and then with a potentially effective desk knife. While much of this behavior was very annoying and potentially destructive, there was never valid question of the therapist's ability to defend himself and protect his property. However, Billy's gestures or assaults elicited considerable anxiety and hostility. The anxiety and hostility seemed basically unwarranted and after careful analysis were found to stem from activated oedipal-castration conflicts.

These patients have by necessity become astute observers of human nature and at least the surface of the human mind. If approached with a negative attitude or a calculated restraint of the negative, they will sense it, sense the therapist as an enemy and play upon his defenses and conflicts until the situation is intolerable. The therapist is then forced to defend himself by withdrawal or counterattack. In either case therapy ends. These patients can be maddening and it is important to sort out the realistic hate they engender so that it can be dealt with in therapy. Unconscious hate in the therapist will be expressed covertly, or out of reaction formation to the unconscious hate the therapist can be too solicitous and supportive. He will consequently inadequately interpret the negative transference, refusing to recognize himself as a monstrous and frightening figure in the patient's mind.

Early in therapy, a fourteen year old, intellectually superior male patient with relatively mild psychopathology but with severely reactive behavior was making excessive noise in the therapist's office. The therapist had had numerous complaints about noise emanating from his office. Consequently, he admonished the patient not to make so much noise as he might disturb the doctor in the adjoining office, a very senior woman analyst who had suffered long from such noises and disturbing patients. The patient's hostile response was, "What's the matter. Are you afraid of her?" There was good reason for asking the patient to be quieter, but his response operated on several levels. It was first a projection of the patient's own fears of his mother onto the therapist; second, it was a transference reaction. However, it was also an incisive interpretation of the anxiety, consequent annoyance and attempts to control which the patient engendered in the therapist by intruding into a mother figure's secret activities with various men (largely). The patient's interpretation provoked some confusion in the therapist. A temporary block ensued concerning the projective aspects of the patient's remark (his own fear of his mother) and the transference aspect (reacting with anger to a simple, realistic request, as if the therapist were the hated mother attempting to control him).

To consider further the therapist's hate for the patient, I would like to point out that I do not use the word hate lightly. I refer to real, murderous rage which often first appears symbolically in the punishment of, or withdrawal from the patient, or it may first appear in the therapist's fantasies and dreams.[11]

During the first hours with Billy, which were excessively trying, the therapist would "facetiously" reply to inquiries from colleagues, that "the prognosis seems pretty good if Billy lives through the next few days"; i.e., if the therapist did not murder him. It is also noteworthy how often people knowledgeable in the ways of the unconscious were perplexed by this reply. Later, Billy escaped the closed ward several times and visited the therapist's home (on two occasions to be sure the therapist was alive), once being admitted by a baby sitter when only she and an infant son were present. This was extremely frightening due to Billy's known destructive potential and evoked consideration of more vigorous restraint (e.g., state hospital). However, the situation also evoked fantasies of fighting Billy or destroying him if necessary to protect home and family. The therapist was not able to deal adequately with his own murderous fantasies until at one of the later "visits" (invasions) Billy pointed out that the therapist looked as though he had been stabbed. This interpretation brought to full awareness the therapist's hostilities and freed him to deal with those hostile feelings, both intrapsychically and with Billy, to the advantage of therapy. The therapist was able to discuss with Billy, his annoyance at Billy's intrusions and was able to interpret more effectively Billy's hostilities toward him, the death wish involved, etc. Following this, Billy stopped coming to the therapist's home.

There are constant communication problems with these patients. Their proclivity for action, their belief in the magic of action and distrust of words, along with a poorly developed ego structure and preconscious system inhibits or prevents them from communicating and facing their conflicts in words. This taxes the therapist, forces greater acumen to read the communications of action and symbolic expression. Besides this being a more difficult task, it deprives the therapist of his usual word feedings from the patient and can (and does) frequently result in increasingly hostile demands for verbal material to feed the therapist and satisfy his infantile curiosity. These hostile demands can lead to further rebellious acting out by the patient, an impasse or interruption of therapy. The therapist in essence often says to the patient, as Glover [8] expresses it: either your associations or your therapeutic life.

Billy has repeatedly stated that he believes in action, that talking "is for the birds." When pressed for verbal communication he frequently warned the therapist to "shut up," stating or implying that he would assault the therapist otherwise and indeed he did so repeatedly when pressed. Also, when pressed to produce verbally he frequently spoke of leaving the hospital and treatment. Once when Billy was being mildly pressured to stop acting and to deal with his conflicts in words, he responded with fantasies of unbearable tension and destruction should he stop acting. He interpreted with considerable anger, the therapist's approach as a "bulldozer technique." At various times, the therapist's curiosity and need for words have been rationalized as "research interest."

The demand for words and associations is unrealistic as it is the task of therapy to interrupt the repetition compulsion and connect the unconscious conflict with words that can be dealt with intrapsychically rather than acted out. Also, there is often considerable urgency to demand ego control from the patient to stop acting. There is much therapeutic reality in the wish to have the patient progress to this point, but the therapist frequently demands conformity, an end to the acting, before he understands the unconscious drives within the patient and thus before he can interpret and work through the impulse-defense system in a therapeutically realistic way. Thus, the therapist's too early demands for conformity (and without adequate understanding and interpretation to the patient) is symptomatic of the therapist's unresolved and injured narcissism and omnipotence. As the patient's acting out is in many ways a dereistic dramatization of omnipotence, the patient's acting and the therapist's demands for conformity can reduce itself to a struggle between two people, both of whom unconsciously see themselves as omnipotent. Also, the therapist unconsciously senses that the acting is a dramatization of phallic masturbatory fantasies.[6] The acting therefore takes on all of the moral opprobrium attached to masturbation, by which the therapist unconsciously feels contaminated. He deems himself responsible for it and thus feels he must stop it. There is the additional factor that the close therapeutic relation has a seductive or regressive effect on the therapist's own ego toward action. If this is a marked factor and remains unconscious, the therapist must stop the patient's acting, interrupt treatment or withdraw, as neither his superego nor society will tolerate even the threat of his id impulses being activated or allowed access to motility. The therapist may seem to understand adequately and interpret the patient's impulse-defense system without therapeutic change. In this context we need to be cognizant that interpretations may be used for the patient's benefit or may be used in a hostile way to command conformity and enforce the therapist's omnipotent wishes. If interpretations are given in this negative way, they are, at the least, ineffective and may result in the patient acting out still more in reaction to the therapist's aggression or attempts to control him.

Mike, a thirteen year old patient being seen twice a week, had moved along in therapy and settled down remarkably. He was comfortably playing with a yo-yo one interview and recounting some of his daily activities. The yo-yo play was interpreted as masturbation and his desire to show this to the therapist. The interpretation was correct, but it had no place in that context. The interpretation was the therapist's unconscious command for Mike to move to id material to satisfy his scoptophilic impulses. The interpretation elicited only anger and the therapist had to backtrack and repair the situation.

Also, the therapist can, if not fully aware of his own reactions and needs, vicariously use the patient to act out for him and then in a guiltless way punish the patient for his (the therapist's) instinctual wishes, in this way projecting the impulse, guilt and subsequent punishment.[9]

Ted (a sixteen year old boy who was delinquent for stealing automobiles and window peeping) and his therapist were discussing the therapist's role in relation to the law should Ted become involved in further legal difficulties. In a conscious attempt to ingratiate himself and be therapeutically supportive, the therapist stated he would come to Ted's rescue under such circumstances. After the interview the therapist was quite anxious when he realized he was unconsciously asking Ted to act out, so that the therapist might rescue him and thus prove his interest and love while allowing social forces (the therapist's projected aggressor) to punish Ted, the transgressor. The negative oedipal factors in the therapist's rescue fantasy are striking. That is particularly true considering Ted's conflicts and defense structure: delinquency as a defense against homosexuality, which was in turn a defense against incest and castration anxiety. The therapist transitorily identified with Ted's id impulses. He projected his own id impulses on Ted, and his aggression on society, which would have then allowed him to rescue Ted and perpetuate a sexualized, mutually defensive relationship on the pattern of Ted's defense structure noted above. At the next interview the therapist told Ted he feared Ted would act out in response to his comments of the previous interview. The therapist pointed out this was unnecessary and undesirable. The reality factors involved in any further legal entanglements were again discussed in the light of the therapist's greater awareness of his own unconscious motivations and mechanisms, which (of course) were not verbally communicated.

A closely related mechanism is the situation where the patient projects his own acrimonious self-rebuke or superego and sadistically attacks the therapist verbally or physically for supposed misdeeds, defections, etc. The patient is then acting as sadistic superego to the therapist, while at the same time the therapist's id is being mobilized by the therapeutic uncovering of the patient's id impulses. This is most trying for the therapist, and it is of little help to realize that the patient is projecting self-criticism and attack by his own superego. In spite of his best efforts and considerable self-awareness, the therapist not infrequently counterattacks, or mobilizes his own infantile superego against the patient's id, ego and superego. This mobilization of the therapist's superego can result in violent rejection of the patient, punishment, or at least hostile demands for conformity. It may be of some support during these trying times, although it is slight, to realize that a stronger positive relationship often develops following the periods of maximum aggression. When the reaction is less pronounced in the therapist, he may respond more benignly with an unconscious desire to reform the patient. Although this may express itself more covertly, it is no less disruptive to therapy in the long run.

These patients with severe character disorders likewise do not as a rule want therapy and so treatment begins in a negative phase. They do not seek out the therapist, but rather the therapist must actively engage the patient. Such cases move slowly, with frequent relapses into acting, the relapses seeming to be an integral part of the illness itself. Such youngsters will often lie to the therapist, trick him, and attempt to degrade him in other ways. These items are, at times at least, a part of the irresistible urge to actively repeat the hurts they have passively sustained in the past, to drive their object away while at the same time suffering masochistically for their aggression.[1] The therapist can be hurt by these phenomena if he has too great a narcissistic investment in the patient and unless his own object relations are secure. These patients also demand immediate gratification and if it is not forthcoming, they will attack or punish the therapist. This interferes with the therapist's own image of himself and his own sublimated, professional, restitution attempts for his sadism. This interference with the sublimation tends to activate his sadistic impulses. Likewise, the slow and difficult course of the more severe cases, their refusal to improve promptly or get well is an affront to the therapist's omnipotence and again an attack on his self-image. Of course, a knowledge of the patient's dynamics offers some protection and tends to diminish the therapist's defensive maneuvers. We should realize that relapses into action are bound to occur, that such is the course of these illnesses. Improvement is perhaps first indicated by a less regressive or primitive quality to the acting and only later do we see less acting out per se.

The therapist who actively seeks out the patient and hammers at defenses can hardly remain even a relatively blank screen and by necessity must reveal more of himself than in the usual therapy situation. This is frightening to many therapists. To conceal themselves and to protect themselves from countertransference reactions, they can suppress all human freedom in relation to the patient and fail to engage actively the patient, to the obvious detriment of treatment. As noted earlier, these patients are by necessity astute observers of others. As therapy proceeds and they become more aware of the existence and manifestations of unconscious conflicts, they will perceive residual or reactivated conflicts in the therapist. At times, such a patient perceives the therapist's current conflicts very clearly and proceeds to interpret them in a hostile way which leaves no doubt how well concealed the therapist is. This causes counter-reactions varying from mild anxiety and annoyance to severe anxiety bordering on panic or the rise of consequent defense mechanisms. It also certainly facilitates the countertransference reaction to the patient as an object or part object from our earlier life experience.

Ted, the 16 year old delinquent mentioned earlier, had just spontaneously broached homosexuality as a defense against incest and the physical and psychological trauma that might in consequence accrue to mother. At the same time, he was dealing with his fear of the castrated female and with his fear of the pain of re-entering the vagina with his penis, comparing it to the infant's birth pain. At this point, Ted accused the therapist of having homosexual feelings himself, stating that the therapist must derive some vicarious satisfaction from looking at his (Ted's) system and went on to suggest that the therapist's purpose in investigating the patient's defense system was to learn about the ones the therapist himself used. While this was Ted's emerging mother transference, it was also a correct interpretation of the unanalyzed therapist's partial motivation. Ted's interpretation produced acute anxiety which it was necessary to handle in supervision.

These patients' lack of conformity to any rule, regulation, mores or wish of the therapist is a well-known and disturbing factor. While the therapist is intellectually aware that acting out is symptomatic, he emotionally responds to it as though it were in the patient's conscious control. He feels that the patient could do better if he wanted to or if he only tried. It is difficult for the therapist to understand emotionally how behavior that produces no ostensible guilt, but rather punishes the environment, can be symptomatic. The patient does not suffer, but rather the therapist and his world suffer. Emotionally, this means the patient is bad, that he "has no conscience." Almost any behavior can be tolerated (e.g., in the severe neuroses) and much can be forgiven if the patient suffers intrapsychically. However, it is virtually impossible to sympathize with a patient's acting out and (as previously noted) it is difficult and threatening to even empathize with his alloplastic modes of adjustment. These countertransference attitudes toward the patient are essentially superego in origin and are in large part evoked by the patient's use of the mechanism of identification with the aggressor by which he projects his guilt and aggression. Identification with the aggressor is a potent defense that does not easily yield. Even when the therapist recognizes the defense, its effectiveness and the patient's unconscious resistance to relinquish it, further facilitate the impression that the patient is stubborn and bad.

The patients with severe character disorders assault the environment in an attempt to establish object relations and secure supplies. They are, of course, extremely ambivalent in this, fearing any love relationship. However, they are intrusive and always explicitly present, forcing awareness of their presence on others and thus causing an ambivalent investment in them. When a child does not respond to the positive investment the therapist has in him and neither loves the therapist nor conforms to his wishes, the therapist is narcissistically injured as noted earlier. As he is consistently unable to elicit direct signs of love from the patient, the therapist focuses in anger on conformity as proof of love. This operates according to a formula that is somewhat as follows: I love you; if you love me you will do as I want. Nonconformity (acting-out) results in narcissistic injury to the therapist, which leads to angry, hostile demands for conformity as proof of love. These demands lead to further nonconformity and so a vicious cycle is established. This results in very real difficulty for all people dealing with the severe character disorders. This sequence of events tends to cause such children to be rejected and at times results in hostile, punitive action by the therapist or others. Improvement in the child is likewise often denied because as he improves, greater demands are made on him and although he may be conforming more than ever before, he may still not conform to the newer demands. This makes it seem that he is as rebellious, uncooperative and unloving as ever. Consequently, countertransference reactions according to the above formula may be continuously present or may be intermittently evoked.

Intuitive and skilled ward nurses could not, for a prolonged period, see Billy's obvious improvement, saying that he was "his same old self." It became apparent that as he adjusted better to the ward, newer demands were made on him and considerable annoyance ensued when he did not adhere to these newer demands. Several relatively detached observers noted that during this period the nurses seemed to aggravate Billy's acting out and provocative behavior by their relatively excessive demands. They then in various, often subtle ways (and at times not so subtle ways) punished him for his lack of adherence to their demands. At that period, he was actually adjusting and cooperating with ward procedure much better than ever before. However, he was as aggravating to ward personnel as ever, as he did not conform (love) enough to bind the ward personnel's negative feelings. This resulted in further demands for conformity as proof of love and the situation operated dynamically according to the formula noted above.

I have found this formula or rule of thumb extremely useful to help interrupt rising countertransference feelings and as a starting point for further analysis of the countertransference, which I feel is essential for any really adequate therapy of these patients. I do not think you can conceal conflicts from the juvenile character disorder patient, and whenever such is consciously or unconsciously attempted, the patient will perceive it as a lack of honesty, a lie, a perpetuation of earlier traumas and rejections. Obviously, no therapist is perfect and I am sure that anyone dealing actively with one of these patients makes many mistakes. These patients demand immediate response and often will not allow the therapist the briefest period to analyze transference and countertransference, even in his own mind. Consequently, the therapist is frequently required to respond quickly, spontaneously and many times when under psychologic and physical attack as noted earlier. Often, the errors seem technical in nature, yet behind these is nearly always some countertransference distortion.

Interpretation to the patient of the therapist's own countertransference can be a highly effective tool, but requires some finesse. Such interpretations must be correctly timed and should be aimed at the most superficial level that is effective. We should try to relate the rising conflictual material to the current stresses within the reality of the therapeutic situation rather than to further instinctual material. This may allude to other and deeper material which I think is communicated nonverbally to the patient and which the patient unconsciously elaborates and uses effectively to resolve his reaction to the therapist's distortions. Here, I refer particularly to the therapist's hostile, rejecting impulses. I doubt that it is constructive, and expect it is destructive, to spontaneously broach erotic countertransference. If the patient makes a correct countertransference interpretation of either aggressive or libidinal material, I think it is best to concede the interpretation with a very brief explanation, here again relating the impulse to the current reality rather than to further instinctual material. I have found this is always effective and would wonder about perpetuation of countertransference distortions if the therapist is impelled to do more.

While playing chess with Billy, the therapist lost (or Billy captured) his queen. The therapist unconsciously shifted his position and adjusted his genitals. Billy pointed out with glee (in the vernacular) that the therapist too had castration fears. The interpretation was conceded and related to the reality loss just sustained. This sufficed to reduce Billy's tension. Billy's anxiety over the loss of his own queen and his reactive counterphobic erection had been pointed out to him on earlier occasions. Although the oedipal factors in the therapist's activated castration anxiety are obvious, they were not broached directly. However, Billy was preconsciously aware of the oedipal factors at that point in treatment. Acceptance of his interpretation probably allowed him to see unconsciously the universal nature of the oedipal situation and gain support and strength through identification with a therapist who could bear his residual oedipal-castration anxiety. Also, his interpretation did not elicit aggression, indicating the more benign nature of the therapist's superego. Over a period of time such experiences tend to moderate the patient's more punitive superego.

The affective responses rising in the therapist and others dealing with the severe character disorders are difficult to manage. The therapist proper needs a considerable understanding of himself, his motivations, weaknesses and vulnerabilities. He also needs someone to whom he can abreact, discharge the affect which he must necessarily contain in the therapeutic situation. In other words, self-awareness, awareness of the dynamic factors at play is not sufficient. The therapist, particularly in the more severe cases, needs a "toilet," to borrow again a term from Glover.[8]

For many weeks at the onset of therapy, Billy constantly and violently bit and attacked his therapist. He was also very seductive in grabbing at the therapist's genitals, exposing his own erect penis (e.g.) and also in the highly sexualized nature of his over-all acting out. For months, Billy's reaction to every situation was accompanied by an erection to which he invariably called attention by "adjusting" his genitals. Billy called all of this "play," but it was at times almost unbearable and each hour with him became an ordeal. The therapist, to bolster himself before each hour, would first have to abreact to his dictaphone while dictating therapy notes. For many weeks the dictaphone was an essential, all-understanding, noncritical ally. Following this abreaction the therapist was able to take the next step and attend the morning nurses' meeting. There he would assure the nurses of Billy's progress, attempt to enlist their support and understanding and would chide them for their rejecting attitudes and their lack of patience. Only after this public demonstration of himself as (or identification with) the good father and mother was the therapist able to engage Billy again.

It is also useful and highly desirable whenever possible to divide the therapeutic and administrative responsibility. The therapist cannot realistically detach himself from the patient's behavior outside of therapy, but it removes a real load if he does not have to feel directly responsible for the control of the patient and likewise does not have to feel he is directly answerable for the patient's behavior. This division of therapeutic and administrative responsibility can only be relative and requires nice teamwork.

The therapist proper or his administrative associate also has to assume the burden of helping others, team members, nurses, hospital administrators, law enforcement officers, lawyers, courts and a multitudinous procession of people to understand and tolerate the patient if therapy is to proceed; indeed, this is an integral part of therapy. It helps these people to understand something of the general dynamics of this type patient, of the hostility they engender (particularly in relation to nonconformity) and of the countertransference problems they cause. Even those without professional training can be helped to tolerate their own hostility through identification with a therapist who can verbalize his hostilities, their meaning and significance and follows this up with a plan to deal with the patient to bring him back into the fold of society.

The extent of these youngsters' involvement with people and agencies is fantastic and these factors must be dealt with if therapy is to continue. During the two years Billy has been in therapy, he has been involved with seven different police departments (two, several hundred miles away); the State Highway Patrol; four juvenile probation groups; the administrators of a well-known bus line (when he was refused permission to ride ever again); passing college students who were so struck by his behavior that they located the therapist and called at his home to report it; and all level personnel, too numerous to recall, from two hospitals (the University Hospital and a State Hospital where Billy has lived for several periods). This is, of course, only a partial list.

Interestingly enough, one of the problems nonprofessional people (especially) have is setting realistic limits for such juvenile character disorders. They tend to let such youngsters impose on them (according to the formula we discussed) until they feel their love, tolerance and patience is being abused, until they feel that the patient is not going to love them or conform. They then tend to retaliate vigorously, to over-react. All of these people can be helped by assisting them to set early, realistic limits to the patient's encroachment so they will not be too much imposed on, ultimately injured, angry and punitive. Also, everyone working with these patients needs an opportunity to abreact, to ventilate the pent-up affects.

It is important and supportive for the therapist to keep in full awareness throughout, his purposes and goals as a therapist; that is, to maintain an adequate, working empathy without identifying with the id impulses, the destructive parents (archaic superego) and without identifying with the wishes of parent and society for conformity. In other words, the therapist can cross-check and maintain a control by measuring and comparing his behavior, activity and affective responses as means to the actual therapeutic goals. The therapist's responses should be adapted to the unconscious needs of the patient and the process of therapy.

People's innate reactions to the severe character disorders in childhood vary according to their own character structure. Some are able to tolerate these patients fairly well, while others reject them immediately, are punitive and can see them only as "bad" children. This brings up the interesting and often noted fact that not all therapists work equally well with these children. As we noted earlier, not all therapists can even empathize with such youngsters. Glover [8] has suggested that the character disorders need a "psychopathic analyst." In elaborating a similar point, Lippman [10] quotes Zulliger as stating that some do not work well with these cases as they are not narcissistic enough. Aichhorn [2] consciously used his own omnipotent wishes as a therapeutic tool in working with wayward youth. I think these psychiatrists hint at the fact that a therapist, to really empathize with such patients, must have dealt with elements in his own character structure that are similar to structural elements in the severe character disorders. That is, the effective therapist must have constructively integrated, via his own spontaneous growth process or personal analysis and preferably both, his own narcissistic omnipotence, severe and terrifying pregenital superego imagos, heightened castration anxiety and the resultant defense mechanisms. A prominent factor in the therapist's motivation in undertaking the treatment of these difficult children is the wish to be a better mother than his own and to do actively in a better way that which he experienced passively in a frustrating way. To consider the dynamics at a different level, this is a sublimation of rage and sadism from an early, pregenital period. This is, I am sure, a factor in all child therapists' motivation. However, to want to be a better mother to an impossible and hateful child is a different degree of things and certainly relates to the degree of early frustration, rage and sadism, whether the rage and sadism are secondary to frustration per se or to an increased aggressive drive endowment with a resultant low frustration tolerance.

Billy was accepted for therapy early in the therapist's wife's first pregnancy. The therapist had openly stated envy of his wife's ability to bear children and be a mother with the close, symbiotic attachment to a child. Analysis of the therapist's unconscious motivations in taking Billy into therapy revealed that he hoped to realize through therapy the wish to bear a child. Taking Billy into therapy and carrying him in therapy was unconsciously equated with carrying him in the womb. The wish to create a new person through therapy or to manage the patient's rebirth through therapy was closely associated with the wish to give birth to a child. (Retrospectively, at the point of writing this paper, Billy was hospitalized for a period of nine months and two weeks.) A further unconscious wish operating in taking Billy into therapy was the wish to be a better mother to an impossible child than the therapist's mother had been to him, or his wife would be to her child.

These factors are in turn closely related to the frightening character of the pregenital superego elements laid down and the consequent degree of narcissism, restitution and sublimation required to maintain a balance. I suggest that the successful therapist of the severe character disorders must have managed these factors within himself without undue repression and thus be able to empathize and work therapeutically with closely related elements in the character disorders.

Bibliography

1. Abraham, K.: The history of an impostor in the light of psychoanalytic knowledge. Psychoanalyt. Quart. *4:* 570–587, 1935.

2. Aichhorn, A.: Wayward Youth. New York, Viking Press, 1951.

3. Crocker, D.: The study of a problem of aggression. Psychoanalyt. Study of the Child *10:* 300–335, 1955.

4. Eissler, K. R.: Ego-psychological implications of the psychoanalytic treatment of delinquents. Psychoanalyt. Study of the Child *5:* 97–121, 1950.

5. Fliess, R.: Countertransference and counteridentification. J. Am. Psychoanalyt. A. *1:* 268–284, 1953.

6. Freud, A.: Certain types and stages of social maladjustment. *In* Eissler, K. R.: Searchlights on Delinquency. New York, International Universities Press, Inc., 1949.

7. Glover, E.: The diagnosis and treatment of delinquency (being a clinical report on the work of the Institute for the Scientific Treatment of Delinquency, during the five years 1937–1941). *In* Radzinowicz, L., and Turner, J. W. C.: Mental Abnormality and Crime. English Studies in Criminal Science. Vol. 2. London, Macmillan and Co., Ltd., 1944.

8. Glover, E.: The Technique of Psychoanalysis. London, Vailliere, Tindale and Cox, 1955.

9. Johnson, A. M.: Sanctions for superego lacunae of adolescents. *In* Eissler, K. R.: Searchlights on Delinquency. New York, International Universities Press, Inc., 1949.

10. Lippman, H. S.: Psychopathic reactions in children. Am. J. Orthopsychiat. *21:* 227–231, 1951.

11. Winnicott, D. W.: Hate in the countertransference. Internat. J. Psycho-Analysis *30:* 69–74, 1949.

12. Zulliger, H.: Berichte und Gedanken zur Erörterung des narzistisch-triebhaften Charakters. Arch. Psychoanalyt. Pädagog. *10:* 149, 1935.

Index